# Elementary Probability
## for the
# Biological Sciences

# Elementary

## Probability

for

**New York**
**APPLETON-CENTURY-CROFTS**

DIVISION OF MEREDITH CORPORATION

# the
# Biological
# Sciences

### James E. Mosimann
**National Institutes of Health**

**LIBRARY ST. MARY'S COLLEGE**

**To My Mother**

5978

688–2

Library of Congress Card Number: 68-17419

PRINTED IN THE UNITED STATES OF AMERICA

E 65310

# PREFACE

A few moments spent with any recent text in general biology suffice to reveal to the reader the extreme diversity of knowledge required of the modern biologist. Certainly, biology is no longer a purely descriptive science, if indeed it ever was. The biologist of today must assimilate and utilize the results of many other scientific fields of endeavor. Ranging from the background of physics and chemistry, which provides an understanding of the genetic code, to a sophisticated knowledge of systems analysis and electronic computers, necessary for modern ecological research, the biologist finds himself drawing continually upon the results of other areas of science. This is not to imply that biology as a science has no area of its own. It is simply to state that the problems encountered in biological work often have a depth and complexity that can be found in few, if any, of the other sciences, and that to properly consider these problems one must be able to apply principles from several disciplines. Thus, from molecular biology to ecology, biology constitutes one of the most challenging areas of science of our time.

In the past it has been almost traditional that the training of the average biologist include little or no mathematics. Today, however, the biologist is often called upon to understand, to use, and even to develop mathematical models of considerable complexity. In particular, one is often called upon to formulate and interpret random or probability models of various phenomena. An understanding of probability theory, the mathematics of uncertainty, has become central to an understanding of the theories and methods of much of biology. For example, evolution, a basic principle of modern biology, can only be understood in probabilistic terms.

This book is an introduction to the mathematical theory of probability designed for the beginning college student who is oriented towards the life sciences. The mathematical knowledge presupposed is high school algebra. The biological knowledge presupposed is of a similar level. By limiting the treatment only to probability on finite sample spaces, it has been possible to give a relatively self-contained mathematical presentation. Throughout the text there are optional sections that deal with specific biological topics. In reading these, the student can decide for himself about the utility of the mathematical theory.

The inclusion of the optional sections, which are essential for the book's biological character, necessitated the deletion of other topics, among them important topics in probability theory. Should a need develop, these other topics could readily be assembled along with other biological materials into a second volume. However, it is with particular regret that the presentation of sections on Bayes theorem, random variables, means and variances, and other topics has been deferred. On the other hand, there are excellent treatments of biostatistics, which expose the biologist to these concepts.

This book had its origins in notes which I wrote for a course given at the University of Arizona in the summer of 1963. More recently, the revised notes have been used for a course in elementary probability for the biological sciences given in the evening school of the National Institutes of Health. The book itself has been prepared for students working without the assistance of an instructor. Most universities do not currently provide a course in probability for biologists. Thus, this book is designed for the student reading supplementary material at home. Accordingly, a conscious effort has been made to include more than a usual number of logical steps in presentation and to provide sufficient examples. Answers to all the exercises are given at the back of the book.

At the end of each chapter references for further reading are given. First, elementary mathematical books are listed; these are at a beginning college level. Next, references pertaining to the optional sections are listed. These include at least one reference to a general treatment of the biological topic considered. They may also include references to specific research publications. It is not assumed that the student will fully understand these but they do, however, give an idea of the current research activity in the biological area treated.

Personally, I hope that this book will serve two purposes. The first is to teach probability to biologists sufficiently early in their careers so that the use of probability models may be an integral part of their daily habits of reasoning. The second is that by reading this book, the beginning biologist may be motivated to study mathematics, alongside his biology, while still an undergraduate.

J. E. M.

# ACKNOWLEDGMENTS

I am grateful to many persons, particularly students, who have aided in the preparation of the manuscript. Unfortunately, it is impossible to acknowledge everyone by name. I would like to thank the following persons, all colleagues at the Division of Computer Research and Technology of the National Institutes of Health: E. K. Harris and A. W. Pratt for their interest and encouragement; R. J. Connor, J. E. Fletcher, R. E. Hackman, M. H. Hudson, F. A. Petro, W. M. Scott, and M. B. Shapiro for their continual flow of comments and criticism.

I would particularly like to acknowledge R. W. Brink, editor of the Mathematical Series at Appleton-Century-Crofts, for his criticism and close reading of the text. For typing and preparing the manuscript Mrs. P. O'Brien and Mrs. P. Maiuzzo have my warmest thanks.

Finally my wife, Jean, and eldest daughter, Theresa, not only were very patient at home, but assisted in working a number of the exercises.

# ACKNOWLEDGEMENTS

# NOTES TO READERS

These notes are addressed particularly to the person reading this book on his own. To read it fruitfully, one should work some exercises at the end of each section. Because this takes time, and one may not have much time, I would like to recommend several possible paths through this book. An ideal path is to follow through all the unstarred sections, and then return to various starred (optional) sections of particular interest.

On the other hand, if one is anxious to see biological applications, stops should be made at various optional sections along the way. The book is planned so that this can be done. However, most of the optional sections are more difficult than the unstarred sections, and one may get bogged down in an optional section. If this should happen I recommend proceeding with unstarred sections, and returning to the optional sections later. The accompanying diagrams suggest various paths that suit different limitations of time and different needs.

No matter which path is chosen, one may find some proof or exposition particularly difficult. If so, it sometimes helps to accept the difficult point or points and to continue reading and working some of the exercises. After doing this, one can return to the beginning of the section in which the difficulty was encountered and try again. Often the problem disappears upon the second reading.

| PATH 1 |    To obtain some experience with precise counting methods
               in biology.

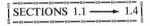

| PATH 2 |    To obtain some knowledge of combinatorial analysis, permutations and combinations.

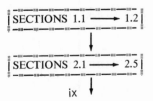

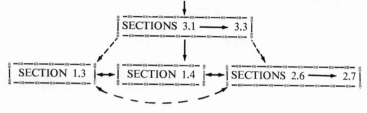

PATH 3 To obtain a working knowledge of one commonly used probability model (Hypergeometric probabilities).

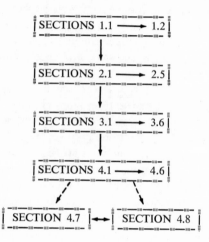

PATH 4 To obtain an introduction to probability theory and probability models in genetics.

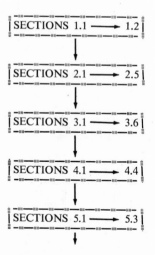

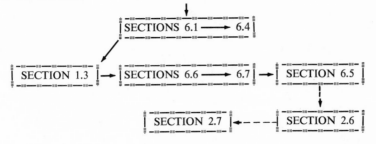

To obtain an introduction to two commonly used probability models (Hypergeometric and Binomial Probabilities).

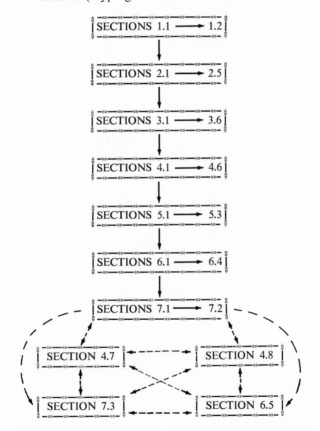

To obtain a general introduction to probability on finite sample spaces with biological applications. The path consists of all unstarred sections in sequence and starred sections as desired.

# CONTENTS[1]

---

[1] Appropriate exercises follow sections.  Starred sections are optional and treat biological topics.
[2] Parts II and III appear in Chapter 6.

# 7    BINOMIAL PROBABILITIES

# A STARTING POINT, A RULE OF COUNTING

## 1.1 A BASIC RULE OF COUNTING

Two graduate students take an exam in biology. Each can either pass or fail. With regard to both students, what can possibly happen? There are four possibilities.

Both pass.
The first passes, the second fails.
The first fails, the second passes.
Both fail.

We can picture these statements by means of a table in which the numeral I corresponds to the first student, and the numeral II to the second student. Their respective grades are indicated by P, for pass, and F, for fail. The table shows the various possibilities.

| Student I \ Student II | P | F |
|---|---|---|
| P | PP | PF |
| F | FP | FF |

There are $2 \times 2 = 4$ possibilities, since for each of the two possible grades for the first student, there are two possible grades for the second student.

Let us look at this problem in another way. Imagine two places, one for each student or

```
└────────┘        └────────┘
 Student I          Student II  .
```

The first place can be filled in one of two ways (pass or fail), so we write a 2 in the first spot, thus

```
└───2────┘        └────────┘
 Student I          Student II  .
```

Similarly the second place can be filled in two possible ways (student 2 either passes or fails), so we write a 2 in the second spot,

```
└───2────┘        └───2────┘
 Student I          Student II  .
```

The number of ways *both* places can be filled is simply

$$2 \quad \times \quad 2 \quad = 4 .$$

Now suppose that the first student (I) is a graduate student and receives a grade of P (pass) or F (fail); while the second student (II), is an undergraduate and receives a grade of A, B, C, D, or F. Then there are ten possibilities, since to each of the two possible grades for student I there correspond five possible grades for student II as shown in the table.

| Student I \ Student II | A | B | C | D | F |
|---|---|---|---|---|---|
| P | PA | PB | PC | PD | PF |
| F | FA | FB | FC | FD | FF |

Again designating a place for each student we have

$$\underbrace{2}_{\text{Student I}} \qquad \underbrace{5}_{\text{Student II}} ,$$

so that there are

$$2 \times 5 = 10$$

possibilities.

EXAMPLE 1.   A pair of dice is tossed.   One die is red, the other white.   Each shows one of six faces.   There are

$$\underbrace{6}_{\text{red}} \times \underbrace{6}_{\text{white}} = 36$$

possibilities.

EXAMPLE 2.   A coin and a die are tossed together. There are

$$2 \times 6 = 12$$

possible tosses.

EXAMPLE 3.   There are two undergraduates, each of whom can make A, B, C, D or F grades.   There are

$$5 \times 5 = 25$$

possible results.

EXAMPLE 4.   A dipeptide chain contains two amino acids, a first one (I) and a second one (II).   Each is one of 20 amino acids.   There are

$$\underbrace{20}_{\text{I}} \times \underbrace{20}_{\text{II}} = 400$$

theoretically possible dipeptides.

EXAMPLE 5. An investigator has determined that the first amino acid of a particular dipeptide is one of three kinds of amino acids. He has no information about the identity of the second amino acid except that it is one of the 20 common naturally occurring amino acids. His dipeptide chain is one of

$$3 \times 20 = 60$$

possibilities.

Let us now formulate the principle we have just illustrated.

> BASIC RULE OF COUNTING.    *Suppose something can happen in $n_1$ ways. Suppose that no matter in which way it does happen, something else can happen in $n_2$ ways. Then the number of possible ways for both to happen together is $n_1 \times n_2$.*

It should be noted that we are *not* proving the above rule. Rather we are accepting it as corresponding with a natural manner of counting. This rule is our unproved starting point, and all the results of the first two chapters stem from this statement.

| PATH 1 ☞ §1.2 | PATH 2 ☞ §1.2 | PATH 3 ☞ §1.2 | PATH 4 ☞ §1.2 | PATH 5 ☞ §1.2 |

## 1.2  EXTENSION OF THE BASIC RULE OF COUNTING

We can extend the basic rule we have just seen to determine the number of ways that more than two things can happen. Suppose there are three students taking an exam, each passing or failing. There are then eight possibilities which are shown in the table:

|     | Student I | Student II | Student III |
|-----|-----------|------------|-------------|
| (1) | P | P | P |
| (2) | P | P | F |
| (3) | P | F | P |
| (4) | P | F | F |
| (5) | F | P | P |
| (6) | F | P | F |
| (7) | F | F | P |
| (8) | F | F | F |

For example, in possibility (7) the first two students fail while the third student passes.

A simple extension of our basic rule permits us to arrive at the answer. There are three places, each of which can be filled in two ways

$$\underbrace{\quad 2 \quad}_{\text{Student I}} \qquad \underbrace{\quad 2 \quad}_{\text{Student II}} \qquad \underbrace{\quad 2 \quad}_{\text{Student III}} \;,$$

and

$$2 \times 2 \times 2 = 8 \,.$$

Had we wished, we could have considered the results of the first two students together as a single category with $2 \times 2 = 4$ possibilities or

$$\underbrace{\qquad\qquad 4 \qquad\qquad}_{\text{Students I and II}} \qquad \underbrace{\quad 2 \quad}_{\text{Student III}} \;.$$

This reduces the three places to two places. No matter what the grades of the first two students, the third can receive either P or F. Hence, we can apply the basic rule of counting in this case, and obtain $4 \times 2 = 8$ as the number of possibilities for all three students together.

Let us now consider the general case where three things can happen in $n_1$, $n_2$, and $n_3$ ways, respectively. Consider that any one of the three things happens. Suppose the number of ways in which it can happen is the same no matter which way the other two happen. We can write and fill in the three places as

$$\underbrace{\; n_1 \;}_{\text{I}} \qquad \underbrace{\; n_2 \;}_{\text{II}} \qquad \underbrace{\; n_3 \;}_{\text{III}} \;.$$

We can also group the first and second places together and treat them as a single category with $(n_1 \times n_2)$ possibilities. This reduces the three things to two or

$$\underbrace{\;(n_1 \times n_2)\;}_{\text{I and II}} \qquad \underbrace{\; n_3 \;}_{\text{III}} \;.$$

We can apply the basic rule again obtaining

$$(n_1 \times n_2) \times n_3 = n_1 n_2 n_3$$

as the total number of ways for the original three things to happen. Thus, using our basic rule (for two places) we have shown that a similar rule is applicable and true for three places.

> EXAMPLE 1.   Two graduate students (grades P or F) and an undergraduate (grades A, B, C, D or F) take an exam. There are
>
> $$2 \times 2 \times 5 = 20$$
>
> possible results for the three students.

EXAMPLE 2. In a chain of three nucleotides, a first, second, and third nucleotide can be distinguished. Each may be one of four types (A, C, G, or U). There are

$$4 \times 4 \times 4 = 64$$

possible chains of three (or "triplets"). For example AAA, AAC, CAA, CAU, CGU, and so forth.

EXAMPLE 3. The sex of three turtles is determined by dissection as male (M) or female (F). There are

$$2 \times 2 \times 2 = 8$$

possible records for the three animals. For example, MMM, MFM, FMM, and so forth.

We can continue extending our rule indefinitely, for if we have four things happening

$$\underbrace{n_1}_{\text{I}} \qquad \underbrace{n_2}_{\text{II}} \qquad \underbrace{n_3}_{\text{III}} \qquad \underbrace{n_4}_{\text{IV}},$$

and we consider the first three together as a single place, then applying our rule for three places we have

$$\underbrace{(n_1 \times n_2 \times n_3)}_{\text{I, II, and III}} \qquad \underbrace{n_4}_{\text{IV}},$$

and then applying the basic rule we obtain

$$(n_1 \times n_2 \times n_3) \times n_4 = n_1 n_2 n_3 n_4$$

as the total number of possibilities for the four things. We could repeat this procedure using five places, then six, etc. However, we content ourselves with simply stating the general rule.

RULE OF COUNTING. *If a first thing can happen in $n_1$ ways, a second thing in $n_2$ ways, a third thing in $n_3$ ways, . . . , and finally a $k$th thing in $n_k$ ways, then the number of ways for all things to happen together is*

$$n_1 \times n_2 \times n_3 \times \ldots \times n_k,$$

*provided that the first thing can happen in $n_1$ ways no matter which way the other things happen, the second thing can happen in $n_2$ ways no matter which way the other things happen, the third thing can happen in $n_3$ ways no matter which way the other things happen, . . . , and the $k$th thing can happen in $n_k$ ways no matter which way the other things happen.*

It should be clear that the validity of this rule follows from the validity of the basic rule of counting, and acceptance of the extended rule follows from acceptance of the basic rule.

EXAMPLE 4. There are four undergraduates, each of whom can get A, B, C, D, or F. There are thus

$$5 \times 5 \times 5 \times 5 = 5^4 = 625$$

possible results.

EXAMPLE 5. There are ten graduate students, each of whom can pass or fail. There are thus

$$2 \times 2 \times 2 \times 2 \times 2 \times 2 \times 2 \times 2 \times 2 \times 2$$
$$= 2^{10} = 1024$$

possible results.

EXAMPLE 6. In a class with 4 graduates using the grading system in Example 5 and 2 undergraduates with the system in Example 4 there are

$$2 \times 2 \times 2 \times 2 \times 5 \times 5 = 400$$

possible results.

EXAMPLE 7. A class has a total of $k$ graduate students, each of whom passes or fails. There are thus

$$2 \times 2 \times \ldots \times 2 = 2^k$$

possible results (if $k = 2$, there are 4; if $k = 4$, there are 16; if $k = 10$, 1024).

EXAMPLE 8. Suppose $k$ things happen. Each can take place in $n$ ways no matter how the others take place. Then there are

$$\underbrace{n}_{1st} \times \underbrace{n}_{2nd} \times \ldots \times \underbrace{n}_{kth} = n^k$$

possible ways for all to happen together.

The extended rule of counting gives the total number of possibilities. In some instances it is convenient to enumerate these possibilities by using a *tree diagram*, which we now illustrate. For example, if three graduate students (grades P or F) take an exam, there are 8 possible results. We can enumerate these by means of the tree diagram given below:

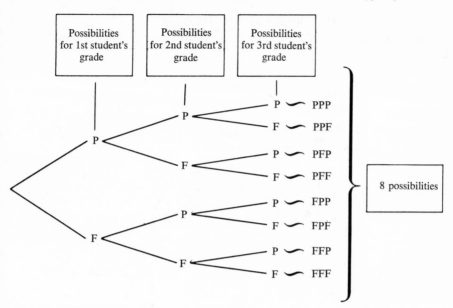

Read this tree diagram by starting at the left and following any single path all the way to the right to arrive at one possible set of grades. Thus the path

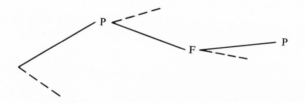

indicates that the first student passes, the second fails, and the third passes or PFP. The path

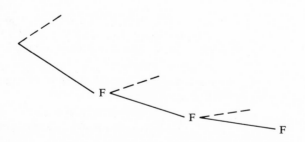

corresponds to the possibility that all three fail or FFF.

If a coin and a die are tossed there are 12 possibilities. The tree diagram looks like

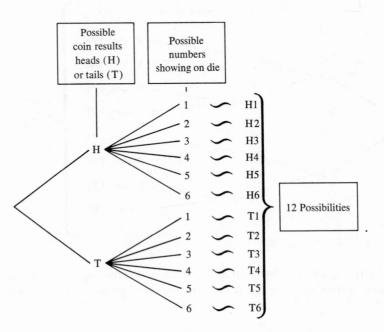

The coin falling heads and the die falling 4 corresponds to the path

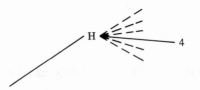

### EXERCISES

1.  Four coins are flipped. Each can fall heads or tails.
    (a) How many different results are possible?
    (b) Enumerate these using a tree diagram.

2.  Two coins are flipped and a "wheel of fortune" (with 36 stopping places) is spun. How many different results are possible?

3.  Five students, two undergraduates (grades A, B, C, D, or F) and three graduate students (grades P or F)

receive their final grades for a course. The actual result is

| Student | 1 | 2 | 3 | 4 | 5 |
|---------|---|---|---|---|---|
| Grade | A | B | P | P | F |

This is one of how many possible results?

4. A forester examines two trees for signs of spruce budworm infestation. He classifies each tree as having a high (H), low (L), or no (N) infestation. As a result of his examination he finds that both trees have a high infestation. He records his findings as follows

| Tree | 1 | 2 |
|------|---|---|
| Rate | H | H |

(a) How many such findings could have been made?
(b) Enumerate these possible findings using a tree diagram.

5. The same forester examines five trees classifying each as H, L, or N. How many possible findings are there?

6. A pollen analyst counts grains of pollen found in a surface soil sample. He identifies the grains to be one of two types — tree pollen (T) or nontree pollen (N). Suppose he records the order in which he counts 10 grains. For example,

TTTNNTTNNT,    TNNNNTTTTT,    or
NTTTTTTTTT.

(a) If each of the above is a distinct "sample," how many different samples of 10 grains are possible?
(b) How many different samples are possible if he counts 100 grains?
(c) If he counts $n$ grains?

7. An octanucleotide is a chain of eight nucleotides. Each nucleotide contains either adenine (A), cytosine (C), guanine (G), or uracil (U). For example, two different possible octanucleotides are

ACGUUUGC    CGUUUGCA.

(a) How many different octanucleotides are theoretically possible?
(b) A hexanucleotide consists of six nucleotides. How many hexanucleotides are theoretically possible?

8. A tripeptide chain consists of three amino acids, which can be distinguished as first, second, and third. Each is one of 20 naturally occurring amino acids. How many tripeptide chains are theoretically possible?

9. A polypeptide chain consists of many amino acids. Each can be one of 20 as in Exercise 8.

(a) How many chains containing 10 amino acids are theoretically possible?

(b) Containing 5 amino acids?

(c) Containing 70 amino acids?

(d) Containing $n$ amino acids?

| PATH 1 ☞ §1.3 | PATH 2 ☞ §2.1 | PATH 3 ☞ §2.1 | PATH 4 ☞ §2.1 | PATH 5 ☞ §2.1 |

## 1.3★   APPLICATIONS OF THE RULE OF COUNTING: CHROMOSOME AND GENE MODELS IN HEREDITY. PART I.[1]  INTRODUCTION

According to the cell theory animals and plants are made up of small, basic units called cells. Some organisms like protozoa, algae, and bacteria are unicellular, that is, consisting of a single cell, while others like the plants and animals of everyday experience are multicellular. Even in a multicellular individual, however, all cells are derived by cell division and growth from a single cell. Multicellular organisms start their lives as a single cell.

In sexually reproducing organisms, such as man, the single cell that gives rise to the quadrillions of cells in the adult is a *fertilized egg*. This is a cell resulting from the union of the respective male and female germ cells — a *sperm cell* from the male parent and an *egg cell* from the female parent. Two facts about the reproduction process are:

(1) Somehow the fertilized egg contains the information needed to construct an adult of a given species (such as an adult human) and not another kind of organism. The amount of information necessary is incredibly large, yet contained in a single cell.

(2) This information comes from a single sperm cell of the male parent and a single egg cell of the female parent, the two germ cells that united to form the fertilized egg. Such is the tenuous connection of one generation with another.

The science of genetics is concerned with heredity — that is, the transmission of hereditary information from parents to offspring. Because of facts (1) and (2) above, which are true for all sexually reproducing plants or animals, it is natural to look within cells for an understanding of the information storage and transmission processes.

### Information Storage in Cells

Information storage within a cell is by means of long nucleic acid molecules,

---

[1] Parts II and III of chromosome and gene models in heredity are to be found in Sections 6.6 and 6.7 of Chapter 6. This section contains basic biological background necessary for reading parts II and III and provides several illustrations of the rule of counting.

which can be thought of as long strings of smaller units known as nucleotides whose structure varies. In deoxyribonucleic acids (usually denoted by DNA) the four common base-structures are thymine or T, cytosine or C, adenine or A, and guanine or G.[2] A hypothetical portion of a nucleic acid might be

$$\ldots ACGTTACGTCGTTAC \ldots$$

The linear sequences of letters (nucleotides) differ among the various kinds of DNA molecules. Thus, different molecules of DNA in the cell can store different information. DNA molecules provide the cell with a means of "writing" and storing information using a four-letter alphabet consisting of T, C, A, and G. Specifically, information is stored as nonoverlapping three-letter "words" like CGG.

How many three-letter words like CGG, AAA, and so forth, are possible using four letters? We can find the answer from the basic rule of counting. There are three places, and the first can be filled in any of four ways. The second place can be filled in any of four ways, and, similarly, for the third. We have

$$\underset{\text{1st}}{\underline{4}} \quad \times \quad \underset{\text{2nd}}{\underline{4}} \quad \times \quad \underset{\text{3rd}}{\underline{4}} \quad = 64$$

possible triplets or three-letter words. A great amount of information can be written and stored in DNA molecules. For example, we can ask how many different sequences are theoretically possible for a single molecule of 1500 bases (by no means the longest DNA molecule). By the rule of counting we have

$$\underset{\text{1st}}{\underline{4}} \quad \times \quad \underset{\text{2nd}}{\underline{4}} \quad \times \ldots \times \quad \underset{\text{1500th}}{\underline{4}} \quad = 4^{1500}$$

This number is greater than $10^{900}$.[3] There is an enormous information storage potential in DNA. (Information storage by means of nucleic acids is considered again in Section 2.6.)

### Transmission of Information from Parents to Offspring

How is the information in DNA transmitted from parent to offspring? DNA is found in chromosomes — more or less linear bodies that are found in plant and animal cells. A sperm cell contains a fixed number of chromosomes (23 in man), and an egg cell has the same number.[4] When sperm and egg unite in fertilization, the result is a cell with double the number of chromosomes in

---

[2] In RNA the ribonucleic acids, thymine or T is replaced by uracil or U.

[3] This number is incredibly large. The star Sirius is 8.6 light years away from earth (1 light year is equivalent to about $6 \times 10^{12}$ miles). If a slowly moving insect were to take one billion years to move one foot, it could complete a trip to Sirius and back in $5 \times 10^{26}$ years. In $10^{900}$ years, the insect could make $2 \times 10^{873}$ such trips. In other words the number of round trips the insect could make is itself an incredibly large number.

[4] In some organisms a special chromosome may be found in one sex and not in the other.

either of the germ cells (46 in man). In man, each of the 23 paternal chromosomes has a matching maternal chromosome, thus, in the fertilized egg there are 23 such matching, or homologous, pairs of chromosomes. Via the chromosomes the offspring receives similar amounts of DNA from each parent. Since DNA sequences differ in the two parents, the information content in the fertilized egg is not identical to that of either parent.

The fertilized egg undergoes cell division, producing two cells which in turn divide and produce more cells. After many such divisions, the quadrillions of cells in the adult man are produced. These divisions are *mitotic* in which each cell with 46 chromosomes divides to produce two cells, each with 46 chromosomes identical in number and type to those of the cell which originally divided. Thus, except for occasional errors, all the cells derived by *mitosis* (mitotic division) contain the same chromosomes and the same DNA sequences.

However, mitosis is not the only kind of cell division possible. In the mature individual some cells divide to produce germ cells (sperm if male, and eggs if female). In this process a kind of cell division known as *meiosis* occurs. During meiosis the number of chromosomes is halved. Germ cells, the products of meiotic divisions, contain one half the original number of chromosomes. Thus the sperm and egg cell in man (or woman) are produced by meiosis and contain 23 chromosomes. As a result the union of the sperm and egg cells of two individuals yields a fertilized cell with 46 chromosomes, the same number as each parent. Of this number 23 chromosomes are from the father and 23 from the mother. Thus a new combination of DNA sequences is found in the fertilized egg which undergoes mitosis, the individual then matures, and the cycle continues.

### The Variety of Germ Cells from an Individual

The number of chromosomes per cell varies among different species of plants and animals. In a given species the fertilized egg contains $N$ pairs of chromosomes, $2N$ chromosomes in all. One chromosome of each pair is contributed by the female parent, the other by the male. Since all the body cells of the individual are derived from the fertilized egg by mitotic divisions, all body cells likewise contain $2N$ chromosomes in $N$ pairs. When a given body cell divides by meiosis to produce germ cells, each resulting germ cell receives one member from each chromosome pair.

For example, consider a hypothetical organism whose body cell contains three pairs of chromosomes — a "long" pair, a "short" pair, and a "bent" pair.

The diagram shows such a cell in which one member of each pair is shaded for purposes of identification. The different shapes of the chromosomes provide a convenient means of identifying a given chromosome pair. It should be recalled, however, that it is the DNA sequences in the chromosome that contain genetic information. The shape of the chromosome is not directly relevant to the kind of information that it contains. In this diagram we assume that no two chromosomes have the same information content. Thus, no two chromosomes have the same sequences of DNA. An individual with body cells as illustrated can produce eight kinds of germ cells, each containing a different set of information. We can determine this by application of the rule of counting. A germ cell receives one of two possible chromosomes from each pair. Hence, we have

$$\underset{\text{long}}{\underline{2}} \quad \times \quad \underset{\text{short}}{\underline{2}} \quad \times \quad \underset{\text{bent}}{\underline{2}} \quad = 8$$

kinds of germ cells possible. These can be enumerated by means of a tree diagram as

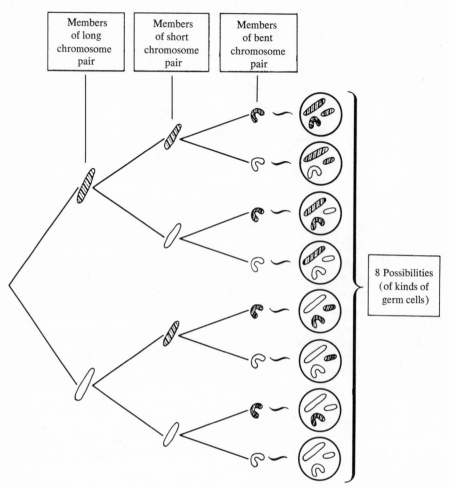

| Members of long chromosome pair | Members of short chromosome pair | Members of bent chromosome pair |

8 Possibilities (of kinds of germ cells)

More generally, consider an individual organism whose body cells each contain $N$ pairs of chromosomes. Suppose also that no two chromosomes contain exactly the same information. A germ cell receives one of two possible chromosomes from each of $N$ pairs. Hence, by the rule of counting we have

$$\underbrace{2}_{\text{1st pair}} \times \underbrace{2}_{\text{2nd pair}} \times \dots \times \underbrace{2}_{\text{Nth pair}} = 2^N$$

kinds of germ cells, each with a different information content.

### The Variety of Offspring from a Mating of Two Individuals

Consider an organism with two pairs of chromosomes — "long" and "bent." Suppose we have a male and a female whose cells are as indicated in the diagram.

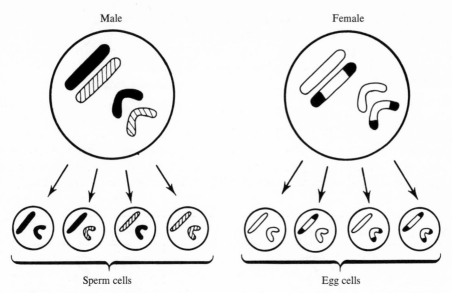

The diagram represents the cells of a particular male and female, along with the $2^2 = 4$ kinds of germ cells that each can produce. Each chromosome is marked differently to indicate that no two of the 8 chromosomes pictured contain identical DNA sequences. When these two individuals mate, the fusion of a sperm and egg cell gives a fertilized egg. For example, one possible fertilized egg is

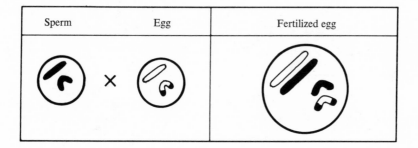

Both the male and female have four distinct kinds of germ cells. By the rule of counting there are

$$\underbrace{4}_{\text{sperm cell}} \times \underbrace{4}_{\text{egg cell}} = 16$$

possible sperm-egg combinations. In this example no two of the eight chromosomes (male and female) are alike in information content. Thus, each of these 16 combinations yields a distinct fertilized egg representing the different kinds of possible offspring that might arise from this mating.

Suppose an organism has cells with $N$ pairs of chromosomes. A given male can produce $2^N$ kinds of germ cells, and likewise for a given female. The number of different sperm-egg combinations is, by the rule of counting,

$$\underbrace{2^N}_{\text{sperm cells}} \times \underbrace{2^N}_{\text{egg cells}} = 2^{2N} = 4^N.$$

However, we cannot conclude that there are $4^N$ different, possible offspring since each sperm-egg combination need not always produce a different fertilized egg. For example, suppose a male and female have two identical germ cells.

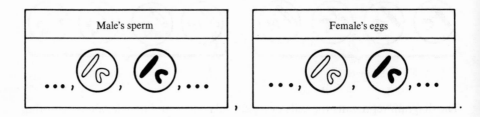

Then two different sperm-egg combinations produce the same kind of fertilized eggs.

Or again it might be that germ cells are

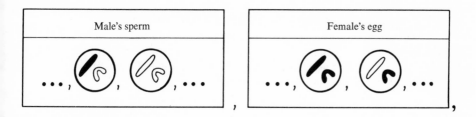

and again two different sperm-egg combinations produce the same kind of fertilized egg.

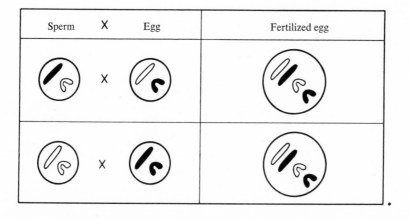

Although caution is called for in counting the number of distinct fertilized eggs, it is not difficult to do so. Consider a male and a female of a species whose body cells have $N$ pairs of chromosomes. Consider any single chromosome pair. Label the two male chromosomes $M_1$ and $M_2$; similarly, label those of the female $F_1$ and $F_2$. In counting the number of distinct fertilized eggs problems arise only when two or more of the four ($M_1$, $M_2$, $F_1$, $F_2$) contain the same information. (Some cases where this is so have just been illustrated.)

If we consider any chromosome pair, and if all four chromosomes ($M_1$, $M_2$, $F_1$, $F_2$) are distinct in information content, then there are four distinct fertilized eggs possible for each pair; namely,

$$F_1M_1, \ F_1M_2, \ F_2M_1, \ F_2M_2.$$

If the four chromosomes are distinct for each of $N$ pairs, there are

$$\underset{\text{1st}}{\underline{4}} \quad \times \quad \underset{\text{2nd}}{\underline{4}} \quad \times \ldots \times \quad \underset{N\text{th}}{\underline{4}} \quad = 4^N$$

different, possible fertilized eggs. This is the same as the number of sperm-egg combinations. (For a case where all four chromosomes are not distinct see Exercise 8.)

The result just stated holds if the chromosomes remain intact. Members of a pair can break and rejoin in various ways; for example, so that a portion of one chromosome becomes part of its partner and vice versa. The number of possible fertilized eggs is then actually greater than $4^N$. Breakage is considered in Section 6.7.

In man a fertilized egg has 23 pairs of chromosomes. A single individual could potentially produce any of $2^{23}$ (over 8 million) different kinds of germ cells. A given couple (with four distinct chromosomes for each pair of chromosomes) could form any of $4^{23}$ (over 70 quadrillion) kinds of fertilized eggs without any chromosome breakage occurring. The immense potential variety of possible offspring from the same parents is a characteristic of sexual reproduction.

## EXERCISES

1. How many 3-letter "triplets" like AAA, AAC, and so forth, can be made using the letters given.
   (a) A and C;            (b) A and T;
   (c) A, C, G;            (d) A, C, G, T.

2. If each base of a nucleic acid is either adenine, guanine, cytosine, or thymine, how many different linear sequences are possible in a nucleic acid of
   (a) 3 bases;            (b) 5 bases;
   (c) 6 bases;            (d) 10 bases.

3. The fertilized cell of a certain organism has 4 pairs of chromosomes; no member of a pair is the same as its partner.
   (a) How many distinct germ cells can a single individual produce?
   (b) If a male mates with a female, and no chromosome has the same information content as any other for both the male and female together, how many different kinds of offspring could a single pair potentially produce?

4. Answer questions (a) and (b) of Exercise 3 where the fertilized egg of the organism has only one homologous pair of chromosomes. Enumerate the possibilities using a tree diagram.

5. Answer questions (a) and (b) of Exercise 3 where there are 10 pairs of chromosomes.

6. In some plants and animals sperm and eggs can be produced by the same individual and self-fertiliza-

tion is possible. In such a self-mating the sets of male and female germ cells are the same; that is, to each possible sperm cell there corresponds a possible egg cell, identical in information content. (The variety of offspring, although less than in a mating of two individuals, is still large as is shown in this and the following exercises).
Suppose the fertilized egg of a hypothetical organism has a single pair of chromosomes. The two chromosomes are distinct in information content. Show by enumeration that although there are 4 possible sperm-egg combinations, there are only 3 kinds of eggs distinct in information content.

7. Consider the problem that is exactly the same as that of Exercise 6 except that the fertilized egg contains 2 pairs of chromosomes.
(a) How many sperm-egg combinations are there?
(b) How many distinct kinds of fertilized eggs are there?

8. Consider a self-fertilizing individual whose body cells contain $N$ pairs of chromosomes. Using the result of Exercise 6 and the rule of counting show that there are $3^N$ distinct fertilized eggs that this individual could potentially produce.

9. Using the results of Exercise 8, how many distinct fertilized eggs are possible from a self-fertilizing individual whose body cells have
(a) 3 chromosome pairs;   (b) 5 chromosome pairs;
(c) 10 chromosome pairs.

| PATH 1 ☞ §1.4 |   | PATH 2 ☞ §1.4, 2.6 |   | PATH 4 ☞ §6.6 |

## 1.4★  APPLICATIONS OF THE RULE OF COUNTING: A PROBLEM IN WOLF BEHAVIOR

A group of wolves (three males and two females) is maintained in semi-natural conditions in a large pen. A zoologist studying social behavior in wolves observes the animals during the mating season and records the courtship patterns of the group. For daily intervals during the breeding season he records whether or not a particular male courts a particular female and vice versa. A result for one time interval might be pictured as follows:

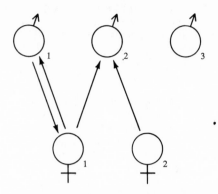

In words this diagram states that during this interval male 1 (represented by
$\male_1$) courted female 1 ( $\female_1$), female 1 courted males 1 and 2, and female 2 courted
male 2. Another possible result is

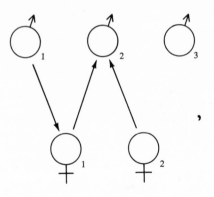

in which both females courted male 2, who did not reciprocate, and male 1
courted female 1. The figures or patterns above indicate whether courtship
occurred, not how many times. Thus, in both the above although $\male_1$ may have
courted $\female_1$ more than once, only a single arrow is drawn from $\male_1$ to $\female_1$.

During any interval it is possible for each male to court all the females, and
for both females to court the three males. It is also possible that no courting
occurs. The two figures below, respectively, represent both these possibilities

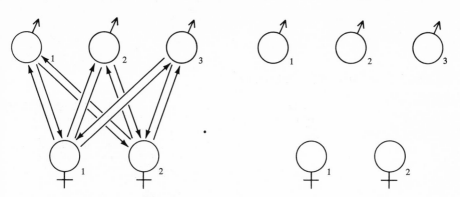

The question arises as to how many different figures or mating patterns of the wolves are possible. We can use the rule of counting to determine this. Before counting the total number of possible figures it may be interesting to test your intuition by guessing whether there are few or many mating patterns.

We now use the rule of counting to answer our question. Consider any male along with any female. For any pair there are four possibilities given by

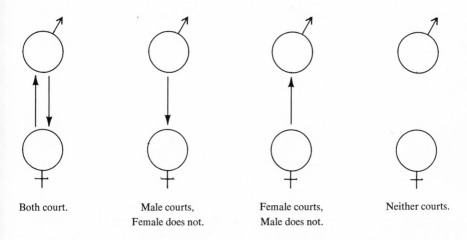

| Both court. | Male courts, Female does not. | Female courts, Male does not. | Neither courts. |

How many different male-female pairs are possible? There are three males and two females. By the rule of counting there are $3 \times 2 = 6$ pairs. For each of the six pairs there are the four possibilities which have just been illustrated. By the rule of counting we have

$$4 \times 4 \times 4 \times 4 \times 4 \times 4 = 4^6 = 4096$$

possibilities in all. The number of possibilities is quite large.

The general problem is readily solved. If there are $n$ females and $m$ males, then by the rule of counting there are $nm$ possible pairs. As before, each pair has four associated possibilities of interaction. By the rule of counting we have

$$\underbrace{4}_{\text{1st}} \quad \times \quad \underbrace{4}_{\text{2nd}} \quad \times \ldots \times \quad \underbrace{4}_{nm\text{th}} \quad = 4^{nm}$$

as the total number of possible mating patterns.

> EXAMPLE 1. With four males and two females, m = 4 and $n = 2$. The number of possible patterns is $4^8 =$ 65,536. With two males and four females, $m = 2$ and $n = 4$, and the number of mating possibilities is $4^8$, the same as the first instance. With three males and one female the number of possible patterns is $4^3 = 64$.

If for some reason certain courtships are regarded as impossible, then the reduced number of patterns is readily calculated using the rule of counting. Suppose, for example, that there are $m$ males and $n$ females, but that one male is sick and does no courting. First, consider the sick male paired with any of the $n$ females. Since this male does not court, there are only two possibilities for each such pair; namely,

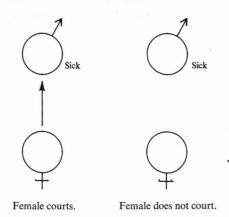

Female courts.          Female does not court.

There are $n$ such pairs. each with two possibilities. Next, consider any pair not involving the sick male. There are $m - 1$ healthy males and $n$ females. Thus there are $n(m - 1)$ such pairs; associated with each pair are the normal four possibilities. In all, we have $nm$ pairs; $n$ pairs each with two possibilities, and $n(m - 1) = nm - n$ pairs each with four possibilities. By the rule of counting we have

$$\underbrace{2 \times 2 \ldots \times 2}_{\substack{n \text{ pairs involving} \\ \text{the sick male}}} \times \underbrace{4 \times 4 \ldots \times 4}_{\substack{n(m - 1) \text{ pairs} \\ \text{not involving} \\ \text{the sick male}}} = 2^n 4^{n(m-1)},$$

$$\underbrace{\phantom{2 \times 2 \ldots \times 2 \times 4 \times 4 \ldots \times 4}}_{nm \text{ pairs in all.}}$$

and this is the total number of possible mating patterns if one male is sick and does no courting.

EXAMPLE 2. With $m = 3$ males (one of which is sick) and $n = 2$ females, the number of possible patterns is

$$2^2 \times 4^4 = 4 \times 256 = 1024.$$

The number of possible patterns when no male is sick is $4^6 = 4096$. There are 1024 patterns in which a particular male (the sick one) does no courting. The proportion of patterns in which one male does no courting is $1024/4096 = \frac{1}{4}$. With $m$ males and $n$ females the number of patterns in which a particular male does no courting is $2^n 4^{n(m-1)}$. This can also be written as

$$2^n 4^{n(m-1)} = 2^n (2^2)^{n(m-1)} = 2^n 2^{2nm-2n}$$
$$= 2^{2nm-n}$$
$$= 4^{nm}/2^n.$$

The total number of possible patterns with all animals possibly courting is $4^{nm}$. The proportion of patterns in which a given male does no courting is thus

$$1/2^n.$$

This proportion decreases as the number of females increases.

We can consider another case in which the number of possible courtships is restricted; as before, there are $m$ males and $n$ females. However, $\male_1$ is faithful to $\female_1$; that is, he either does or does not court $\female_1$, while she, herself, may court any male including $\male_1$. However, she is jealous of $\male_1$ and permits no other female to court him. We know there are $nm$ possible male-female pairs. First, consider the pair $\male_1$-$\female_1$. For this pair there are the four normal possibilities. Next, consider $\male_1$ paired with any of the $n - 1$ remaining females. For any such pair there is only one possibility; namely, that no courtship occurs. $\male_1$ does not court another female, and none of them is allowed to court him. Finally, consider any male other than $\male_1$ paired with any female including possibly $\female_1$. There are $m - 1$ males and $n$ females, and hence $n(m - 1)$ such pairs. Each pair has the normal four possibilities. Using the rule of counting we have

$$\underbrace{4}_{\substack{\text{one pair:} \\ \male_1\text{-}\female_1}} \times \underbrace{1 \times 1 \times \ldots \times 1}_{\substack{n - 1 \text{ pairs:} \\ \male_1\text{-other females}}} \times \underbrace{4 \times 4 \ldots \times 4}_{\substack{n(m - 1) \text{ pairs:} \\ \text{all other males-all females}}}$$

$$= 4 \times 4^{n(m-1)} = 4^{nm-n+1}$$

as the total number of possible patterns.

Before closing this section we consider still a third case of restricted mating. There are $m$ males and $n$ females; $\male_1$ is faithful to $\female_1$, $\female_1$ reciprocates and is faithful to $\male_1$. (Any other male may court $\female_1$, and any other female may court $\male_1$.) The following sets of pairs must be considered: The pair $\male_1$-$\female_1$, the $n - 1$ pairs of $\male_1$ with other females, the $m - 1$ pairs of $\female_1$ with other males, and the $(n - 1)(m - 1)$ pairs of other males with other females. Considerations similar to those we have already seen lead to

$$\underbrace{4}_{\substack{\text{one pair:} \\ \male_1\text{-}\female_1}} \times \underbrace{2 \times \ldots \times 2}_{\substack{n - 1 \text{ pairs:} \\ \male_1\text{-other females}}} \times \underbrace{2 \times \ldots \times 2}_{\substack{m - 1 \text{ pairs:} \\ \female_1\text{-other males}}}$$

$$\times \quad \underbrace{4 \times \ldots \times 4}_{(n - 1)(m - 1) \text{ pairs:}} \quad = 4(2^{n+m-2})4^{(n-1)(m-1)}$$

all other males-all other females

as the number of possibilities. Note that all $nm$ pairs are accounted for since

$$1 + (n - 1) + (m - 1) + (n - 1)(m - 1) = nm.$$

The number of possibilities can be written in several ways. A convenient form is

$$4(2^{n+m-2})4^{(n-1)(m-1)} = 2^{n+m}4^{(n-1)(m-1)}.$$

> EXAMPLE 3. Suppose there are three males and four females ($m = 3$ and $n = 4$). Suppose that $\male_1$ is faithful to $\female_1$, and vice versa. Then the number of mating possibilities is $2^{n+m}4^{(n-1)(m-1)}$. We have
>
> $$2^7 \times 4^6 = 128 \times 4096 = 524{,}288$$
>
> possible patterns. With two males and one female ($m = 2$ and $n = 1$), we have
>
> $$2^3 \times 4^0 = 2^3 = 8$$
>
> possible patterns.

### EXERCISES

1.  Suppose there are two males and one female.
    (a) How many possible courtship patterns are there?
    (b) Enumerate these.
    (c) Would you consider enumerating the patterns for two males and two females?

2.  (a) There are 4 males and 3 females. How many mating patterns are there?
    (b) With 3 males and 3 females, how many patterns are there?

3.  Suppose there are 2 males and 3 females with the restriction that none of the females does any courting. How many overall mating patterns are possible?

4.  There are 4 males and 3 females. However, male 1 is faithful to female 2 (that is, he does or does not court

female 2; he courts no other females).
Other males may court all females (including female
2). Females may court any males.
(a) How many mating patterns are possible?
(b) What proportion do these constitute of the
answer to part (a) of Exercise 2?

5. Solve the same problem as in Exercise 4 except that
female 2 is also faithful to male 1. She either courts
or does not court him and courts no other males.
Other females may court any males (including male
1).
(a) How many mating patterns are possible?
(b) What proportion do these constitute of the total
possible patterns (Hint: Compare with part (a) of
Exercise 2)?

6. There are 2 males and 3 females. Female 1 allows no
other female to court male 1. She herself may or may
not court either male. Any male may court any
female. How many mating patterns are possible?

7. There are 3 males and 3 females. Male 1 may court
any female. He allows no other male to court at
all. Female 3 is sick and does no courting (she herself may be courted). Females 1 and 2 may court any
males.
(a) How many patterns are possible?
(b) What proportion do these constitute of the total
mating possibilities when there are no restrictions on
courtships?

8. There are 3 males and 3 females. Male 2 is scorned
by all females and is never courted. (He himself may
court any female). The other males may court any females.
(a) How many mating patterns are possible?
(b) The same situation prevails, but male 1 always
actively courts female 2 and no other female. How
many patterns are possible?

9. There are *m* males and *n* females. Male 1 is faithful
to female 2 as in Exercise 4. The other males may
court any female.
(a) How many mating patterns are possible?
(b) What proportion do these constitute of the total
number of possibilities when there are no restrictions?

| PATH 2 §1.3, 2.6 |

## REFERENCES

### General

GOLDBERG, S., *Probability An Introduction* (Englewood Cliffs, N. J.: Prentice-Hall, Inc., 1960), Ch. 1, Section 2.

KEMENY, J. G., SNELL, J. L., and THOMPSON, G. L., *Introduction to Finite Mathematics* (Englewood Cliffs, N. J.: Prentice-Hall, Inc., 1956), Ch. 3.

### Optional Section 1.3

ELLIOTT, A. M., *Zoology*, 3rd ed. (New York: Appleton-Century-Crofts, 1963), Ch. 2, 3, 24.

ELLIOTT, A. M., and RAY, C., *Biology*, 2nd ed. (New York: Appleton-Century-Crofts, Inc., 1960), Ch. 2, 3, 29.

NASON, A., *Textbook of Modern Biology* (New York: John Wiley & Sons, Inc., 1965), Ch. 4, 11.

### Optional Section 1.4

KLOPFER, P. H., and HAILMAN, J. P., *An Introduction to Animal Behavior* (Englewood Cliffs, N. J.: Prentice-Hall, Inc., 1967).
[A general introduction to the study of behavior.]

RABB, G. B., WOOLPY, J. H., and GINSBURG, B. E. "Social Relationships in a Group of Captive Wolves," *American Zoologist*, Vol. 7, No. 7 (1967), pp. 305, 311.

# USE OF THE RULE TO COUNT PERMUTATIONS

## 2.1 PERMUTATIONS OR ARRANGEMENTS IN A LINE

In how many ways can the three letters ABC be arranged in a line? By actual arrangements we find that there are six possibilities or

$$ABC, ACB, BCA, BAC, CAB, CBA.$$

We can look at the problem and use the rule of counting. There are three places

$$\underbrace{\quad}_{\text{1st}} \quad \underbrace{\quad}_{\text{2nd}} \quad \underbrace{\quad}_{\text{3rd}} \; .$$

We can fill the first place with an A, B, or C — in other words in three ways; thus,

$$\underbrace{3}_{\text{1st}} \quad \underbrace{\quad}_{\text{2nd}} \quad \underbrace{\quad}_{\text{3rd}} \; .$$

Whatever letter we fill the first place with is used up, so there remain two letters. There are then two ways of filling the second place or

$$\underbrace{3}_{\text{1st}} \quad \underbrace{2}_{\text{2nd}} \quad \underbrace{\quad}_{\text{3rd}} \; .$$

There is then only one letter remaining for the third place; hence, we write a "one" in that spot or

$$\underbrace{3}_{\text{1st}} \quad \underbrace{2}_{\text{2nd}} \quad \underbrace{1}_{\text{3rd}} \; .$$

Invoking the rule of counting, we see that the total number of ways of filling the three places is

$$3 \times 2 \times 1 = 6.$$

Suppose we have $n$ distinguishable things to arrange in a line. How many arrangements are possible? Consider $n$ places

$$\underbrace{\quad}_{\text{1st}} \quad \underbrace{\quad}_{\text{2nd}} \quad \underbrace{\quad}_{\text{3rd}} \quad \ldots \quad \underbrace{\quad}_{\text{$n$th}} \; .$$

The first place can be filled with any of the $n$ things, thus in any of $n$ ways. This leaves $n - 1$ things remaining, and thus $n - 1$ ways of subsequently filling the second place. After the second place is filled there are $n - 2$ things remaining, and thus $n - 2$ ways of filling the third place. Finally, after all but the last place are filled, there is only one thing left to fill the $n$th place. Thus, we have

$$\underbrace{n}_{\text{1st}} \quad \underbrace{n-1}_{\text{2nd}} \quad \underbrace{n-2}_{\text{3rd}} \quad \cdots \quad \underbrace{1}_{n\text{th}} \ .$$

Invoking the rule of counting we have

$$n \times (n - 1) \times (n - 2) \times \ldots \times 1$$

ways of filling the places. Hence, we have the following result[1]

*The number of arrangements in a line (or permutations) of n distinguishable things is*

$$n \times (n - 1) \times (n - 2) \times \ldots \times 1$$

In the sections to follow the words *permutations* and *arrangements in a line* are used interchangeably.

EXAMPLE 1. The number of arrangements in a line is given for cases listed.
(a) For the letters ABCD,     $4 \times 3 \times 2 \times 1 = 24$.
(b) For the letters AB,       $2 \times 1 = 2$ (AB and BA).
(c) For the letter A,         one.
(d) For five different individuals, $5 \times 4 \times 3 \times 2 \times 1 = 120$.

EXAMPLE 2. Six students in a biology class are ranked in order of performance. Excluding the possibility of ties, how many possible rankings of each student are there? Here $n = 6$, and there are

$$6 \times 5 \times 4 \times 3 \times 2 \times 1 = 720$$

possible rankings.

EXAMPLE 3. In a class with $k$ students and with ties excluded there are

$$k \times (k-1) \times \ldots \times 2 \times 1$$

possible rankings.

EXAMPLE 4. Suppose in a class of five students that one particular individual is assured of highest honors. Given this fact how many possible rankings are there for the other students? Since a given individual must come first, there is only one way of filling the first place. The second place can be filled in any of four ways; the third, in any of three; and so forth; giving

$$\underbrace{1}_{\text{1st honors}} \quad \underbrace{4}_{\text{2nd honors}} \quad \underbrace{3}_{\text{3rd}} \quad \underbrace{2}_{\text{4th}} \quad \underbrace{1}_{\text{5th}} \ .$$

---

[1] In the next section the factorial notation is introduced, which makes it possible to state this result more succinctly.

By the rule of counting there are 24 possible rankings.

EXAMPLE 5.   Consider Example 4 but with a change in restrictions stating that one student is assured of second honors. There are also 24 possible rankings in this case. The ways of filling the places are

$$
\underbrace{\quad 4 \quad}_{\text{1st honors}} \quad \underbrace{\quad 1 \quad}_{\text{2nd honors}} \quad \underbrace{\quad 3 \quad}_{\text{3rd}} \quad \underbrace{\quad 2 \quad}_{\text{4th}} \quad \underbrace{\quad 1 \quad}_{\text{5th}} \; .
$$

It may be convenient to use a tree diagram to enumerate possible permutations. For example, to enumerate the permutations of the three letters A, B, C we can write

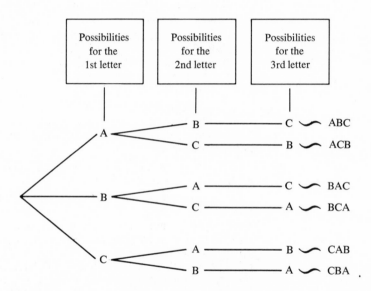

After the letter A is chosen, then only B and C are available. After A and C are both chosen, then B must be the third letter. This particular case is indicated as

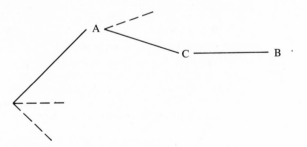

This path corresponds to the permutation ACB.

**EXERCISES**

1. (a) How many permutations are there of the letters xyz?
   (b) Enumerate these using a tree diagram.

2. (a) How many permutations are there of the letters ABCD?
   (b) Enumerate these using a tree diagram.

3. (a) How many permutations are there of the letters in the word *forecast*?
   (b) How many permutations are there of the letters in the word *universal*?

4. How many permutations are there of the letters ABCDE in which:
   (a) The permutation begins with the letter A?
   (b) The permutation begins with A and ends with C?
   (c) The permutation begins with B?

5. Ten different pots (each representing a different soil treatment) are to be arranged in a row on a greenhouse shelf. How many different arrangements of the pots are possible?

6. Four pollen grains (1 pine, 1 fir, 1 oak, 1 alder) are in a microscopic slide preparation. In how many possible orders can these four be tabulated if each is counted only once?

7. A person is tested on his ability to identify pollen grains of various pine species. He is presented the grains for identification.
   (a) There are three preparations — 1 of Virginia pine pollen, 1 of loblolly pine, and 1 of longleaf pine. He is presented the preparations in the order of longleaf, Virginia, loblolly. This is one of how many possible orders of presentation?
   (b) There are five preparations of pine pollen (1 each of Virginia, longleaf, loblolly, slash, and pitch pine). He is presented the grains in this order. This is one of how many possible orders of presentation?

8. A log crosses a small stream. A fox (F), a deermouse (D), and an ecologist (E) use the log to cross at night. Each crosses only once a night. When the fox arrives he waits at the log for prey. If the mouse arrives next he is eaten by the fox who then leaves. If the ecologist arrives while the fox is waiting the fox flees into the night. One order of arrival is FDE. (Here the fox arrives first, and the deermouse arrives next and is eaten.)
   (a) How many possible orders of arrival are there?
   (b) How many of these result in the fox eating?

(c) How many result in the fox fleeing without eating?

(d) How many result in the fox waiting all night?

9. A male sheeptick waits at the end of a blade of grass for a passing sheep to which to attach himself. There are three sheep in the pasture — one with a female tick (F), one with a male tick (M), and one with no ticks (N). There is also a farm truck (T) which drives through the pasture once a day. If the farm truck drives near the waiting tick, he retreats to the bottom of the blade of grass and stays there, inactive, for the rest of the day. Suppose each sheep and the truck pass exactly once by the tick's blade of grass during the day.

(a) How many different orders of arrival are there? (A possible order is TMNF.)

(b) In how many of these does the truck arrive before any of the sheep? (In these cases the tick does not attach himself at all.)

(c) In how many possibilities does the tick attach himself to the sheep with the female? (In these cases a mating is possible.)

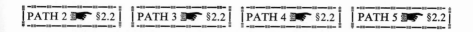

PATH 2 §2.2    PATH 3 §2.2    PATH 4 §2.2    PATH 5 §2.2

## 2.2 FACTORIAL NOTATION

We have just seen that numbers like

$$4 \times 3 \times 2 \times 1 = 24,$$

$$6 \times 5 \times 4 \times 3 \times 2 \times 1 = 720,$$

and

$$n \times (n - 1) \times (n - 2) \times \ldots \times 2 \times 1$$

give the number of arrangements in a line of 4, 6, and $n$ distinct things, respectively. We now introduce a notation to aid us in handling such numbers.

DEFINITION. *If $n$ is a positive integer, the symbol $n!$, which is read "$n$ factorial" is used to denote the product of the first $n$ positive integers*

$$n! = 1 \times 2 \times 3 \times \ldots \times n.$$

*As a special case, if $n = 0$ so that $n$ is not a positive integer, we define*

$$0! = 1.$$

Thus,

$$4! = 1 \times 2 \times 3 \times 4 = 24,$$

where we read "four factorial" for the symbol "4!." Similarly,

$$6! = 1 \times 2 \times 3 \times 4 \times 5 \times 6 = 720,$$

and we read this as "six factorial." 4! is another way of writing the number 24. Likewise, 6! is another symbol for the number 720. It makes no difference whether we write the integers in order of increasing or decreasing magnitude. Thus, we may write

$$4! = 1 \times 2 \times 3 \times 4 = 4 \times 3 \times 2 \times 1 = 24.$$

We often write the integers in decreasing order as

$$n! = n \times (n - 1) \times (n - 2) \times \ldots \times 2 \times 1 = 1 \times 2 \times \ldots \times n.$$

EXAMPLE 1.   We illustrate factorial notation in the following examples.
(a) $7! = 7 \times 6 \times 5 \times 4 \times 3 \times 2 \times 1 = 5040$.
(b) $3! = 3 \times 2 \times 1 = 6$.
(c) $2! = 2 \times 1 = 2$.
(d) $1! = 1$.

EXAMPLE 2.   We have noted for example, that 3! is another way of writing the number 6. Thus, $(3!)^2 = 6^2 = 36$.
(a) $(2!)^2 = 2^2 = 4$.
(b) $(3!)^2 - (2!)^2 = 36 - 4 = 32$.
(c) $7!/6! = 5040/720 = 7$.
(d) $4! - 3! = 18$.

The expression $(3 + 3)!$ is the number 720, since

$$(3 + 3)! = 6! = 720.$$

Note that $(3 + 3)!$ is not $3! + 3!$, which is $6 + 6 = 12$. The factorial symbol applies to the entire expression in the parentheses. Consequently, for example,

$$(3 + 3)! = 6!,$$
$$(5 + 2)! = 7!,$$
$$(6 + 1)! = 7!.$$

Consider 7!; this is

$$7! = 7 \times 6 \times 5 \times 4 \times 3 \times 2 \times 1.$$

We can also write this as

$$7! = 7 \times (6 \times 5 \times 4 \times 3 \times 2 \times 1)$$
$$= 7 \times 6!.$$

Similarly,

$$5! = 5 \times 4 \times 3 \times 2 \times 1$$
$$= 5 \times (4 \times 3 \times 2 \times 1)$$
$$= 5 \times 4!.$$

These examples illustrate an important relationship between the factorial of a number $n$ and the factorial of the number one greater than $n$ or $n + 1$; namely,

$$(n + 1)! = (n + 1) \times n \times (n - 1) \times \ldots \times 1$$
$$= (n + 1) \times [n \times (n - 1) \times \ldots \times 1]$$
$$= (n + 1) \times n!.$$

This relationship holds for any positive integer $n$. Thus, if $n = 6$ we have

$$(6 + 1)! = (6 + 1) \times 6! = 7 \times 6!$$
$$6! = 6 \times 5!$$
$$1000! = 1000 \times 999!.$$

It is easy to determine the ratios of certain factorials using this relationship. Thus,

$$\frac{7!}{6!} = \frac{7 \times 6!}{6!} = 7,$$

and

$$\frac{1000!}{999!} = \frac{1000 \times 999!}{999!} = 1000.$$

In general,

$$\frac{(n + 1)!}{n!} = \frac{(n + 1) \times n!}{n!} = (n + 1).$$

Dividing one factorial into another is often a simple matter of canceling factors. For example

$$\frac{8!}{6!} = \frac{8 \times 7 \times 6 \times 5 \times 4 \times 3 \times 2 \times 1}{6 \times 5 \times 4 \times 3 \times 2 \times 1}$$
$$= \frac{8 \times 7 \times 6!}{6!} = 8 \times 7 = 56.$$

In the case of very large numbers this may be an important technique to remember. 100! and 98! are both very large numbers but the ratio,

$$\frac{100!}{98!} = \frac{100 \times 99 \times 98 \times \ldots \times 1}{98 \times \ldots \times 1}$$
$$= \frac{100 \times 99 \times 98!}{98!} = 9900$$

is easily calculated.

We first defined factorials for positive integers, and then included a definition of 0! ("zero factorial"). Why was this chosen to have the value 1? For any *positive* integer $n$, we have

$$(n + 1) \times n! = (n + 1)! \ .$$

Therefore, 0! is defined so that this relationship also holds for $n = 0$. Letting $n = 0$, we have

$$(0 + 1)! = (0 + 1) \times 0!$$
$$1! = 1 \times 0!$$
$$1 = 1 \times 0!$$
$$1 = 0! \ .$$

Thus, $1 = 0!$ is a reasonable definition of 0!. Using this definition,

$$(n + 1) \times n! = (n + 1)!$$

holds for $n$ a positive integer or $n$ equal to zero.

EXAMPLE 3. The following examples illustrate various manipulations involving numbers expressed as factorials.

(a) $(2 + 2)! = (3 + 1)! = (5 - 1)! = (6 - 2)! = 4!$ .

(b) $4! = 4 \times 3! = 4 \times \quad 6 = \quad 24$ ;
$5! = 5 \times 4! = 5 \times \quad 24 = 120$ ;
$6! = 6 \times 5! = 6 \times 120 = 720$ .

(c) $\quad 10! = 10 \times 9!$ ; $\quad \dfrac{10!}{9!} = 10$ ; $\quad \dfrac{12!}{11!} = 12$ ;

$\dfrac{1001!}{1000!} = 1001$ ; $\quad \dfrac{73!}{72!} = 73$ .

(d) $\dfrac{10!}{8!} = \dfrac{10 \times 9 \times 8!}{8!} = 90$ ;

$\dfrac{50!}{48!} = 50 \times 49 = 2450$ ;

$\dfrac{8!}{5!} = \dfrac{8 \times 7 \times 6 \times 5!}{5!} = 336$ ;

$\dfrac{6!}{3!} = \dfrac{6 \times 5 \times 4 \times 3!}{3!} = 120$ .

(e) $0! + 0! = 2$ ; $\quad 0! + 0! + 0! = 3$ ; $\quad \dfrac{3!}{0!} = 3! = 6$ .

## EXERCISES

1. $7! = 5040$. What do the following equal?
   (a) $8!$ ;         (b) $4!$ ;         (c) $(4!)^2 - 5!$ ;
   (d) $1! - 0!$ ;    (e) $(1 + 0)!$ ;   (f) $10!$ ;
   (g) $6!$ ;         (h) $7! - 6!$ ;    (i) $(7 - 6)!$ ;
   (j) $(6 + 4)!$ .

2. Determine the value of:
   (a) $(3 + 2)!$ ; (b) $(3 + 2 - 4 + 1)!$ ; (c) $(6/2)!$ ;
   (d) $6!/2!$ ; (e) $10!/7!$ ; (f) $25!/24!$ .

3. Evaluate the following:
   (a) $4! \times 2!$ ;         (b) $(4 \times 2)!$ ;
   (c) $6!/(4! \times 2!)$ ;     (d) $10!/(8! \times 2!)$ .

4. Evaluate the following:
   (a) $\dfrac{10!}{9!\,1!}$ ;    (b) $\dfrac{10!}{10!\,0!}$ ;    (c) $\dfrac{10!}{8!\,2!}$ ;    (d) $\dfrac{10!}{5!\,5!}$ .

5. Complete the following table:

   | | | | | |
   |---|---|---|---|---|
   | $0! = 1$ | $3! = 6$ | $6! =$ | $9! =$ | $12! =$ |
   | $1! = 1$ | $4! =$ | $7! =$ | $10! =$ | $13! =$ |
   | $2! = 2$ | $5! =$ | $8! =$ | $11! =$ | |

6. Determine the value of $(n + r)!$ for
   (a) $n = 2, r = 2$ ;        (b) $n = 3, r = 1$ ;
   (c) $n = 5, r = 1$ ;        (d) $n = 4, r = 2$ ;
   (e) $n = 7, r = 0$ .

| PATH 2 ☞ §2.3 | | PATH 3 ☞ §2.3 | | PATH 4 ☞ §2.3 | | PATH 5 ☞ §2.3 |

## 2.3 MORE ON PERMUTATIONS OF DISTINCT OBJECTS

Using factorial notation we can now state the result of Section 2.1 in a succinct fashion.

GENERAL STATEMENT. *The number of permutations of n distinct objects is n*!

This result applies to arranging $n$ distinct objects in $n$ places in a line. In this section we consider an extension of this.

Consider the letters A, B, C, D. There are $4! = 24$ ways of arranging these four letters in four places in a line. Suppose we have four letters, but only two places in which to arrange them. How many different permutations can we form by choosing any two letters and then arranging them in a line? By actual arrangement we find that there are 12 such arrangements:

$$AB, \quad BA, \quad CA, \quad DA,$$

$$AC, \quad BC, \quad CB, \quad DB,$$

$$AD, \quad BD, \quad CD, \quad DC.$$

This number can readily be determined using the rule of counting. There are two places

$$\underset{\text{I}}{\lfloor\underline{\quad}\rfloor} \qquad \underset{\text{II}}{\lfloor\underline{\quad}\rfloor} .$$

The first place can be filled with any of four letters. Three letters remain from which to choose the second letter. Thus the second place can be filled in any of three ways. There are

$$\underset{\text{I}}{\underline{4}} \times \underset{\text{II}}{\underline{3}} = 12$$

ways of filling the two places.

EXAMPLE 1. In a class of seven students, one receives first honors; another, second honors; and still another, third honors. Any of seven students can take first honors; there remain six possibilities for second honors, and five for third. We have

$$\underset{\text{1st}}{\underline{7}} \times \underset{\text{2nd}}{\underline{6}} \times \underset{\text{3rd}}{\underline{5}} = 210$$

possible ways for this to happen. This is the number of permutations that can be formed by choosing any of three things from seven.

EXAMPLE 2. Suppose that of five male wolves, one emerges as a dominant male (I). He dominates the other four. Suppose also that a second emerges as a subdominant male (II). He dominates the remaining three. In how many ways can a dominant male and a subdominant male be chosen from the five. There are two places. The number of ways is

$$\underset{\text{I}}{\underline{5}} \times \underset{\text{II}}{\underline{4}} = 20 \,.$$

This is the number of permutation of two things chosen from five things.

The problem can be posed in a general manner. There are $n$ distinct objects. In how many ways can any $r$ of these be arranged in a line. There are $r$ places:

$$\underset{\text{1st}}{\underline{\quad}} \qquad \underset{\text{2nd}}{\underline{\quad}} \qquad \underset{\text{3rd}}{\underline{\quad}} \cdots \underset{r\text{th}}{\underline{\quad}} \cdot$$

The first place can be filled with any of $n$ objects, and hence in any of $n$ ways. There remain $n-1$ objects and thus $n-1$ ways of filling the second place. There then remain $n-2$ objects with which to fill the third place and so forth. In how many ways can the $r$th place be filled? We know that $r-1$ objects have been used to fill the previous $r-1$ places. There remain $n-(r-1)$ $= n-r+1$ objects, and hence that many ways of filling the $r$th place. By the rule of counting we obtain

$$\underset{\text{1st}}{\underline{n}} \times \underset{\text{2nd}}{\underline{(n-1)}} \times \underset{\text{3rd}}{\underline{(n-2)}} \times \ldots \times \underset{r\text{th}}{\underline{(n-r+1)}} =$$

$$n(n-1)(n-2)\ldots(n-r+1).$$

This is the number of permutations of $n$ objects chosen $r$ at a time. It is understood that the first term in the product is $n$, the last term is $n - r + 1$, and that there are $r$ terms in the product. For example, in arranging any two of the four letters A, B, C, D into two places we have $n = 4$ and $r = 2$. The first term in the product is $n = 4$. The last term is $n - r + 1 = 4 - 2 + 1 = 3$. We then obtain as before

$$4 \times 3 = 12.$$

The general result can be succinctly stated in factorial notation. Note that

$$n! = n \times (n - 1) \times (n - 2) \times \ldots \times (n - r + 1) \times$$
$$(n - r) \times (n - r - 1) \times \ldots \times 2 \times 1,$$

and

$$(n - r)! = (n - r) \times (n - r - 1) \times \ldots \times 2 \times 1.$$

Thus,

$$\frac{n!}{(n - r)!} = n(n - 1)(n - 2) \ldots (n - r + 1).$$

Thus, we have the following

GENERAL STATEMENT.    *Given n distinct objects, the number of ways of choosing and arranging r of these in a line is*

$$\frac{n!}{(n - r)!}.$$

A symbol in frequent use for the number of permutations that can be formed from $n$ distinct objects is $_nP_r$, which can be read as *the number of permutations of n things r at a time.* Thus,

$$_nP_r = n!/(n - r)!$$

EXAMPLE 3.    In Example 1, there are seven students and three places so $n = 7$, $r = 3$. The first number in the product is $n = 7$, the last is $n - r + 1 = 7 - 3 + 1 = 5$. We obtain as before

$$_7P_3 = 7 \times 6 \times 5 = 210.$$

In Example 2, there are five wolves and two places. The first number in the product is $n = 5$; the last, $n - r + 1 = 4$. We find that

$$_5P_2 = 5 \times 4 = 20.$$

EXAMPLE 4.    Given 7 letters ABCDEFG, the number of permutations which can be formed by first choosing any 4 letters and then arranging these in a line is

$$7!/(7 - 4)! = 7!/3! = 840.$$

**EXERCISES**

1. Evaluate $_nP_r$ for
   (a) $n = 8, r = 3$ ;      (b) $n = 8, r = 2$ ;
   (c) $n = 3, r = 1$ ;      (d) $n = 3, r = 3$ ;
   (e) $n = 100, r = 1$ ;    (f) $n = 100, r = 3$ .

2. From ten different pots (each containing a different soil treatment), three pots are to be selected and arranged in a row on a greenhouse shelf. How many ways are there of choosing and arranging the three pots?

3. From four persons (J,M,S, and T) a chairman and a secretary are to be chosen. In how many ways can this be done?

4. In how many ways can we arrange the letters ABCDE into three places, one letter per place?

5. In a small population there are 7 females and 3 males. Each male must mate, and each mates with one and only one female. No female may mate more than once. How many different mating patterns are there for the population? (Hint: Represent the females by seven letters ABCDEFG and the males by three places.) Two mating patterns differ if one pattern has a mating of two individuals not found in another.

6. From 50 people, a president and a vice-president are to be chosen. In how many ways can this be done?

7. Consider Exercise 5 except now there is a population of 10 females and 4 males. How many mating patterns are possible?

| PATH 2 ☞ §2.4 |   | PATH 3 ☞ §2.4 |   | PATH 4 ☞ §2.4 |   | PATH 5 ☞ §2.4 |

## 2.4 PERMUTATIONS WITH ONE CLASS OF INDISTINGUISHABLE OBJECTS

Suppose we have the letters AAB, where the two A's are indistinguishable. In how many different ways can these three letters be arranged in a line? By actual arrangement we find there are only three; namely,

BAA,    ABA,    AAB.

If the two A's were distinguishable ($A_1$ and $A_2$) there would be $3! = 6$ permutations possible or

$BA_1A_2$,    $A_1BA_2$,    $A_1A_2B$,

$BA_2A_1$,    $A_2BA_1$,    $A_2A_1B$.

Consider a permutation beginning with B,

$$B\_ \_.$$

With identical A's there is only one way of filling the empty places,

$$B \underline{A} \underline{A}.$$

However, with different A's ($A_1$ and $A_2$) there are two ways of filling the empty places; namely,

$$B \underline{A_1 A_2} \quad \text{and} \quad B \underline{A_2 A_1}$$

and these represent the 2! arrangements of $A_1$ and $A_2$. Thus, to each of the distinct arrangements (when the A's are identical) we can associate two arrangements when the A's differ:

$$B \underline{A} \underline{A}; \qquad \{B \underline{A_1 A_2}, \quad B \underline{A_2 A_1}\};$$
$$\underline{A} B \underline{A}; \qquad \{\underline{A_1} B \underline{A_2}, \quad \underline{A_2} B \underline{A_1}\};$$
$$\underline{A} \underline{A} B; \qquad \{\underline{A_1 A_2} B, \quad \underline{A_2 A_1} B\}.$$

There are 3! = 6 arrangements of $BA_1A_2$. *For each distinct arrangement when the A's are indistinguishable the 2! = 2 permutations of $A_1$ and $A_2$ are lost.* This suggests dividing 3! by 2! in order to obtain the number of distinct permutations of the letters AAB or

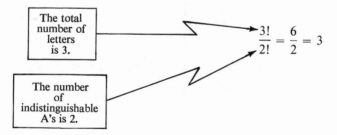

We now prove that this result is generally true.

GENERAL STATEMENT.    *The number of distinct permutations of n things when r of these are indistinguishable is*

$$\frac{n!}{r!}.$$

Before proceeding with the proof of this stated result, several illustrations of its use are given in the examples.

EXAMPLE 1.    There are four distinct permutations of the letters AAAB given by

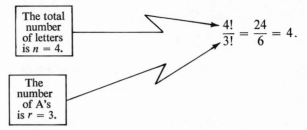

These are readily enumerated using a tree diagram.

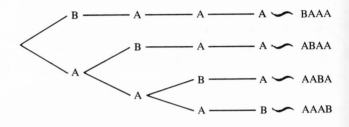

For each distinct arrangement, the $3! = 6$ arrangements of $A_1$, $A_2$, and $A_3$ are lost.

EXAMPLE 2.   The number of permutations of the letters ABCC is

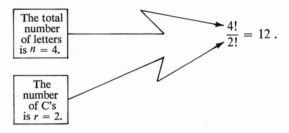

In proceeding we reconsider the example of the letters AAB in a slightly more formal fashion.  As we have seen, if we consider the A's as distinct then there are three distinguishable things — $A_1$, $A_2$, and B — for which there are $3! = 6$ different permutations.  Take any one of these like

$$A_1BA_2.$$

Call any other permutation a "sister" permutation if it is *the same except for some rearrangement of the A's among themselves.*  Thus,

$$A_2BA_1$$

is a sister permutation of $A_1BA_2$.  Since there are only two permutations of $A_1$ and $A_2$, only two permutations can be sisters of each other.  How many different "families" of sister permutations are there? There are three or

$$\{BA_1A_2, \quad BA_2A_1\}, \qquad \{A_1BA_2, \quad A_2BA_1\}, \qquad \{A_1A_2B, \quad A_2A_1B\}.$$
$$\text{family 1: BAA} \qquad \text{family 2: ABA} \qquad \text{family 3: AAB}$$

Note that

(1) Any one of the 3! = 6 permutations must belong to some family.
(2) A permutation can only belong to one family.
(3) There are 2! = 2 sister permutations in each family.

There is a total of six permutations, two different ones in each family, and the number of families can be determined as

$$\frac{3!}{2!} = \frac{6}{2} = 3.$$

But each family corresponds to a distinct permutation when $A_1$ and $A_2$ are indistinguishable. This is generally true, for if the A's are indistinguishable, then permutations from the same family are indistinguishable. However, two permutations from different families must differ in some way other than a rearrangement of the A's among themselves. They are distinguishable whether or not the A's are distinguishable. Therefore, *the number of distinct permutations when the A's are indistinguishable is simply the number of families.*

The general result readily follows. There are *n* things, and *r* of these are indistinguishable. Contrary to the true situation, we first suppose that the *r* identical things are distinguishable. We label these $(A_1, A_2, \ldots, A_r)$. Then there is a total of *n* distinguishable things and there are *n*! permutations of these. There are *r*! sister permutations in any family since $A_1, \ldots, A_r$ can be rearranged among themselves in *r*! ways. Then there is a total of *n*! permutations of which there are *r*! different ones in each family. Each permutation must be in one family and no other. *The number of families is then*

$$\frac{n!}{r!}.$$

But the number of families is the number of distinct permutations when the *r* things are indistinguishable. This proves the general result.

EXAMPLE 3.  Consider the permutations of the letters ABCC, where the two C's are indistinguishable. Using a tree diagram we find there are 12 of these:

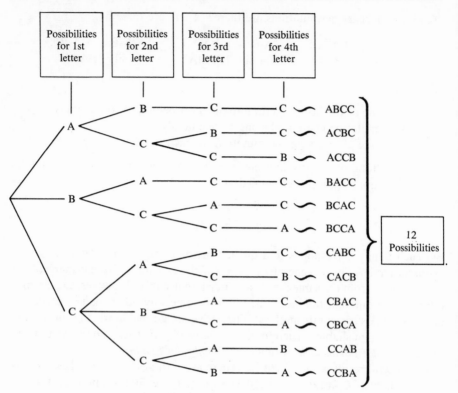

If the C's were different ($C_1$ and $C_2$) there would be 4! = 24 different permutations. There would also be 2! permutations of the C's among themselves, and hence there are two sister permutations in each family. For example,

$$\{ABC_1C_2, \quad ABC_2C_1\} \sim \text{"the ABCC family,"}$$
$$\{BAC_1C_2, \quad BAC_2C_1\} \sim \text{"the BACC family"}$$

and so forth. The number of families (and hence the number of distinct permutations when the C's are indistinguishable) is

$$\frac{4!}{2!} = \frac{24}{2} = 12.$$

EXAMPLE 4. There are one male (M) and four females (F's), the latter being indistinguishable. There are then five distinct permutations given by

MFFFF,    FMFFF,    FFMFF,    FFFMF,
FFFFM .

With distinguishable females ($F_1$, $F_2$, $F_3$, $F_4$) there are 5! = 120 different permutations. The number of sister permutations in each family is 4! = 24 (the permutations of $F_1$, $F_2$, $F_3$, and $F_4$). There are thus

$$\frac{5!}{4!} = 5$$

families. This is the number of distinct permutations when the F's are indistinguishable.

EXAMPLE 5. How many permutations of the letters FFFFFM are there? Here $n = 6$ and $r = 5$, and there are

$$6!/5! = 6$$

distinct permutations.

EXAMPLE 6. How many permutations are there of the letters in the word *future*. There are two U's. The number of permutations of the letters in this word is

$$6!/2! = 360 .$$

EXAMPLE 7. In the word *glosses* there are three S's; therefore, $n = 7$ and $r = 3$. The number of permutations of the letters in this word is

$$7!/3! = 840 .$$

(NOTE that in Examples 6 and 7 the word permutation is used without the adjective *distinct*. When we refer to permutations, distinct permutations are understood. It should be clear in the context of a given problem whether things are to be treated as distinguishable or not.)

### EXERCISES

1.  How many permutations are there of the four letters in the word *moon*?

2.  (a) How many permutations are there of the four letters AAAB ?
    (b) Enumerate these using a tree diagram.

3.  (a) How many permutations can be formed from the letters in the word *sibling*?
    (b) How many from the letters in the word *babbit*?

4.  A microscope slide preparation contains six pine pollen grains (P), and one each of fir (F), oak (O), and alder (A). In how many possible orders can these grains be tabulated? (One possible order is PPPFPOAPP.)

5.  A botanist conducts an experiment on the growth of tomato seedlings. Each of two trays has a different

soil treatment. One tray is labeled A, the other B; there are in addition two identical control trays (C). When the trays are arranged in a row on a greenhouse shelf, how many distinct arrangements are possible?

6. A tree swallow (T), a bank swallow (B), a cliff swallow (C), and six rough winged swallows (R) are on a telephone wire. An observer can tell the species apart, but not individuals within a species. He observes the arrangement RBCTRRRRR. This is one of how many possible observations?

7. An investigator is tested on his ability to distinguish *Carpinus* pollen from *Ostrya* pollen. He is shown twenty grains of pollen, one after the other. There are nineteen *Carpinus* grains and only one *Ostrya* grain. Each grain is shown once. In how many distinct orders can the grains be shown?

8. A log crosses a small stream. A fox (F), three deermice (D), and a man (M) use the log to cross at night. Each crosses once. If the fox arrives first he waits at the log for prey and eats all mice arriving after him; however, if the man arrives while the fox is waiting the fox flees into the night and does not return.
(a) How many orders of arrival are possible? (One possibility is FDDDM, in which the fox eats three mice)
(b) Enumerate the possible orders using a tree diagram.
(c) In how many of these is exactly one mouse eaten? Two mice? Three mice?
(d) In how many does the fox neither eat any mice nor flee from the man?

9. The problem is the same as the preceding except that there are 100 deermice (D) and one fox (F) with no man in the area. The fox's capacity is ten mice after which he leaves the area. The fox does not recognize individuals among the deermice.
(a) How many orders of arrival are possible?
(b) In how many of these are ten mice eaten?
(c) In how many of these are exactly five mice eaten?
(d) In how many are no mice eaten?

| PATH 2 ☞ §2.5 | | PATH 3 ☞ §2.5 | | PATH 4 ☞ §2.5 | | PATH 5 ☞ §2.5 |

## 2.5 PERMUTATIONS WITH MORE THAN ONE CLASS OF INDISTINGUISHABLE OBJECTS

Let us pass to the case with more than one class of indistinguishable things: For example, consider the letters AABB. There is a total of four letters — two indistinguishable A's and two indistinguishable B's. How many distinct permutations are there? By actual arrangement we find there are six given by

$$\text{AABB,}\qquad\text{BBAA,}\qquad\text{ABAB,}\qquad\text{BABA,}\qquad\text{ABBA,}\qquad\text{BAAB.}$$

In this section we show that this number can be determined as follows:

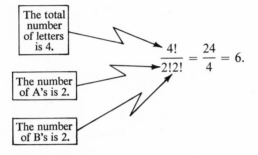

$$\frac{4!}{2!2!} = \frac{24}{4} = 6.$$

Now suppose that we have the letters AAABBCDD, where there are three A's, two B's, and two D's. We show that the number of distinct permutations of these eight letters is

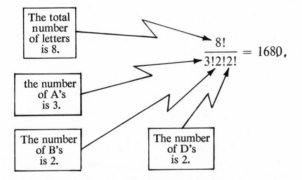

$$\frac{8!}{3!2!2!} = 1680,$$

The general result which is proved in this section is as follows.

GENERAL STATEMENT.    *The number of distinct permutations of n things where m are indistinguishable of type 1, r are indistinguishable of type 2, ..., and s are indistinguishable of type k, is*

$$\frac{n!}{m!r! \ldots s!}.$$

This result follows readily. The only difference between this development and that of the general statement of Section 2.4 is in the determination of the number of sister permutations within a family. As before, consider the indistinguishable things as being distinguishable. Label those of the first type, $A_1, \ldots, A_m$; those of the second, $B_1, \ldots, B_r$; ...; those of the $k$th type, $K_1, \ldots, K_s$. There are then $n$ distinct things, and $n!$ permutations of these things.

Consider any one of the $n!$ permutations. "Sister" permutations are permutations which have the same configuration of letters forgetting the subscripts. Thus, two permutations are sisters if they are the same except for one or more of the following types of rearrangement:

(1) the A's among themselves,
(2) the B's among themselves,

.

.    ,

.

($k$) the K's among themselves.

How many permutations can be sisters? The A's can be arranged among themselves in $m!$ ways; the B's in $r!$ ways; ...; and finally, the K's in $s!$ ways. By the rule of counting the number of permutations that can be sisters is simply

$$m! \times r! \times \ldots \times s! = m!r! \ldots s!.$$

This is the number of sister permutations in any family. We note that

(1) Each of the $n!$ permutations belongs to some family.
(2) Each belongs to only one family.
(3) There are $m!r! \ldots s!$ sister permutations in a family.

There are thus $n!$ permutations with $m!r! \ldots s!$ different ones in each family. The number of families must then be

$$\frac{n!}{m!r! \ldots s!},$$

and this is also the number of distinct permutations when the A's are alike, and the B's are alike, and so forth. Just as in Section 2.4, when these letters are indistinguishable among themselves then members of the same family are also indistinguishable, but members of two different families are distinguishable whether or not the various letters are indistinguishable among themselves.

EXAMPLE 1. There are ten distinct permutations of the letters AAABB.

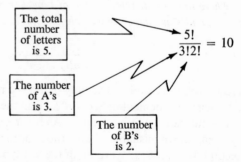

These are readily enumerated using a tree diagram or

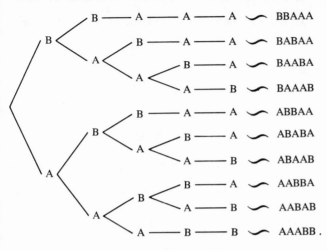

B —— A —— A —— A ⌒ BBAAA
B —— A —— A ⌒ BABAA
B —— A ⌒ BAABA
A —— B ⌒ BAAAB
B —— A —— A ⌒ ABBAA
B —— A ⌒ ABABA
A —— B ⌒ ABAAB
B —— A ⌒ AABBA
A —— B ⌒ AABAB
A —— B —— B ⌒ AAABB .

EXAMPLE 2.  The number of permutations of the letters

AABBBBCDDD

is

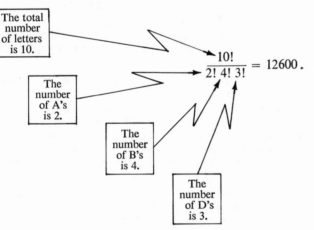

The total number of letters is 10.

The number of A's is 2.

The number of B's is 4.

The number of D's is 3.

$$\frac{10!}{2!\,4!\,3!} = 12600 .$$

EXAMPLE 3.  How many permutations are there of the letters in the word *banana*?
Here $n = 6$, $m = 3$, and $s = 2$.

$$\frac{6!}{3!2!} = 60 .$$

EXAMPLE 4.  The number of permutations of the letters

CCCCGGUAA

is

$$\frac{9!}{4!2!2!} = 3780 .$$

EXAMPLE 5.   The number of permutations of the letters
CCGGUUAAA
is

$$\frac{9!}{2!2!2!3!} = 7560 .$$

## EXERCISES

1. (a) How many permutations are there of the letters
in the word *coffee*?
(b) How many are there of the letters in the word
*professor*?

2. (a) How many permutations are there of the letters
CCCGGUUAAA?
(b) Of 4 A's and 3 U's?
(c) Of 2 A's, 2 C's, and 3 G's?

3. A nucleic acid molecule can be thought of as a permutation of bases (or letters) of four types — C,A,G,U.
(a) How many hypothetical nucleic acids of eight
bases can be formed from 2 C's, 4 U's, 1 A, and 1 G.
(One possibility is CCUUUUAG.)
(b) A nucleic acid of 10 bases is known to have 5 U's,
2 A's, 2 G's, and 1 C. How many hypothetical
molecules are there with this composition?

4. How many permutations are there of the letters
FFFFMMMM?

5. In a microscope slide preparation there are 10 pollen
grains of pine (P), 6 of oak (O), 2 of fir (F), 5 of
alder (A), and 4 of cypress (C). An investigator
tabulates the grains, counting each one once. How
many orders of tabulation are possible? (Leave the
answer in factorial notation.)

6. There are five pots with one soil treatment and five
with another. The five pots of each treatment are
indistinguishable. The pots are arranged in a row on
a greenhouse shelf. How many distinct arrangements are possible?

7. An investigator tabulates 100 grains of pollen on a
slide as follows:

| pine | fir | oak | alder | spruce |
|------|-----|-----|-------|--------|
| 70   | 5   | 10  | 12    | 3 .    |

He did not record the *order* in which these were
counted. In how many possible orders could these
results have been tabulated? (Leave the answer in
factorial form.)  For another slide he tabulated

| pine | fir | oak | alder | spruce |
|------|-----|-----|-------|--------|
| 99   | 0   | 1   | 0     | 0      |

In how many possible orders could these have been tabulated?

8. An investigator is studying size differences between male and female turtles of the same species. He has a sample of four males and six females. The turtles are arranged according to increasing size (no two are of the same size.) He finds the arrangement

FFFFFMMFMM.

(a) This is one of how many possible arrangements?
(b) How many possible arrangements are there in which the two largest specimens are male?
(c) How many possible arrangements are there if the three smallest specimens are females?

9. A research worker is studying sex ratios in human families. He is particularly interested in whether there is a tendency for the early children in a family to be of one sex or the other. He studies families with five children.
How many possible orders of birth are there for the following families?
(a) Families with 2 boys and 3 girls;
(b) Families with 1 boy and 4 girls;
(c) Families with 5 girls;
(d) Families with 3 boys and 2 girls?

PATH 2 ☞ §3.1    PATH 3 ☞ §3.1    PATH 4 ☞ §3.1    PATH 5 ☞ §3.1

## 2.6★  APPLICATIONS OF PERMUTATIONS: THE GENETIC CODE AND NUCLEIC ACID SEQUENCES. PART I.[2] INTRODUCTION

A problem of major importance in biology today is that of determining sequences of bases within nucleic acids. Nucleic acids are chains of smaller units known as nucleotides. These latter are covalently bonded in a linear array to form the nucleic acid molecule. There are four commonly occurring bases in nucleotides that are denoted by the letters C, A, G, and U,[3] and a nucleic acid can be thought of as a linear sequence or permutation of these bases. For example, one might have a nucleic acid like

ACGAUUUUGCCU.

The chemical nature of the nucleotides need not concern us here. What is

---

[2] Part II of the genetic code and nucleic acid sequences follows in Section 2.7.

[3] These letters refer to cytosine, adenine, guanine, and uracil, respectively. These are the four common bases in RNA (ribonucleic acid). In DNA (deoxyribonucleic acid) uracil is replaced by T (thymine).

important is that organisms use nucleic acids as stored words,[4] which contain specific instructions to the cell for the manufacture of proteins. Although it has been known since the early days of the microscope that a single fertilized ovum (or egg) contains all the information necessary to produce, for example, a catfish and not a dog, it is only within the last fifteen years that it has been understood how this prodigious amount of information is stored in a single cell. This is accomplished by means of the stored "words" in different sequences of bases within nucleic acids. Different nonoverlapping triplets of bases in nucleic acids determine what proteins are manufactured by the cell. (Proteins are themselves chains of building-block molecules known as amino acids. There are **twenty** common naturally occurring amino acids. Different proteins have different amounts and sequences of amino acids.)

When a cell is manufacturing a protein, a nucleic acid sequence is "read." During this "reading," different nonoverlapping triplets of nucleotides determine, or "code for," different amino acids. These are added to the protein chain under construction in the same order in which the triplets are read. For example, if the nucleic acid

UUU CGA UUC

is read then the following three amino acids are added to the protein chain in this order,

phenylalanine-arginine-phenylalanine,

since UUU and UUC both code for phenylalanine while CGA codes for arginine. As triplets are read in the nucleic acid, different amino acids are added to the protein chain being built. Thus different proteins are built as a result of different instructions contained in the sequences of bases in nucleic acids.

### EXERCISES

1. How many triplets of different sequence with possibly repeating letters (like AAA, AAG, GGU, etc.) can be formed from the four letters C, A, G, U.

2. The three bases of a particular triplet are known to be A, C, G, but their order is not known.
   (a) How many triplets are possible in this case?
   (b) If the bases are A, A, G, how many possible triplets are there?

3. Could each of the 20 common naturally occurring amino acids be coded with a different doublet (*e.g.*, UU, AU, etc.) formed from the four bases C, A, G, U?

4. A nucleic acid of 10 bases is known to contain 3 A's, 2 U's, 2 C's, and 3 G's.
   (a) How many possible molecules are there with this composition?

---

[4] See also Section 1.3.

(b) If the molecule is known to terminate with the letters AAG, how many possibilities are there?

5. A nucleic acid of 15 bases is known to contain 4 A's, 4 C's, 4 G's, and 3 U's. (Leave answers in factorial form.)

(a) How many possible molecules are there with this composition?

(b) If the molecule is known to begin with the bases AC and terminate with AA, how many possible molecules are there?

6. Suppose it is known that the amino acid phenylalanine is coded only by the triplets UUU and UUC, while the amino acid histidine is coded only by the triplets CAC and CAU. Suppose the code consisted of *overlapping* triplets, so that, for example, the nucleic acid ACGUU codes successively for *three* amino acids as follows:

ACGUU,     ACGUU,     ACGUU,

1st amino acid     2nd amino acid     3rd amino acid

(a) If overlapping triplets coded amino acids as above, what is the maximum number of kinds of amino acids which could follow the amino acid phenylalanine in a protein chain?

(b) If the code were overlapping as above, could histidine ever follow phenylalanine in a protein?

| PATH 2 ☞ §2.7 |     | PATH 4 ☞ §2.7 |

## 2.7★ APPLICATIONS OF PERMUTATIONS: THE GENETIC CODE AND NUCLEIC ACID SEQUENCES. PART II. DETERMINATION OF SEQUENCES

It can be seen that the task of determining the sequences of bases within a nucleic acid is an important one; it is, unfortunately, extremely difficult to do. The first nucleic acid sequence was determined in 1965 by R. W. Holley and his co-workers at Cornell University. It contained 77 bases, which is short as nucleic acids go and was not of a type which directly codes for protein sequences. For various practical reasons the sequences of nucleic acid chains with more than 9 bases (or so) cannot, at present, be directly determined. However, a longer chain can be broken into smaller chains or fragments whose internal sequences can be determined. This method was used by Holley, and it is called the *fragmentation stratagem.*

Suppose one has a preparation of a large number (say $10^{16}$) of nucleic acid molecules of identical sequence. One can introduce into the preparation an enzyme which cuts (or digests) the nucleic acid into smaller sequences or fragments by breaking the original chain after certain bases. The sequences within these smaller fragments can then usually be determined. There are currently two commonly used enzymes. The first, if allowed to react with the preparation for a sufficient amount of time, cuts the sequence after each G; the second, after each C and U. Introduction of the {G} enzyme into a preparation of a hypothetical nucleic acid

CCGGUCCGAAAG

yields after letting the reaction run its course the following fragments

CCG, G, UCCG, AAAG.

If one lets the {C, U} enzyme attack the same sequence, one would find the fragments

C, C, GGU, C, C, GAAAG.

Both enzymes break the molecule into fragments whose letter-sequences can be determined. However, the order of these fragments within the original molecule is *not* known.

Knowing only the fragments from both enzymes, is it possible to determine the sequence of the original chain from the two sets of fragments? In our example the answer is yes. However, with very long chains the answer is almost always no. Let us examine the fragments enumerated above of the {C, U} digest. We obtained a fragment GAAAG that does not end in C or U; hence, it must be the terminal fragment. There remain five fragments, four of which are alike,

C, C, C, C, and GGU.

By application of the general statement (Section 2.5) about the number of distinct permutations of distinguishable and indistinguishable objects there are $5!/4! = 5$ distinct permutations of these fragments. There exist 5 molecules that could give these fragments — namely,

(1)   C, C, C, C, GGU, GAAAG

(2)   C, C, C, GGU, C, GAAAG

(3)   C, C, GGU, C, C, GAAAG

(4)   C, GGU, C, C, C, GAAAG

(5)   GGU, C, C, C, C, GAAAG.

One of these five must be the original sequence. Although each of these gives the fragments for the {C, U} digest, only the third one gives the same fragments observed for the {G} digest, and hence it must be the original sequence. For example, the fragment UCCG, which is observed in the {G} digest, can be produced only by molecule (3). In this simple example we are able to arrive at a single solution.

### Permutations of Fragments and Permutations of Letters

Suppose that a preparation of a nucleic acid of 12 bases is digested with the {C, U} enzyme. Suppose also that the reaction is stopped before all the C and U breaks have been made by the enzyme. When this is done the digest is said to be *partial*, as opposed to *complete* if all the breaks have been made. Suppose the following fragments are obtained and are known by some means to be non-overlapping

UGACU, UGAC, GAC.

(Note that with these partial digest fragments the bases C and U can occur in other than terminal positions.) Since the fragments are nonoverlapping and comprise a total of 12 bases (that is, the number in the original molecule) then some permutation of them is the original molecule. There are 3! = 6 permutations; namely,

(1)  UGACU, UGAC, GAC        (2)  UGACU, GAC, UGAC

(3)  UGAC, UGACU, GAC        (4)  UGAC, GAC, UGACU

(5)  GAC, UGAC, UGACU        (6)  GAC, UGACU, UGAC.

Here is a special result: Permutations (2) and (3) are different permutations of fragments — yet they yield the same permutation of letters! In fact, there are not 6 molecules which could yield these fragments but only 5. In other words *it can happen that different permutations of fragments yield the same permutation of letters.*

We now show that such an eventuality is *not* possible for fragments from a single complete digest. In other words we show that for such fragments each distinct permutation of fragments does, in fact, yield a distinct permutation of letters.

> GENERAL STATEMENT.    *Given all fragments from a complete digest with a single enzyme, the number of distinct permutations of fragments is also the number of possible molecules yielding these fragments.*

Note: The proof of this statement may be tedious. If you find it to be so you can accept this stated result and proceed directly to the exercises from this point.

Suppose we observe the following fragments from a complete digest where the enzyme used breaks the molecule after each C or U:

AG, C, U, GC, GC, GU, AAU, AGGAC.

Since the enzyme breaks the molecule after each C or U, no two fragments overlap. It is possible that one fragment not terminating in C or U is produced. In the original molecule such a fragment must be terminal. Thus, the AG fragment in this example is terminal, and its position is known. Each permutation of the fragments ending in C or U gives a molecule that could have produced the observed fragments. The AG fragment does not enter into these permutations and is ignored for the remainder of the discussion. (To obtain the whole molecule the fragment AG is simply added at the end of the permutation.)

Excluding the AG fragment, there are seven fragments, only two of which are alike. There are

$$\frac{7!}{2!} = 2520$$

distinct permutations of fragments. We now show that each of these yields a distinct permutation of letters, that is, a distinct molecule capable of producing the observed fragments. Let B stand for the kinds of letters after which the enzyme breaks (or cuts), and let X stand for the kinds of letters after which the enzyme does not cut. In this example B stands for C or U; X for A or G. Then any complete digest fragment can be denoted as a sequence of X's followed by a terminal B. For example, in this notation, the fragments

$$C, U, GC, GC, GU, AAU, AGGAC$$

are, respectively,

$$B, B, XB, XB, XB, XXB, XXXXB.$$

The respective lengths are

$$1, 1, 2, 2, 2, 3, 5.$$

Any distinct permutation of these seven numbers corresponds to a permutation of the fragments. From such a permutation we can tell exactly what position the B's occupy in the resulting sequence.

For example, the permutation

$$3, 5, 2, 1, 2, 2, 1$$

denotes a sequence like

| X X B | X X X X B | X B | B | X B | X B | B |
|---|---|---|---|---|---|---|
| 1  2  3 | 4  5  6  7  8 | 9  10 | 11 | 12  13 | 14  15 | 16. |

The positions of the B's in this sequence are determined by the permutation of the fragment lengths. The first fragment is of length 3. Hence, the first two letters of the original sequence must be X's and the third letter B. The next fragment is of length 5; hence, the next B is five places beyond the third place or it is in position $3 + 5 = 8$. The next fragment is of length 2; thus, the next B is two places beyond the eighth place or in position $8 + 2 = 10$. Continuing in this manner we determine the positions of all the B's in the over-all sequence of letters:

$$3, 3 + 5 = 8, 8 + 2 = 10, 10 + 1 = 11,$$
$$11 + 2 = 13, 13 + 2 = 15, 15 + 1 = 16.$$

A different permutation of fragment lengths like

$$2, 1, 5, 3, 2, 2, 1$$

denotes the sequence

$$\underset{1\;\;2}{\underline{\text{X B}}} \quad \underset{3}{\underline{\text{B}}} \quad \underset{4\;\;5\;\;6\;\;7\;\;8}{\underline{\text{X X X X B}}} \quad \underset{9\;\;10\;\;11}{\underline{\text{X X B}}} \quad \underset{12\;\;13}{\underline{\text{X B}}} \quad \underset{14\;\;15}{\underline{\text{X B}}} \quad \underset{16}{\underline{\text{B}}} \;,$$

and the positions of the B's are similarly determined to be 2, $2 + 1 = 3$, $3 + 5 = 8$, and so forth. Each different permutation of fragment lengths corresponds to a different set of positions for the B's in the resulting sequence. *Hence with fragments of the form X . . . XB, no two distinct permutations of fragment lengths can yield the same over-all sequence of letters.*

There are seven fragments with lengths 1, 1, 2, 2, 2, 3, 5. There are two fragments of length 1 and three of length 2. There are

$$\frac{7!}{2!3!} = 420$$

different permutations of fragment lengths and 420 different sets of positions for the B's.

Now suppose we return to the particular permutation of fragment lengths, which we have already dealt with, 3, 5, 2, 1, 2, 2, 1 corresponding to the sequence:

$$\underset{1\;\;2\;\;3}{\underline{\text{X X B}}} \quad \underset{4\;\;5\;\;6\;\;7\;\;8}{\underline{\text{X X X X B}}} \quad \underset{9\;\;10}{\underline{\text{X B}}} \quad \underset{11}{\underline{\text{B}}} \quad \underset{12\;\;13}{\underline{\text{X B}}} \quad \underset{14\;\;15}{\underline{\text{X B}}} \quad \underset{16}{\underline{\text{B}}} \;.$$

How many distinct letter arrangements of A, C, G, and U are possible given this length arrangement? We are free to permute the fragments of length 1 among themselves, those of length 2 among themselves, and so forth. Such permutations do not change the arrangement of fragment lengths. For example, in the above arrangement we might have two different letter sequences by interchanging two fragments of length 2, GC and GU, as follows:

$$\ldots \underset{12\;\;13}{\underline{\text{G C}}} \quad \underset{14\;\;15}{\underline{\text{G U}}} \ldots$$

or

$$\ldots \underset{\ldots\;12\;\;13}{\underline{\text{G U}}} \quad \underset{14\;\;15\;\ldots}{\underline{\text{G C}}} \ldots \;.$$

In this example (see second paragraph after the general statement for the fragments), there are two fragments of length 1 (C and U) and 2! permutations possible for these. Of the three fragments of length 2, two are alike (there are two GC's and one GU). Thus, there are $3!/2! = 3$ permutations of these. There is one each of length 3 and 5, and hence 1 permutation only for these.

The total number of ways of rearranging fragments without changing a length arrangement is

$$2! \times \frac{3!}{2!} \times 1 \times 1 = 6.$$

For each length arrangement there are six distinct letter arrangements resulting from these six distinct permutations of fragments.

Finally the number of distinct letter arrangements is the number of distinct length arrangements (or different positions of B's) times the number of distinct permutations within a length arrangement. We obtain

$$\frac{7!}{2!3!} \times \frac{2! \times 3!}{2!} = \frac{7!}{2!} = 2520$$

distinct permutations of letters. But this is also the number of distinct fragment permutations. *Hence, each distinct permutation of fragments must yield a distinct permutation of letters.*

The general proof follows the same line of reasoning as that of the example just given; however, the notation is cumbersome. There are $n$ complete digest fragments obtained by breaking a sequence with a single enzyme. The sequence may be composed of letters of four types (like A, C, G, U) or of any finite number of types of letters. In the notation already given, any of the fragments is of the form

$$X \ldots XB.$$

A possible terminal fragment not ending in B is not included in the $n$ fragments. The $n$ fragments are nonoverlapping and together contain all the letters of the original sequence except for any letters in a terminal fragment not ending in B.

There are $n$ complete digest fragments produced by a single enzyme. Of these, there are $D$ of length 1, $E$ of length 2, ..., and $K$ of the longest length $k$. Among the $D$ fragments of length 1 there are $r$ types. (In the example already given $r = 2$, the two types being C and U.) Let $d_1$ denote the number present of type 1; $d_2$ the number of type 2; ...; $d_r$ the number of type $r$. Among the $E$ fragments of length 2 there are $s$ types. (In the example already given $s = 2$, the two types being GC and GU.) Let $e_1$ denote the number present of type 1; $e_2$ the number of type 2; ...; $e_s$ the number of type $s$. Continue labeling in this fashion until finally for the $K$ longest fragments, let $k_1$ be the number present of type 1; $k_2$ the number of type 2; ...; $k_t$ the number of type $t$. Note that

$$d_1 + \ldots + d_r = D;$$
$$e_1 + \ldots + e_s = E;$$
$$\cdot$$
$$\cdot$$
$$k_1 + \ldots + k_t = K;$$
$$D + E + \ldots + K = n.$$

The number of distinct permutations of fragments is

$$\frac{n!}{d_1! \ldots d_r! e_1! \ldots e_s! \ldots k_1! \ldots k_t!} . \tag{1}$$

The number of permutations of fragment lengths is

$$\frac{n!}{D! E! \ldots K!} . \tag{2}$$

Each of these denotes a different set of positions for the B's, and thus no two give the same overall arrangement of letters. For a given permutation of fragment lengths we may have one or more of the following types of distinct permutations of different fragments of similar length:

(1) types of fragments of length 1 among themselves,
(2) types of fragments of length 2 among themselves,

$$\cdot$$
$$\cdot \qquad ,$$
$$\cdot$$

($k$) types of fragments of length $k$ among themselves.

By the rule of counting, the number of distinct permutations of the individual letters for a given permutation of fragment lengths is the product of:

[the number of distinct permutations of type (1)]
times [the number of distinct permutations of type (2)]

$$\cdot$$
$$\cdot \qquad ,$$
$$\cdot$$

times [the number of distinct permutations of type ($k$)].

This number is

$$\frac{D!}{d_1! \ldots d_r!} \times \frac{E!}{e_1! \ldots e_s!} \times \ldots \times \frac{K!}{k_1! \ldots k_t!} . \tag{3}$$

Each permutation counted in (3) results in a distinct letter arrangement within a given permutation of fragment lengths. This is the number of distinct permutations of letters for each permutation of fragment lengths. To obtain the total number of distinct letter permutations we multiply formula (2) by formula (3), cancelling $D! E! \ldots K!$. We obtain

$$\frac{n!}{d_1! \ldots d_r! e_1! \ldots e_s! \ldots k_1! \ldots k_t!}$$

as the number of distinct permutations of letters resulting from permutations of fragments. But this is the same as the number of distinct permutations of fragments given in formula (1). Hence, we have shown that each distinct permutation of complete digest fragments produced by a single enzyme yields a distinct letter arrangement, and the number of molecules possibly giving these fragments is given in formula (1).

## EXERCISES

1. A nucleic acid with 10 bases yields the following fragments from a single complete {G} digest (thus the fragments are nonoverlapping):

   ACG, UUA, CG, CG.

   How many possible molecules are there that give these fragments?

2. A nucleic acid with 12 bases yields the following fragments from two complete digests:

   {G}    : ACG, UACG, UA, UCG
   {C, U} : A, GU, C, GU, AC, GU, AC.

   (a) How many possible molecules could produce the {G} digest results?
   (b) How many could produce the {C, U} digest results?
   (c) Enumerate the {G} digest possibilities. Could more than one of these give the {C, U} fragments observed? (Note that the original sequence cannot be uniquely determined from these fragments.)

3. A nucleic acid chain is known to contain 28 bases. The following fragments are observed in a complete digest with the {C, U} enzyme:

   C, U, AU, AC, GU, GC, GAU, AGU, AAU, AGC, GAC, GGC.

   (a) How many possible molecules could yield these fragments?
   (b) Suppose a computer can produce a permutation of these fragments and print the result at the rate of 900 a minute. How long would it take the computer, working continuously, to produce the list of all possible molecules?

4. A nucleic acid chain contains 10 bases. The following fragments are produced by a *partial* {C, U} digest:

   ACGUAC, AC, GU.

   Suppose it is somehow known that these fragments are nonoverlapping. How many molecules could give these fragments?

5. Suppose a molecule yields the following fragments on a single complete {G} digest:

   AG, CG, AG, UUG, AG.

(a) How many molecules could give this result?
(b) How many molecules could start with CG?
(c) How many could start with AG?
(d) Suppose the fragments are

AG, CG, UG, CACG,

How many possible molecules are there?

6. Observe the two possible molecules giving the fragments in Exercise 2. Suppose there were an enzyme available which cut after A. Examine the fragments made by cutting each sequence after each A.

(a) Are the two sequences distinguishable using only the A fragments that result from a complete digest?

(b) If available would a complete digest either with an enzyme cutting after {C} alone or with one that cuts after {U} alone distinguish between these two sequences?

PATH 2 ☞ §1.3, 1.4

## REFERENCES

### General

GOLDBERG, S., *Probability An Introduction* (Englewood Cliffs, N. J.: Prentice-Hall, Inc., 1960), Ch. 3.

KEMENY, J. G., SNELL, J. L., and THOMPSON, G. L., *Introduction to Finite Mathematics* (Englewood Cliffs, N. J.: Prentice-Hall, Inc., 1956), Ch. 3.

MOSTELLER, F., ROURKE, R. E. K., and THOMAS, G. B., *Probability with Statistical Applications* (Reading, Mass.: Addison-Wesley Publishing Company, Inc., 1961), Ch. 2.

[A particularly readable introduction.]

MOSTELLER, F., ROURKE, R. E. K., and THOMAS, G. B., *Probability: A First Course* (Reading, Mass.: Addison-Wesley Publishing Company, Inc., 1961), Ch. 2.

[Also particularly readable.]

### Optional Sections 2.6, 2.7

CROW, J. F., *Genetics Notes*, 6th ed. (Minneapolis, Minn.: Burgess Publishing Company, 1966), Ch. 16, 17, 18.

ELLIOTT, A. M., *Zoology*, 3rd ed. (New York: Appleton-Century-Crofts, 1963), Ch. 2, 3, 24.

ELLIOTT, A. M. and RAY, C., *Biology*, 2nd ed. (New York: Appleton-Century-Crofts, Inc., 1960), Ch. 2, 3, 29.

HOLLEY, R. W., EVERETT, G. A., MADISON, J. T., MARQUISEE, M. and ZAMIR, A., "Structure of a Ribonucleic Acid," *Science*, Vol. 147, (1965), PP. 1462–1465.

MOSIMANN, J. E., SHAPIRO, M. B., MERRIL, C. R., BRADLEY, D. F., and VINTON, J. E., "Reconstruction of Protein and Nucleic Acid Sequences: IV. The Algebra of Free Monoids and the Fragmentation Stratagem," *Bulletin of Mathematical Biophysics*, Vol. 28, (1966), PP. 235–260.

WATSON, J. D., *Molecular Biology of the Gene*, (New York: W. A. Benjamin, Inc., 1965).
[An excellent account.]

# SETS AND SAMPLE SPACES

## 3.1 SETS

The notion of a collection or group of things is familiar to each of us — the coins in our pockets, the fish in a lake, the students in a given class, the solutions to an equation, and so forth. Beginning with this notion let us say that a *set* is a *well-defined collection of objects.* For example, the set of the first three letters of the alphabet is the collection consisting of the letters a, b, c. We can write this in set notation by enclosing the objects in braces

$$\{a, b, c\}.$$

Here each letter a, b, or c is an *element* of the set, which has three elements. We have defined this set by listing its elements. We could also describe this set as being the collection whose only elements are the first three letters of the alphabet. In either case the set represented is the same. If Tom's sisters are Theresa, Mary, Michelle, and Kateri then the set of his sisters has four elements and can be written as

$$\{\text{Theresa, Mary, Michelle, Kateri}\}.$$

We could also write this set as

$$\{\text{Mary, Michelle, Kateri, Theresa}\},$$

for the order in which the elements are listed does not change the set.

Each of the sets mentioned so far has a finite number of elements. By *finite*, we mean that in counting the elements in the collection we come to a last element. The set of integers greater than 2,

$$\{3, 4, 5, 6, \ldots\}$$

does not have a last element and therefore is not finite. All its elements cannot be listed. In this book we work only with sets containing a finite number of elements.

The notion of a set is very simple, and like many simple notions is difficult to define in terms of simpler ones. In our definition of *set* the word *collection* is not defined, but an appeal is made to the reader's understanding of this notion. Our definition is, however, rendered more precise by the use of the words *objects* and *well-defined*. From the examples already given one can see that the objects may be abstract or concrete, real or imagined. A collection is *well-defined* if it is possible to determine positively whether or not any object is or is not a member of the collection.

EXAMPLE 1.   The set of distinct letters found in the word *cocoa* is the set {a, c, o}.

EXAMPLE 2.   The set of permutations of the letters ABC is {ABC, ACB, BAC, BCA, CAB, CBA}.
This is not a set of letters; its elements are permutations. ABC is a single element of this set.

EXAMPLE 3.   The collection of integers
$$\{-1, 2, 16\}$$
is well-defined although one may not know (at first glance) whether
$$x = \frac{12^2 - 11^2}{2} - \frac{7!}{5!\,2!} + \frac{23}{2}$$
is in the set or not. (It is.)

## EXERCISES

1.  How many elements does each of the following sets contain?
    (a) {3, 1, 2, 6};
    (b) {ABC, BCA, CBB};
    (c) the set of distinct letters found in the word *gene*;
    (d) the set of distinct letters found in the word *professor*.

2.  List the elements in each of the following sets:
    (a) the integers greater than zero and less than 12;
    (b) the odd integers in the set described in (a).
    (c) the even integers in the set described in (a).

3.  If three students take an exam, each passes or fails.
    (a) How many elements does the set of possible outcomes contain?
    (b) List its elements.

4.  Which of the sets below are finite and can be defined by listing all elements, and which cannot?
    (a) the integers greater than 26;
    (b) the integers greater than 26 and less than 1,000;
    (c) universities in the United States in 1966;
    (d) the species of turtles found in the St. Lawrence River in 1955.

5.  If the letters AAAB are permuted:
    (a) How many elements does the set of distinct permutations contain?
    (b) List these.

6. A tree swallow (T), a bank swallow (B), a cliff swallow (C), and six rough winged swallows (R) are on a telephone wire. An observer can tell the species apart but cannot distinguish among individuals of the same species. His observation consists of the order in which the birds are sitting on the wire. For example, a possibility is

TBCRRRRRR .

How many elements are in the set of possible observations?

| PATH 2 ☞ §3.2 | | PATH 3 ☞ §3.2 | | PATH 4 ☞ §3.2 | | PATH 5 ☞ §3.2 |

## 3.2 EQUALITY OF SETS AND SUBSETS

DEFINITION. *If two sets contain exactly the same elements they are said to be* **equal**. *They are* **unequal** *if and only if one contains an element not found in the other. Two sets must be either equal or unequal.*

Thus,

$$\{a, b, c\} = \{b, c, a\}$$
$$\{0, 1, 2\} = \{1, 0, 2\}.$$

Note that the order in which the elements are listed is irrelevant. On the other hand

$$\{a, b\} \neq \{a, b, c\}.$$

EXAMPLE 1. The following pairs of sets are equal:

$$\{a\} = \{a\},$$
$$\{1, 2, 3, 4\} = \{4, 2, 1, 3\},$$
$$\{ABC, BCA\} = \{BCA, ABC\}.$$

Note that ABC is a single element.
The following pairs are unequal:

$$\{ABC, CBA\} \neq \{ABC, BCA\},$$
$$\{AB, BC, ABC\} \neq \{A, B, C\},$$
$$\{1, 2, 3, 5\} \neq \{1, 2, 4, 3\}.$$

DEFINITION. *If all the elements of one set are also elements of another set, the former is a* **subset** *of the latter.*

Thus,

$$\{a, b\}$$

is a subset of

$$\{a, b, c, d\},$$

and Tom's brown-haired sisters

{Theresa, Michelle}

is a subset of Tom's sisters

{Theresa, Mary, Michelle, Kateri}.

By our definition a set is also a subset of itself. Thus, {a, b, c, d} is a subset of {a, b, c, d}.

DEFINITION.    *A set with no elements is a special set called* **the empty set** *and is denoted by* $\varnothing$.

We say "The" because there is only one empty set. This follows from the definition of equality of two sets. Any two sets with no elements are equal. Neither set contains an element not in the other, and thus by our definition they are not unequal. But two sets must be equal or unequal, hence they are equal. By special definition the empty set is a subset of any set (including itself).

EXAMPLE 2.    The first set of each pair below is a subset of the second:

(a) {a, b}  , {a, b, c, d, e, f};
(b) {a, c}  , {a, c};
(c) {a, b}  , {a, b, c, d};
(d) {BCA} , {ABC, BCA};
(e) {1, 2}  , {4, 2, 3, 1}.

The first set of each of the following pairs is not a subset of the second:

(a) {a, b}  , {b, c, d, e, f};
(b) {a, c}  , {a};
(c) {1, 2}  , {1, 4, 3, 6}.

The set {2, 3, 4} has eight subsets given by:

{2, 3, 4};

{2, 3};        {2, 4};        {3, 4};

{2};        {3};        {4};        $\varnothing$.

## EXERCISES

1.   Which of the following pairs of sets are equal?
(a) {A, B}   , {B, A};
(b) {A, B}   , {B, A, C};
(c) {A, B, C} , {1, 2, 3};
(d) {1, 2}   , {2, 1, 3};
(e) {a, b, c}  , {a, b}.

2.   Is the set    {1, 2, a, b, d, 12}    equal to the set

{a, b, 12, d, 1, 2} ?

3.  The set $\{2, 4\}$ is a subset of which of the following
    sets?
    (a) $\{2, 24\}$ ;                    (b) $\{2, 4\}$ ;
    (c) $\{1, 2, 4\}$ ;                  (d) $\{4, 3, 1, 12\}$ ;
    (e) $\{2, 6\}$ ;                     (f) $\{2, 8\}$ .

4.  The empty set $\varnothing$ is a subset of which of the following
    sets?
    (a) $\{1, 2\}$ ; (b) $\varnothing$ ; (c) $\{6, 10, 12\}$ ; (d) $\{a, b, c\}$ .

5.  There are four different subsets of the set $\{4, 5\}$ .
    List them.

6.  Which of the following are subsets of the set
    $\{A, B, C\}$ ?
    (a) $\{A\}$;       (b) $\{C, B, A\}$;  (c) $\{C, A\}$;  (d) $\varnothing$ ;
    (e) $\{A, B\}$;    (f) $\{C, B\}$;     (g) $\{B\}$;     (h) $\{C\}$.

7.  Suppose that a set has three elements. How many
    different subsets are there? Label each of the ele-
    ments 1, 2, 3, and now consider the set $\{1, 2, 3\}$.
    One can designate each element as "present" (p) or
    "absent" (a) in order to identify each subset. By the
    rule of counting there are

    $$2 \times 2 \times 2 = 2^3 = 8$$

    different ways of designating each of the 3 elements
    as p or a. Hence, there are 8 subsets. These are
    listed for the set $\{A, B, C\}$ in Exercise 6. Note that
    when all three elements are absent we obtain the
    empty set.
    Satisfy yourself by using the rule of counting that the
    *number of subsets of a finite set of n elements is $2^n$.*

| PATH 2 ☞ §3.3 | | PATH 3 ☞ §3.3 | | PATH 4 ☞ §3.3 | | PATH 5 ☞ §3.3 |

## 3.3  COUNTING SUBSETS AND COMBINATIONS

Suppose we have the set of letters

$$\{A, B, C\}.$$

How many different subsets of two letters are there? There are three given by

$$\{A, B\}, \{A, C\}, \{B, C\} .$$

That is to say there are three ways of selecting two letters from the three given
letters. Note particularly that the order in which the letters are picked is of no
consequence since, for example,

$$\{A, B\} = \{B, A\}.$$

The number of two-letter subsets of a set of three letters is the number of ways of choosing two letters from three. This number could have been determined as follows. From the second general statement of Section 2.3 we know that the number of ways of (1) choosing any two letters from three *and* (2) arranging them in order is

$$_3P_2 = \frac{3!}{1!} = 6.$$

These six ways are, in this case,

$$AB, \ AC, \ BC,$$
$$BA, \ CA, \ CB.$$

For each choice of two letters there are $2! = 2$ arrangements. To determine the number of choices we can divide six by two and obtain the answer we have already seen; namely, three.

More generally, how many ways are there of choosing $r$ things from $n$? From Section 2.3 we recall that the number of ways of choosing *and* arranging $r$ things from $n$ things is $_nP_r = n!/(n - r)!$. We also have that

$$\begin{bmatrix} \text{the number of} \\ \text{choices of } r \\ \text{things from } n \end{bmatrix} \times \begin{bmatrix} \text{the number} \\ \text{of permutations} \\ \text{of } r \text{ things} \end{bmatrix} = \ _nP_r$$

The number of permutations of $r$ things is $r!$. There are $r!$ permutations for each different choice of $r$ things. Thus to obtain the number of choices of $r$ things from $n$ we divide $_nP_r$ by $r!$. We obtain

$$\frac{_nP_r}{r!} = \frac{n!}{r!(n - r)!}.$$

This is the number of ways of choosing $r$ things from $n$ or in other words the number of $r$-element subsets of a set of $n$ elements. A common way of referring to an $r$-element subset of a set of $n$ elements is as a "combination of $r$ things from $n$."

For example, there may be five people, two of whom are to be chosen for a committee. There are then

$$\frac{5!}{2!3!} = 10$$

possible committees. Each committee is a subset of two persons from the set of five different people.

EXAMPLE 1.   Consider the set of four letters $\{A, B, C, D\}$ There are four subsets of three letters; namely,

$$\{A, B, C\} \ , \{A, B, D\} \ , \{A, C, D\} \ , \{B, C, D\} \ .$$

Here, $n = 4$, $r = 3$, and $n - r = 1$; we have

$$\frac{4!}{3!1!} = 4 \ .$$

EXAMPLE 2. The set $\{A, B, C\}$ has three subsets of two letters; namely,

$$\{A, B\}, \{A, C\}, \{B, C\}.$$

here, $n = 3$ and $r = 2$; we have $3!/(2!1!) = 3$.

EXAMPLE 3. From the set of four letters $\{A, B, C, D\}$, how many subsets of four letters can be formed? There is only one, $\{A, B, C, D\}$. Here, $n = 4, r = 4$, and using the general result we obtain

$$\frac{4!}{4!(4-4)!} = \frac{4!}{4!0!} = 1.$$

EXAMPLE 4. How many subsets of one letter are there from $\{A, B, C, D\}$?
Here, $n = 4, r = 1$, and we have

$$\frac{4!}{1!(4-1)!} = \frac{4!}{1!3!} = 4.$$

The subsets are

$$\{A\}, \{B\}, \{C\}, \{D\}.$$

EXAMPLE 5. From six people, a committee of two is formed. In how many ways can this be done? There is a set of six people; a committee of two is a subset with two people. The number of possible committees is therefore

$$\frac{6!}{2!4!} = 15.$$

We now introduce a special symbol which is useful. The *number* of subsets of three elements that can be chosen from a set of seven elements can be indicated by

$$\binom{7}{3} = \frac{7!}{3!(7-3)!} = \frac{7!}{3!4!} = 35.$$

This is the number of combinations of three things from seven. Similarly, the number of subsets of seven elements is

$$\binom{7}{7} = \frac{7!}{7!(7-7)!} = \frac{7!}{7!0!} = 1,$$

while the number of subsets with no elements is

$$\binom{7}{0} = \frac{7!}{0!(7-0)!} = \frac{7!}{0!7!} = 1.$$

The subset with no elements is the empty set.

GENERAL STATEMENT.    *In general, the number of r-element subsets of a set of n elements or the number of combinations of r things chosen from n is, and can be denoted by,*

$$\binom{n}{r} = \frac{n!}{r!(n-r)!}.$$

We only use this symbol when the number $n$ is a positive integer. Should it happen that the integer $r$ is greater than $n$ or that $r$ is negative, then we define the value of this symbol to be zero. For example,

$$\binom{5}{6} = 0, \qquad \binom{5}{-2} = 0.$$

This is intuitively logical, since there can be no 6-element subsets of a set of 5 elements nor can there be subsets with a negative number of elements.

EXAMPLE 6.    Of four species of trees present in a forest, two are to be classed as "dominants." How many subsets of two dominants are there?

$$\binom{4}{2} = \frac{4!}{2!2!} = 6.$$

EXAMPLE 7.    A committee is to consist of 2 botanists and 3 zoologists. If there are 6 botanists and 5 zoologists from whom to choose, how many committees are possible? We have a set of six botanists, and we need a subset of two. There are

$$\binom{6}{2} = \frac{6!}{2!4!} = 15$$

ways to choose the two botanists. There is also a set of 5 zoologists. There are

$$\binom{5}{3} = \frac{5!}{3!2!} = 10$$

subsets of three zoologists.
Using the rule of counting we can choose first the botanists and then the zoologists in $15 \times 10$ ways, and so get 150 possible committees.

## EXERCISES

1.  Evaluate the following:

(a) $\binom{3}{2}$ ;    (b) $\binom{10}{1}$ ;    (c) $\binom{7}{4}$ ;

(d) $\binom{7}{3}$ ;    (e) $\binom{8}{0}$ ;    (f) $\binom{8}{-1}$ ;

(g) $\binom{5}{2}$ ;    (h) $\binom{6}{7}$ ;    (i) $\binom{10}{2}$ .

2.  The product $\binom{4}{2}\binom{3}{1} = 6 \times 3 = 18$. Evaluate the following:

(a) $\binom{4}{3}\binom{4}{0}$ ;

(b) $\binom{5}{2}\binom{7}{1}$ ;

(c) $\binom{3}{0}\binom{3}{4}$ ;

(d) $\binom{10}{2}\binom{5}{1}$ .

3.  A given set has 6 elements.
    (a) How many 2-element subsets are there?
    (b) 3-element subsets?
    (c) 7-element subsets?

4.  There is a set of 100 different persons. Four people are to be chosen for an award.
    (a) In how many ways can this be done?
    (b) In how many ways can two people be chosen?
    (c) One person?

5.  From 10 faculty members, how many doctoral committees of 3 people each can be chosen?

6.  From 10 different pine pollen grains and 10 different oak pollen grains how many different samples of 6 grains each can be chosen such that there are 2 pine grains and 4 oak grains in each sample? How many samples with 3 pine grains and 3 oak grains in each are there?

7.  From 20 different pollen grains (10 pine and 10 oak), how many samples of size 6 are possible? What proportion of these contain 2 pine and 4 oak grains? 3 pine and 3 oak? (Leave answers in general form.)

8.  From among 4 botanists, 3 palynologists, and 5 geologists, a doctoral committee is to be chosen so that there are 2 botanists, 1 palynologist, and 1 geologist comprising it. In how many ways can this be done?

| PATH 2 ☞ §1.3, 1.4, 2.6 | PATH 3 ☞ §3.4 | PATH 4 ☞ §3.4 | PATH 5 ☞ §3.4 |

## 3.4  THE SAMPLE SPACE, A SET OF POSSIBILITIES

When we say that a coin lands heads or tails, we are certainly not considering all possible happenings for a real coin flip — if the coin is flipped in an orbiting space capsule, it may not land at all. Yet in many cases we are certainly willing to limit ourselves to discussions of coin flipping in which the only possible results are heads (H) or tails (T), and we can denote this set of possibilities as

$$\{H, T\}.$$

If we did wish to consider possible results in a space capsule a breakdown of interest might be that the coin does not land but is

"out of reach when five minutes have elapsed" (O)

or

"in reach when five minutes have elapsed" (I),

and we would denote this set of possibilities as the collection

{O, I}.

Or we might consider a different breakdown, at five minutes the coin might be

(a) "less-than-or-just one foot from switch A,"
(b) "more than one foot and not more than two feet from switch A,"
(c) "more than two feet from switch A,"

and we can denote this set of possibilities as

{a, b, c}.

The above simply illustrates the necessity of agreeing what we are talking about, for if we say the coin lands heads or tails it is generally understood that we are not talking about coin flipping in a space capsule. Two persons gambling are apt to come to blows over a coin which lands at an angle against a cigarette wrapper, because of a lack of agreement as to whether this was or was not meant to be a possible outcome of their game. Likewise, someone trying to determine if a coin is fairly balanced is not apt to include in his results the toss that ends up on edge in the mud.

By establishing our set of possibile outcomes, we are simply defining our *universe of discourse*, or in other words we are precisely limiting the scope of our statements. Each of the three sets of possibilities — {H, T}, {O, I}, {a, b, c} — is an example of a *sample space*.

> DEFINITION.    *A* **sample space** *is a set. Specifically, it is a set of possibilities for a real or conceptual experiment in which:*
> (1) *each possibility (element of the set) denotes one possible outcome of the experiment,*

*and*

> (2) *each repetition of the experiment has an outcome corresponding to one and only one element in our set of possibilities.*

> DEFINITION.    *Each element of a set which is a sample space is called a* **simple event**.

The sample space {H, T} contains two simple events.

EXAMPLE 1. A coin and a die are tossed. A possible sample space for this experiment is

{H1, H2, H3, H4, H5, H6, T1, T2, T3, T4, T5, T6} .

There are 12 simple events.

EXAMPLE 2. Two coins are flipped. Possible sample spaces are

$$\{HH, HT, TH, TT\} ;$$
$$\{Ha, Hb, Hc, Hd, Ta, Tb, Tc, Td\} .$$

where a, b, c, d, are the possibilities that the angle $\theta$ which the second coin makes with the surface is

(a) $0° < \theta \le 45°$,     (b) $45° < \theta \le 90°$,
(c) $90° < \theta \le 135°$,    (d) $135° < \theta \le 180°$;

and

$$\{2, 1, 0\}$$

where the numbers simply represent the numbers of heads which can result.

An important point to realize is that the sample space is not necessarily unique, more than one sample space can describe the same experiment. *In this book we consider only finite sample spaces; that is, sample spaces with only a finite number of simple events.*

## EXERCISES

1. A slide contains 3 arboreal and 3 nonarboreal pollen grains — 1 pine, 1 fir, 1 oak, 1 Chenopod-amaranth, 1 grass, and 1 sedge. A spot is chosen on the slide at random, and the stage moved until the first grain is encountered. This is recorded. Which of the following are possible sample spaces for this experiment, and which are not?
   (a) {pine, fir, oak, cheno-am, grass, sedge} ;
   (b) {pine, fir, oak, grass, sedge} ;
   (c) {pine, fir} ;
   (d) {arboreal, non-arboreal} .

2. Specify an appropriate sample space for each of the following experiments:
   (a) a penny and a nickel are flipped simultaneously and the results noted;
   (b) a bank swallow (B) and five cliff swallows (C) are observed sitting in a certain order on a telephone wire.
   (c) 3 pollen grains are tabulated from a soil sample containing only pine and oak grains and the order of tabulation is recorded.
   (d) the same situation as in part (c) but now the only

interest is in recording the *number* of pine grains observed;

(e) the order of arrival of 100 mice and 1 fox at a particular spot is recorded;

(f) three coins are flipped simultaneously and the number of heads is recorded.

3. Five food pellets are in a container. Two contain poison (P), the remaining three are normal (N). A rat eats the pellets one at a time. He continues eating until he eats a poisoned pellet. When this happens death follows quickly and no further pellets are eaten. The number of pellets eaten, as well as the order in which they are eaten, may be observed. Which of the following can be used as a sample space for this experiment?

(a) {P, NP, NNP, NNNP} ;

(b) {PP, PN, NP, NN} ;

(c) {1, 2, 3, 4}, where a number indicates the number of pellets eaten;

(d) {P, NNP} ;

(e) {N} ;

(f) {P, N} .

4. Five balls are in an urn. Two are purple (P); the remaining three are neutral-colored (N). Balls are drawn from the urn one at a time. A ball once drawn is not replaced in the urn. Drawings continue until a purple ball is drawn. When this happens, the drawings stop. The number of balls drawn, as well as the order in which they are drawn, may be observed. Which of the sets in (a) through (f) of Exercise 3 can be used as a sample space for this experiment? (In (c) interpret the numbers as the number of balls drawn.)

| PATH 3 ☞ §3.5 |  | PATH 4 ☞ §3.5 |  | PATH 5 ☞ §3.5 |

## 3.5  EVENTS, SUBSETS OF SAMPLE SPACES

Let us consider a model for coin flipping where two coins are tossed, each falling heads or tails with no other possibilities. Then our sample space contains four simple events:

$$\{HH, HT, TH, TT\}.$$

Now think of the event "the first coin falls heads." This occurs whenever the first coin falls heads, regardless of how the second coin lands. The simple events for which the first coin falls heads are {HH} and {HT}. Together these form the following subset of the sample space:

$$\{HH, HT\}.$$

In fact, rather than write a word sentence "the first coin falls heads," we could simply write down this subset. Again, consider the event "at least one coin falls heads." For this statement we could simply write the subset

$$\{HH, HT, TH\}.$$

DEFINITION.    *An* **event** *is any subset of the sample space.*

Thus, the subset

$$\{HH, HT, TH\}$$

is in words the event that "at least one coin falls heads." We can say that this event *occurs* if both coins fall heads, since the simple event {HH} is contained in the above event. To say then that a particular event *occurs* is merely to say that the happening which takes place in our idealized experiment corresponds to a *simple event* contained in that particular event. Thus, we say that the event "at least one coin falls tails," or {HT, TH, TT}, occurs if both coins fall tails TT, but does not occur if both coins fall heads since HH is not contained in this event.

EXAMPLE 1.    An event is a subset. If the sample space is {HH, HT, TH, TT}, then
(a) the event "both coins land similarly" is {HH, TT};
(b) the event "both coins land differently" is {HT, TH};
(c) The event "either one, two, or no heads occur" is {HH, TH, HT, TT} (note that this event is the entire sample space);
(d) the event "both coins land heads" is {HH}.
Now if the outcome of our experiment is that both coins fall heads (a), (c), and (d) occur but not (b). If the outcome is two tails, then events (a) and (c) occur but not events (b) and (d).

Now consider the event "both coins fall tails" or {TT}. Also, consider the event "neither the first nor the second coin falls heads" or {TT}. These two events are equal, since an event is just a set, and {TT} = {TT}. However, the event "the first coin falls tails" or

$$\{TH, TT\}$$

is *not* equal to the above event since there is a simple event {TH} that is contained in this latter but not in the former. Since events are sets, the definition of equality of events is the same as that previously given for sets, we repeat it for convenience.

DEFINITION.    *Let* A *and* B *be any two events of a given sample space. We say that event* A *equals event* B (A = B) *if* A *and* B *contain exactly the same simple events.*

A *and* B *are said to be* **unequal** (A ≠ B) *if and only if either* A *or* B *contains a simple event not in the other.*

*The events* A *and* B *must be either equal or unequal.*

EXAMPLE 2.   Consider the sample space for the arrangements of three bank swallows and one tree swallow on a phone wire

$$\{BBBT, BBTB, BTBB, TBBB\}\;.$$

(a) the event "all bank swallows are together" = {BBBT, TBBB} = C;
(b) the event "one bank swallow is separated from the other two" = {BBTB, BTBB} = D ;
(c) the event "the tree swallow is between two bank swallows" = {BBTB, BTBB} = F ;
(d) the event "the tree swallow is next to only one bank swallow" = {BBBT, TBBB} = G .
Then,

$$D = F\,, F \neq G\,, C \neq F\,, G = C\,.$$

If the actual arrangement is BBTB, then we say event D (or F) occurs.

## EXERCISES

1.   A person is tested on his ability to identify pollen of three pine species — Virginia (V), longleaf (L), pitch (P). He is presented one grain of each in a randomly chosen order.  The sample space of possible orders of presentation is

$$\{VLP, VPL, PLV, PVL, LVP, LPV\}\;.$$

Give the *simple events* contained in the following events:
(a) the Virginia pine grain is first;
(b) the Virginia pine grain is presented just before that of the longleaf pine;
(c) the pitch pine grain is presented second;
(d) the pitch pine grain separates the other two in order of presentation;
(e) the Virginia pine grain is presented first, and the longleaf pine grain last;
(f) the pitch pine grain is presented first, and the longleaf pine grain last.
Which, if any, of the above events are equal?

2.   The sample space for exam results in which a graduate student passes or fails and an undergraduate student makes A, B, C, D, or F is
   {PA, PB, PC, PD, PF, FA, FB, FC, FD, FF} .
List the simple events in the following events:
(a) both students fail;
(b) the undergraduate's grade is B or better;
(c) one, but only one, student fails;

    (d) the undergraduate's grade is C;
    (e) the graduate's grade is P.
3.   Three pollen grains (1 fir and 2 alder) are counted
    on a slide-preparation. The sample space for possible
    orders of counting is

$$\{AAF, AFA, FAA\}$$

    (a) Given this sample space how many different
    events (subsets) are possible? (Include the event
    $\{AAF, AFA, FAA\}$ as well as the empty event $\varnothing$
    in your answer). How many events containing two
    simple events are possible?
    (b) If a sample space contains $n$ simple events, how
    many events containing exactly $r$ simple events ($n \geq$
    $r$) are possible?

| PATH 3 ☞ §3.6 |    | PATH 4 ☞ §3.6 |    | PATH 5 ☞ §3.6 |

## 3.6 INTERSECTIONS, UNIONS, AND COMPLEMENTS OF EVENTS

Consider again our model of flipping two coins with the sample space

$$\{HH, HT, TH, TT\}.$$

Think of the event "the second coin falls heads" or

$$\{TH, HH\},$$

and also of the event "the first coin falls tails" or

$$\{TT, TH\}.$$

If we now consider the event "the second coin falls heads *and* the first coin falls tails," we have

$$\{TH\},$$

which is just the event containing the simple event common to both of the above events. This illustrates the following definition.

> DEFINITION.   *Given a sample space and two of its events* A *and* B *then the event that consists of only those simple events that are common to both* A *and* B *is called the* **intersection** *of these two events, and is denoted by*

$$A \cap B.$$

In words we form intersections of events by means of the word *and*. Thus, "$A \cap B$ occurs" can be stated simply as "both A *and* B occur."

EXAMPLE 1.   Given the sample space for two coin flips or
$$\{HH, HT, TH, TT\} \ .$$

(a) Let
$$A = \text{"the two coins land similarly"} = \{HH, TT\} \ ,$$
and
$$B = \text{"the first coin is heads"} \qquad = \{HT, HH\} \ ,$$
then
$$A \cap B = \text{"the two coins land similarly \textit{and} the first coin is heads"} = \{HH\} \ .$$

(b) Let A and B be the events above, and in addition let
$C = $ "anything has happened" $= \{HH, HT, TH, TT\}$ ,
$D = $ "neither coin is tails" $= \{HH\}$ ,
$E = $ "at least one coin is not tails" $= \{HH, HT, TH\}$ ,
$F = $ "the first coin is tails" $= \{TH, TT\}$ ,
$G = $ "both coins are heads" $= \{HH\}$ ,
$I = $ "the coins land differently" $= \{HT, TH\}$ ,

then

$C \cap D = \{HH\} = $ "anything has happened \textit{and} neither coin is tails,"

$A \cap E = \{HH\} = $ "the two coins are alike \textit{and} both coins are not tails,"

$G \cap B = \{HH\} = $ "both coins are heads \textit{and} the first coin is heads."

Now $G \cap B$ itself is an event. Consider its intersection with C or
$$(G \cap B) \cap C = \{HH\} \ .$$

Also, $B \cap C = \{HT, HH\}$ is an event. Consider \textit{its} intersection with G or
$$G \cap (B \cap C) = \{HH\} \ .$$

(This example anticipates an extension of the definition of intersection found later in this section)

(c) Let A, B, C, D, E, F, G, I be as above, then
$$C \cap E = \{HH, HT, TH\}, \quad I \cap B = \{HT\} \ ,$$
$$(C \cap E) \cap B = B, \quad F \cap C = F \ ,$$

(d) Note that $G \cap I$ contains no simple events, for there are none common to both G and I. $G \cap I$ is the empty event.

Now consider the event "the first coin falls heads \textit{and} the first coin falls tails." This is impossible because the intersection of the events
$$\text{"the first coin falls heads"} = \{HT, HH\}$$

and

$$\text{"the first coin falls tails"} = \{TH, TT\}$$

contains no simple events and is the empty event $\emptyset$. The empty event is an impossible event. We now give the following definition.

> DEFINITION.    *Given a sample space and two of its events* A *and* B, A *and* B *are said to be* **mutually exclusive** *if their intersection is empty; that is if*
>
> $$A \cap B = \emptyset .$$

In other words two mutually exclusive events have no simple events in common. Hence mutually exclusive events cannot occur together. The two events "the first coin falls heads" and "the first coin falls tails" are mutually exclusive since their intersection is the empty event. Note that any two different simple events are mutually exclusive events, since each simple event contains only one element.

EXAMPLE 2.   Consider the sample space for the arrangements of three bank swallows and one tree swallow on a phone wire, or

$$\{BBBT, BBTB, BTBB, TBBB\} .$$

The following are examples of mutually exclusive pairs of events:

$$\{BBBT, BBTB\} \quad \text{and} \quad \{BTBB\} ,$$
$$\{BBBT, BBTB\} \quad \text{and} \quad \{BTBB, TBBB\} ,$$
$$\{BBBT, BBTB, BTBB\} \quad \text{and} \quad \{TBBB\} ,$$
$$\{BBBT\} \quad \text{and} \quad \{TBBB\} ,$$
$$\{BBBT\} \quad \text{and} \quad \emptyset .$$

The following are *not* mutually exclusive pairs of events;

$$\{BBBT, BBTB\} \quad \text{and} \quad \{BTBB, BBTB\} ,$$
$$\{BBBT, BBTB, BTBB\} \quad \text{and} \quad \{BTBB\} ,$$
$$\{BBBT, TBBB\} \quad \text{and} \quad \{BTBB, BBBT, TBBB\} .$$

Let us return once more to our well-worn coins and consider the event "the second coin falls heads" or

$$A = \{TH, HH\},$$

and also the event "neither coin falls heads" or

$$B = \{TT\}.$$

If we now think of the event "the second coin falls heads *or* both coins fall tails," then we have the following possibilities

$$C = \{TH, HH, TT\},$$

which is simply the event containing *all* the simple events in either of the two events A and B. This illustrates the following definition.

DEFINITION.    *Given a sample space of which* A *and* B *are two events then the event that consists of all the simple events contained in either* A *or* B *is called the union of* A *and* B *and is denoted by*

$$A \cup B.$$

In words we form unions of events by means of the word *or* meaning not only *either, or* but also *both.* Thus "the event A $\cup$ B occurs" is equivalent to the event either A occurs or B occurs, or both A and B occur. Keeping this in mind, we can read "A $\cup$ B" simply as A *or* B.

EXAMPLE 3.    Consider the events
A = "the second coin falls heads" = {TH, HH} ,
B = "the first coin falls heads" = {HT, HH} ,
A $\cup$ B = "the second coin falls heads *or* the first coin falls heads" = {HT, TH, HH} .
If, in fact, both coins fall heads then A, B, and A $\cup$ B all occur since {HH} is contained in each of these.

EXAMPLE 4.    Consider the sample space for three bank swallows and one tree swallow sitting on a wire

$$\{BBBT, BBTB, BTBB, TBBB\} .$$

A = "the tree swallow is on the end" = {BBBT, TBBB},
B = "the tree swallow is not at the extreme right" = {TBBB, BBTB, BTBB} ,
C = "something happens" = {BBBT, BBTB, BTBB, TBBB} ,
D = "the tree swallow is at the extreme right" = {BBBT} .

Thus,

$$A \cup B = C, \quad A \cup C = C, \quad B \cup C = C,$$
$$D \cup B = C, \quad D \cup C = C, \quad A \cup D = A.$$

The union (D $\cup$ B) is itself an event. We can thus form the union of this event with C, or

$$(D \cup B) \cup C = C.$$

Also, (B $\cup$ C) is an event. Form the union of this with D and obtain

$$D \cup (B \cup C) = C .$$

Since

$$(D \cup B) \cup C = D \cup (B \cup C),$$

we can forget the parentheses and write simply

$$D \cup B \cup C = C .$$

(This anticipates the extension of the definition of union to follow.)

The definitions given previously of both *intersection* and *union* can be readily extended to the case of more than two events as follows.

DEFINITION.     *Given a sample space and k of its events* $A_1, A_2, \ldots, A_k$, *then;*

*The* **intersection** *of* $A_1, A_2, \ldots, A_k$ *is the event that consists of those simple events that are common to all of the k events, and is denoted by*

$$A_1 \cap A_2 \cap \ldots \cap A_k,$$

*and read*

"$A_1$ and $A_2$ and . . . and $A_k$."

*The* **union** *of* $A_1, A_2, \ldots, A_k$ *is the event that consists of all of the simple events found in any of the k events, and is denoted by*

$$A_1 \cup A_2 \cup \ldots \cup A_k,$$

*and read*

"$A_1$ or $A_2$ or . . . or $A_k$."

Finally we introduce the notion of the complement of an event.

DEFINITION.     *Given a sample space* S *and one of its events* A, *then the event that consists of every element in* S *that is not found in* A *is called the* **complement** *of* A *and is denoted by*

$$A'.$$

If we have the sample space $\{HH, HT, TH, TT\}$ and the event

$$A = \{HH\},$$

then the complement of A is

$$A' = \{HT, TH, TT\}.$$

We can read $A'$ as "S but not A" or simply "not A."

For any sample space S and any of its events A, this definition implies that

$$A \cap A' = \emptyset$$
$$A \cup A' = S.$$

EXAMPLE 5.    In the sample space for Example 4, $\{BBBT, BBTB, BTBB, TBBB\}$, the event "the tree swallow is at the extreme right" is $\{BBBT\}$. Its complement is the event $\{BBTB, BTBB, TBBB\}$. This is the event "the tree swallow is *not* at the extreme right."

EXAMPLE 6.    In the diagram below, called a Venn diagram for the English logician John Venn, 1834–1923, the rectangle represents the sample space S and the two circles represent the events A and B.

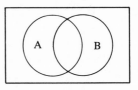

The shaded portions of the diagrams below represent the corresponding events labeled below:

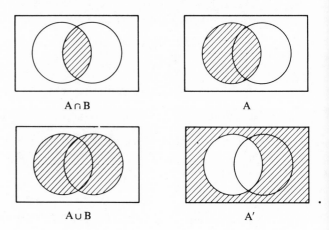

EXAMPLE 7.   Consider the Venn diagrams

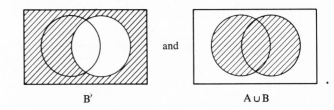

B′ is an event, so also is A ∪ B.  Their intersection is the
shaded portion common to both diagrams

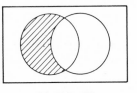

B′∩ (A∪B)

This is the event "B does not occur" *and* "A or B occurs."
This intersection is simply the event "A but not B occurs"
as shown in the diagram.

## EXERCISES

1.  Consider a sample space {a, b, c, d}.
    (a) Form the intersection and unions of the follow-
    ing pairs of events.  (For example, if we have {a} and
    {b}, then {a} ∪ {b} = {a, b}, {a} ∩ {b} = ∅.
      (i) {a} and {c} ,            (ii) {a, c} and {b, d} ,
    (iii) {a} and {b, c, d} ,     (iv) {a, b, c} and {c, d} .
    (b) Which of the above pairs are mutually exclusive?

2.  A pollen analyst has a core taken from a dry lake bed.
    From past experience in the area he knows that two
    vegetation zones — pine parkland and oak woodland
    — may be represented in the core.  Miscellaneous
    other zones are possibly present.  Possible observa-
    tions are given in the table in which + means *present*
    and o means *absent*.  For example, + + o means
    pine parkland and oak woodland are present and
    other zones are absent.

| Vegetation Zones | | |
|---|---|---|
| Pine Parkland | Oak Woodland | Miscellaneous Others |
| + | + | + |
| + | + | o |
| + | o | + |
| + | o | o |
| o | + | + |
| o | + | o |
| o | o | + |
| o | o | o |

Consider the sample space consisting of the eight possibilities presented in the preceding table:

$$\{+++,++o,...,ooo\}\ .$$

Write the following statements in terms of events, for example, "the only zone in the core is pine parkland" is $\{+oo\}$.

(a) "Parkland and woodland are absent."

(b) "No zones are present" (for example, no pollen is found).

(c) "Miscellaneous zones are present."

(d) "Parkland is present."

(e) "Parkland is present, but not woodland."

(f) "Parkland, woodland, and miscellaneous zones are present."

3.   The sample space for possible orders of counting 3 pollen grains (2 alder, 1 fir) is

$$S = \{AAF, AFA, FAA\}\ .$$

Let

$A = \{AAF, AFA\}$,    $B = \{FAA\}$,
$C = \{AFA\}$,    $D = \{AFA, FAA\}$.

Find the simple events in

(a) $A \cap B$ ;  (b) $A \cap B \cap D$;

(c) $(C \cup D \cup A) \cap (A \cup B)$ ;  (d) $D \cap B$ ;

(e) $D \cap S$ ;  (f) $D \cup S$.

4.   Given the sample space for the position of three bank swallows and one tree swallow on a wire

$$S = \{BBBT, BBTB, BTBB, TBBB\}\ ,$$

form the complements of the following events:

(a) "the tree swallow is on the extreme right";

(b) "the tree swallow is not on the extreme right";

(c) "the tree swallow is on either end";

(d) $\{BBBT, BTBB\}$ .

5.   In Exercise 1 there are four parts, each with a pair of sets. In which of the four parts is the second set of the pair the complement of the first set? If the second set of a pair is the complement of the first set, is the first set then a complement of the second?

6.   In the Venn diagram

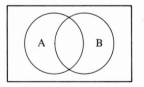

shade in the appropriate portions of the diagram for

the events given below:
(a) B ;          (b) B' ;         (c) A ∩ B' ;
(d) A ∪ S ;      (e) B ∪ S ;      (f) (A ∩ B')∪ B .

7.  Take the sample space of Exercise 2 and represent it
    as a Venn diagram:

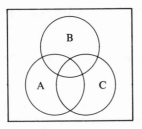

Let A be the event "a parkland zone is represented in
the core," B the event "a woodland zone is represented in the core," and C the event "some miscellaneous zone is in the core." Shade the area on the diagram corresponding to the events in (a) through (f) of
Exercise 2. For example, the event "parkland, woodland, and miscellaneous zones are in the core" is
represented by

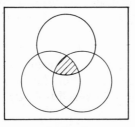

A∩B∩C

PATH 3 ☞ §4.1    PATH 4 ☞ §4.1    PATH 5 ☞ §4.1

## REFERENCES

### General

ALLENDOERFER, C. B., and OAKLEY, C. O., *Fundamentals of Freshman Mathematics*
(New York: McGraw-Hill Book Company, Inc., 1959), Ch. 6.

GOLDBERG, S., *Probability An Introduction*, (Englewood Cliffs, N. J.: Prentice-
Hall, Inc., 1960), Ch. 1.

KEMENY, J. G., SNELL, J. L., and THOMPSON, G. L., *Introduction to Finite Mathematics* (Englewood Cliffs, N. J.: Prentice-Hall, Inc., 1956), Ch. 2.

# ASSIGNMENT OF PROBABILITIES ON SAMPLE SPACES

## 4.1 PROBABILITIES OF EVENTS, A MATHEMATICAL DEFINITION OF PROBABILITY

All of us have at sometime expressed our degree of uncertainty about a particular happening with statements like "he'll probably be late" or "there's a better than even chance he'll never come." Or we have heard remarks relating to an observed or conjectured frequency of occurrence of some happening relative to a larger number of happenings — "nine times out of ten he'll let you down" or "six out of ten mice will survive."

In this section we give a mathematical definition of probability which lends precision to the notions of *frequency of occurrence* or *degree of uncertainty* just illustrated. With this definition, probabilities become simply numbers, and can be manipulated precisely and elegantly without necessarily considering their application to the real world. Mathematically, we define probabilities relative to a sample space. We speak of probabilities of events or of subsets of the sample space.

Although quite abstract, the mathematical definition of probability originates from man's experience of the real world. Before presenting the mathematical definition of probability, we present a related notion, that of *relative frequency*. Let us consider once again an experiment in which two coins are flipped, and for which the sample space is

$$\{HH, HT, TH, TT\}.$$

Suppose this experiment has been repeated 1000 times with the following results:

| Simple event | Number of occurrences |
|:---:|:---:|
| HH | 257 |
| HT | 246 |
| TH | 252 |
| TT | 245 |
| Total | 1000 |

Out of the 1000 repetitions the event "both coins fall heads," or $\{HH\}$, occurred 257 times while the event "the first coin falls heads and the second falls tails," or $\{HT\}$, occurred 246 times. The relative frequency with which $\{HH\}$ occurred is 257/1000, and that with which $\{HT\}$ occurred is 246/1000.

How many times did the event

$$\{HH\} \cup \{HT\} = \{HH, HT\}$$

occur? This is the event "both coins fall heads" *or* "the first coin falls heads and the second falls tails." This is the same as the event "the first coin falls heads." The first coin falls heads whenever either $\{HH\}$ or $\{HT\}$ occurs. This happened $257 + 246 = 503$ times out of 1000 tries. The relative frequency with which $\{HH, HT\}$ occurred is, then, $503/1000$. This could have been determined by adding the relative frequencies of its two simple events $\{HH\}$ and $\{HT\}$,

$$\frac{257}{1000} + \frac{246}{1000} = \frac{503}{1000}.$$

How many times did the event $\{HH, HT, TH, TT\}$ occur? This event occurred 1000 times out of 1000, for it is the entire sample space and occurred whenever $\{HH\}$, $\{HT\}$, $\{TH\}$, or $\{TT\}$ occurred. Its relative frequency is $1000/1000 = 1$. This can also be determined by summing the relative frequencies of its simple events

$$\frac{257}{1000} + \frac{246}{1000} + \frac{252}{1000} + \frac{245}{1000} = \frac{1000}{1000} = 1.$$

Finally, how many times did "both coins fall tails" *and* "both coins fall heads"? This is the empty event

$$\{TT\} \cap \{HH\} = \varnothing.$$

This event is not possible and never occurred. Its relative frequency is

$$\frac{0}{1000} = 0.$$

The foregoing examples illustrate some everyday facts about relative frequencies; namely,

(1) any relative frequency is some number ranging from zero to one;
(2) the relative frequency with which the event S, the entire sample space, occurs is 1.

Further, the relative frequency of any event is simply the sum of the relative frequencies of all the simple events contained in that event.

Finally, we note that

(3) The relative frequency of the empty event is zero.

The calculations we have just illustrated are not abstract. They apply to the *observed results* of a repeated experiment. In the mathematical definition of probability which we now present, the probabilities defined are abstract quantities. However, if we wish, we can think of probabilities as *idealized relative frequencies.* Thus, suppose we have a real or imagined experiment repeated many times. We can think of a result that occurs about 4 times out of every 10 experiments. In constructing a probability model of this experiment we could assign the probability 4/10 to the event corresponding to this result. From the definition to follow it is readily seen that the properties of mathematical probabilities reflect the properties illustrated for relative frequencies.[1]

We now give a mathematical definition of the probability of an event of a finite sample space.

DEFINITION.    *Given a sample space, associate with each of its simple events a number (not necessarily the same for all simple events) such that*

(1) *this is some number p ranging from zero to one ($0 \leq p \leq 1$),*

(2) *The sum of these numbers for all simple events in the sample space is 1.*

*The **probability** of any event is the sum of the numbers associated with the simple events contained in that event.*

*In addition, we define*

(3) *the probability of the empty event to be zero.*

We now illustrate this abstract definition of probabilities of events using our two-coin flip sample space. Let us associate a number with each simple event as follows:

$$\{HH, HT, TH, TT\}$$
$$\tfrac{1}{4}, \tfrac{1}{4}, \tfrac{1}{4}, \tfrac{1}{4}$$

Here each number associated with a simple event is the *probability of that simple event.* Thus, the probability of the event "both coins fall heads" is $\tfrac{1}{4}$, the number associated with $\{HH\}$. What about the probability of the event "the coins show two heads or two tails, or one head and one tail"? This event is the entire sample space

$$\{HH, HT, TH, TT\}$$
$$\tfrac{1}{4}, \tfrac{1}{4}, \tfrac{1}{4}, \tfrac{1}{4}$$

Since it contains all the simple events this event must occur, and its probability is 1. If we add the probabilities of the simple events we obtain

$$\tfrac{1}{4} + \tfrac{1}{4} + \tfrac{1}{4} + \tfrac{1}{4} = 1.$$

Similarly, if we seek the probability of the event "the first coin falls heads," or

$$\{HH, HT\}$$
$$\tfrac{1}{4}, \tfrac{1}{4},$$

---

[1] It is not however, necessary that mathematical probabilities be thought of as idealized relative frequencies. The definition of mathematical probability given is equally consistent with the notion of expressing a "degree of personal conviction", without reference to relative frequency (*cf.* the reference to Schlaifer's book at the end of this chapter).

we add the probabilities of its simple events and obtain $\frac{1}{2}$ for its probability. Likewise, the probability of "a tail on the first throw" is $\frac{1}{2}$, since we have

$$\{TH, TT\}$$
$$\frac{1}{4}, \frac{1}{4}$$

with $\frac{1}{4} + \frac{1}{4} = \frac{1}{2}$. If we seek the probability of the event "both coins fall tails" we find that this is $\frac{1}{4}$, since this event is $\{TT\}$ and the probability attached to $\{TT\}$ is $\frac{1}{4}$. Suppose, however, we seek the probability of an impossible event such as "the first coin falls tails and both coins fall heads." The set of simple events corresponding to this happening is the empty event, and the probability of the empty event is zero. Therefore, the probability of the impossible event is zero.

We repeat what was stated in the definition of *probability* and what has been illustrated by the examples given; *to calculate the probability of any event we simply:*

(1) *determine the simple events in the given event and*

(2) *sum their individual probabilities.*

*The resulting sum is the desired probability.*

We use more than one notation to denote the probability of an event. A common notation is the following: *Given a sample space* S *and one of its events* A *the probability of* A *is denoted by* $P(A)$. Other notations are given later.

EXAMPLE 1.    Given the sample space with its associated probabilities

$$\{HH, HT, TH, TT\}$$
$$\frac{4}{9}, \frac{2}{9}, \frac{2}{9}, \frac{1}{9},$$

We can see that the probability of the simple event $\{HH\}$ is $\frac{4}{9}$, the probability of $\{HT\}$ is $\frac{2}{9}$, and the probabilities of the following events are:

$$\{HH, HT\}, \frac{6}{9};$$
$$\{HT, TH\}, \frac{4}{9};$$
$$\{HH, HT, TH, TT\}, 1.$$

EXAMPLE 2.    Given the sample space of Example 1, let $A = \{HH, HT\}$, $B = \{HT, TH\}$, and $C = \{HH, TT\}$. To determine $P(A \cap B)$ we note that $A \cap B = \{HT\}$. Thus, $P(A \cap B) = \frac{2}{9}$. To determine $P(A \cup C)$ we note that $A \cup C = \{HH, HT, TT\}$. Thus, $P(A \cup C) = \frac{4}{9} + \frac{2}{9} + \frac{1}{9} = \frac{7}{9}$. In a similar fashion we find that $P(A \cap C) = \frac{4}{9}$, and $P(A \cup B) = \frac{8}{9}$.

EXAMPLE 3.    Given the sample space with associated probabilities

$$\{HH, HT, TH, TT\}$$
$$p_1, p_2, p_3, p_4$$

then
the probability of $\{HH, HT, TH, TT\}$ is $p_1 + p_2 + p_3 + p_4 = 1$,
the probability of $\{HH, TH\}$ is $p_1 + p_3$,
the probability of $\{TT\}$ is $p_4$,
the probability of $\{TH, TT\}$ is $p_3 + p_4$,
the probability of $\{TH\}$ is $p_3$,
the probability of $\varnothing$ is 0.

EXAMPLE 4.   Using the sample space of Example 3, let
$A = \{HH\}, B = \{HT, TT\}$, and $C = \{TT\}$. Then,

$$P(A) = p_1; \qquad P(A \cup C) = p_1 + p_4;$$
$$P(B) = p_2 + p_4; \qquad P(B \cup C) = p_2 + p_4;$$
$$P(C) = p_4; \qquad P(A \cap C) = 0.$$

## EXERCISES

1.   Given the sample space with its associated probabilities

$$\{a, \ b, \ c, \ d\}\ ,$$
$$\tfrac{1}{11}, \tfrac{2}{11}, \tfrac{3}{11}, \tfrac{5}{11}$$

What is the probability of the following events?
(a) $A = \{c\}$ ;  (b) $B = \{a, c, d\}$ ;
(c) $C = \{a, c\}$ ;  (d) $D = \{b, c, d\}$ ;
(e) $A \cup D$ ;  (f) $B \cup D$ ;
(g) $B \cap D$ ;  (h) $A \cap B \cap C$.

2.   A small chimpanzee is given five wooden letters AAAAB which he arranges in a line on a board. The sample space is

$$\{AAAAB, AAABA, AABAA, ABAAA, BAAAA\}$$
$$\tfrac{1}{10}\ , \quad \tfrac{1}{5}\ , \quad \tfrac{2}{5}\ , \quad \tfrac{1}{5}\ , \quad \tfrac{1}{10}$$

The chimp spells a word:
(a) What is the probability that he spells AAAAB?
(b) That he spells either AAAAB or ABAAA?
(c) That he spells AAAAB and BAAAA?

3.   The problem is the same as in Exercise 2 except that the probabilities assigned on the sample space are

$$\{AAAAB, AAABA, AABAA, ABAAA, BAAAA\}$$
$$\tfrac{1}{5}\ , \quad \tfrac{1}{5}\ , \quad \tfrac{1}{5}\ , \quad \tfrac{1}{5}\ , \quad \tfrac{1}{5}$$

Let $A = \{AAAAB\}$ represent "he spells AAAAB";
let $B = \{BAAAA\}$, "he spells BAAAA";
and let $C = \{AABAA, AAABA, ABAAA\}$.
What is the probability of each of the events listed below?

(a) $A \cup B \cup C$;
(b) $A \cap B$;
(c) "the chimp spells AABAA or AAABA or ABAAA";
(d) $A \cup B$.

4. Given the sample space
$$\begin{array}{c} \{1, 2, 3, 4\} \\ \tfrac{1}{4}, \tfrac{1}{4}, r, s \end{array} .$$

(a) If $r = \tfrac{1}{4}$, what must $s$ equal?
(b) If $r = \tfrac{1}{8}$, what must $s$ equal?
(c) If $A = \{1, 2, 3\}$ and the probability of this event is $\tfrac{1}{2}$ that is, $(P(A) = \tfrac{1}{2})$, what must $s$ equal?
(d) If $P(A) = \tfrac{7}{10}$, what must $s$ equal?

5. Given the sample space
$$\begin{array}{c} \{a, b, c\} \\ \tfrac{1}{5}, r, s \end{array} .$$

Suppose $A = \{a, b\}$, $B = \{b\}$, and $C = \{c\}$.
(a) If $P(A) = \tfrac{1}{2}$, determine $P(B)$ and $P(C)$.
(b) If $P(B) = \tfrac{1}{2}$, determine $P(A)$ and $P(C)$.
(c) If $P(C) = \tfrac{4}{5}$, determine $P(A)$ and $P(B)$.

6. An observer observes three bank swallows (B) and one tree swallow (T) on a telephone wire. A model in which there is some preference for the bank swallows to group together is given by the sample space
$$\begin{array}{c} \{BBBT, TBBB, BTBB, BBTB\} \\ \tfrac{1}{3}, \quad \tfrac{1}{3}, \quad \tfrac{1}{6}, \quad \tfrac{1}{6} \end{array} .$$

Let $A = \{BBBT, TBBB\}$ or "the bank swallows are together"; $C = \{BTBB, BBTB\}$; and $D = \{BBBT, BTBB\}$. Find the probabilities of
(a) A;        (b) C;        (c) D;
(d) $A \cup C$;    (e) $A \cap C$;    (f) $D \cap A$;
(g) $A \cap C \cap D$;    (h) $C \cup D$;    (i) $\varnothing$.

7. The problem is the same as in Exercise 6; however, there is no preference for the bank swallows to group together. The sample space is
$$\begin{array}{c} \{BBBT, TBBB, BTBB, BBTB\} \\ \tfrac{1}{4}, \quad \tfrac{1}{4}, \quad \tfrac{1}{4}, \quad \tfrac{1}{4} \end{array} .$$

Define A, C, and D as before, and answer parts (a) through (i) of Exercise 6.

| PATH 3 ☞ §4.2 | PATH 4 ☞ §4.2 | PATH 5 ☞ §4.2 |

## 4.2  PROBABILITIES OF EVENTS,
## THEIR UNIONS AND COMPLEMENTS

In this section we consider two simple but important consequences of the definition of probability. The first result concerns the probability of an event that is the union of two events.

GENERAL STATEMENT.     *Given a sample space* S *and two of its events* A *and* B, *then*

$$P(A \cup B) = P(A) + P(B) - P(A \cap B).$$

This can be stated in words as "(the probability of the event A or B) is equal to (the probability of event A) plus (the probability of event B) minus (the probability of the event A and B)." This can also be stated as "(the probability that A or B) occurs is (the probability that A occurs) plus (the probability that B occurs) minus (the probability that both occur)."

The second result concerns the complement of an event.

GENERAL STATEMENT.     *Given a sample space* S *and one of its events* A, *and the complement of* A, *denoted by* A′, *then*

$$P(A) = 1 - P(A').$$

In words "(the probability of the event A) is equal to (one) minus (the probability of the event not-A)." This can also be stated as "(the probability that A) occurs is (one) minus (the probability that A does not occur)."

The proof of the second general statement is given as an exercise at the end of this section. We show here that the first general statement is true. First, we consider an example.

Suppose we have the following sample space along with its associated probabilities,

$$S = \{e_1, e_2, e_3, e_4, e_5\}$$
$$p_1, p_2, p_3, p_4, p_5 \quad .$$

Consider the events

$$A = \{e_1, e_2, e_3\}, \qquad B = \{e_3, e_4\},$$

then

$$A \cap B = \{e_3\}, \qquad A \cup B = \{e_1, e_2, e_3, e_4\}.$$

From the definition of probability we have that

$$P(A) = p_1 + p_2 + p_3, \qquad\qquad P(B) = p_3 + p_4,$$
$$P(A \cap B) = p_3, \qquad\qquad P(A \cup B) = p_1 + p_2 + p_3 + p_4.$$

Note in particular that $P(A \cup B) = p_1 + p_2 + p_3 + p_4$. Let us compare this with the sum $P(A) + P(B)$. We find that

$$P(A) + P(B) = p_1 + p_2 + 2p_3 + p_4.$$

This is *not* equal to $P(A \cup B)$. The probability $p_3$ is represented twice. This is because the simple event $\{e_3\}$ occurs in both A and B; that is, in $A \cap B$. To adjust the sum $P(A) + P(B)$ so that the result is equal to $P(A \cup B)$ we can subtract $P(A \cap B) = p_3$. We obtain

$$P(A) + P(B) - P(A \cap B) = (p_1 + p_2 + 2p_3 + p_4) - p_3$$
$$= p_1 + p_2 + p_3 + p_4$$
$$= P(A \cup B).$$

The result illustrated is generally true. Suppose we have a sample space and two of its events A and B. Then $A \cup B$ consists of all the simple events found in A or B. $P(A \cup B)$ is the sum of the probabilities associated with these particular simple events. In this sum the probability for each simple event is represented once. Suppose we add the separate probabilities $P(A)$ and $P(B)$, and consider this sum. Probabilities associated with simple events found only in A or only in B are represented once; however, probabilities associated with simple events found in both A and B, that is, in $A \cap B$, are represented twice. Since probabilities associated with simple events in $A \cap B$ are represented twice, subtracting $P(A \cap B)$ from the sum $P(A) + P(B)$ gives a sum in which they are represented only once. Thus,

$$P(A) + P(B) - P(A \cap B)$$

is the sum in which the probability for each simple event in A or B is represented only once. But as we saw in the preceding paragraph such a sum is $P(A \cup B)$.

EXAMPLE 1.    In the sample space

$$\{HH, HT, TH, TT\},$$
$$\tfrac{1}{9}, \quad \tfrac{2}{9}, \quad \tfrac{2}{9}, \quad \tfrac{4}{9}$$

Let $A = \{HH, HT\}$ and $B = \{HH, TH\}$. Then, $A \cap B = \{HH\}$ and $A \cup B = \{HH, HT, TH\}$. We see that

$$P(A) = \tfrac{3}{9}, \qquad P(B) = \tfrac{3}{9}, \qquad P(A \cap B) = \tfrac{1}{9}.$$

Thus,

$$P(A \cup B) = \tfrac{3}{9} + \tfrac{3}{9} - \tfrac{1}{9} = \tfrac{5}{9}.$$

We could also determine $P(A \cup B)$ directly by adding the probabilities of its simple events $\{HH\}$, $\{HT\}$, and $\{TH\}$ to obtain

$$P(A \cup B) = \tfrac{1}{9} + \tfrac{2}{9} + \tfrac{2}{9} = \tfrac{5}{9}.$$

To apply the result of the second general statement, note that $A' = \{TH, TT\}$, and $P(A') = \tfrac{6}{9}$. $P(A')$ could have been determined by noting that $P(A) = \tfrac{3}{9}$ and writing

$$P(A') = 1 - \tfrac{3}{9} = \tfrac{6}{9}.$$

Similarly $P(B') = 1 - \tfrac{3}{9} = \tfrac{6}{9}$.

EXAMPLE 2.   Consider the sample space given in Example 1 along with its associated probabilities. Let A = {HH, HT} and B = {TH, TT}. Then, A ∩ B = ∅. We have $P(A) = \frac{3}{9}$, $P(B) = \frac{6}{9}$, and $P(A \cap B) = 0$.

$$P(A \cup B) = \tfrac{3}{9} + \tfrac{6}{9} - 0 = \tfrac{3}{9} + \tfrac{6}{9} = 1.$$

Note that whenever A and B are *mutually exclusive*, then $P(A \cup B) = P(A) + P(B)$.

EXAMPLE 3.   Four rats are injected with a drug. The number dying within two hours is observed. The sample space is {0, 1, 2, 3, 4}. Suppose A is the event "two or more rats die," or {2, 3, 4}, and B is the event "three or fewer rats die," or {0, 1, 2, 3}. Then, A ∪ B = S, and $P(A \cup B) = 1$. Suppose $P(A) + P(B) = \frac{12}{10}$. What is the probability that two or three rats die? This is the event A ∩ B. Its probability can be determined from $P(A \cup B) = P(A) + P(B) - P(A \cap B)$. We have

$$1 = \tfrac{12}{10} - P(A \cap B),$$

or

$$P(A \cap B) = \tfrac{2}{10}.$$

This is the desired answer. What is the probability that 0 or 1 or 4 rats die? This is the complement of A ∩ B; that is, (A ∩ B)'. Its probability is

$$P(A \cap B)' = 1 - \tfrac{2}{10} = \tfrac{8}{10}.$$

### EXERCISES

1.  Consider the sample space S given by

$$\{ \underset{\tfrac{1}{10}}{a}, \ \underset{\tfrac{2}{10}}{b}, \ \underset{\tfrac{3}{10}}{c}, \ \underset{\tfrac{4}{10}}{d}, \ \underset{0}{e} \}.$$

Determine $P(A)$ and $P(A')$ for
(a) A = {e};               (b) A = {a, b};
(c) A = {b, c, d};         (d) A = ∅.

2.  Using the sample space S and associated probabilities of Exercise 1, determine $P(A \cup B)$ for the following pairs of events:
(a) A = {e}, B = {a, b, e};
(b) A = {a, b}, B = {d, c};
(c) A = S, B = ∅;
(d) A = {a, b}, B = {a, b}.

3.  Given a sample space S and two of its events A and B, determine $P(A')$, $P(B')$, and $P(A \cup B)$, where
(a) $P(A) = \frac{1}{3}$, $P(B) = \frac{2}{3}$, and $P(A \cap B) = \frac{1}{6}$;
(b) $P(A) = \frac{1}{16}$, $P(B) = \frac{1}{8}$, and $P(A \cap B) = \frac{1}{32}$;
(c) $P(A) = 1$, $P(B) = \frac{1}{2}$, and $P(A \cap B) = \frac{1}{2}$;
(d) $P(A \cap B) = 1$;
(e) $P(A) = 1$, $P(B) = \frac{1}{3}$.

4. Five mice are observed in a cage after having been injected with a heart-stimulating drug. The number of mice dying within one hour is recorded. Suppose that the probability that exactly three mice die is $\frac{1}{3}$, and the probability that four or five mice die is $\frac{1}{3}$.
(a) What is the probability that three or more mice die?
(b) What is the probability two or fewer mice die?
(c) If A is the event three mice die and B is the event four or five mice die, what is the probability of $A \cap B$? What is the probability of $A \cup B$?

5. Each of ten rats is injected with an experimental drug. The number of rats dying within one week after the injection is observed.
(a) If the probability that 8 or more rats die is $\frac{1}{5}$, what is the probability that 7 or fewer rats die?
(b) Suppose that in addition to the facts given in (a), the probability that 8 or fewer rats die is $\frac{17}{20}$. What is the probability that exactly 8 rats do not die?

6. Prove the result of the second general statement of this section using the result of the first general statement. (Hint: Recall from Section 3.6 that $A \cap A' = \emptyset$ and $A \cup A' = S$.)

7. Each of ten rats is injected with an experimental drug. The number of rats dying within three days following the injection is observed. Suppose that the probability that nine or fewer rats die is $\frac{3}{10}$, while the probability that one or more rats die is $\frac{7}{10}$.
(a) What is the probability that exactly four rats die?
(b) What is the probability that exactly four, five, or six rats die?
(c) What is the probability that no rats die?
(d) What is the probability that 10 rats die?

| PATH 3 ☞ §4.3 |      | PATH 4 ☞ §4.3 |      | PATH 5 ☞ §4.3 |

## 4.3  EQUIPROBABLE SIMPLE EVENTS

Suppose we have a sample space containing five simple events representing the color of a toy chosen by a small chimpanzee given by

$$\{\text{red, white, blue, green, yellow}\},$$
$$p_1, \quad p_2, \quad p_3, \quad p_4, \quad p_5$$

where the $p$ below each simple event is its probability. Suppose also that we wish to model the situation in which the chimpanzee has no preference for any one of these colors, so we think of a conceptual experiment in which each color is as likely to be chosen as any other. This notion can be rendered precise by saying that the same probability is assigned to each simple event of the sample space. We can denote this common value by $p$, so that

$$p_1 = p_2 = p_3 = p_4 = p_5 = p.$$

Since from our definition of probabilities, the sum of these probabilities must be 1, we have

$$p_1 + p_2 + p_3 + p_4 + p_5 = 5p = 1,$$

or

$$p = \tfrac{1}{5}.$$

The probabilities assigned must then be

$$\{red, white, blue, green, yellow\}.$$
$$\tfrac{1}{5}, \quad \tfrac{1}{5}, \quad \tfrac{1}{5}, \quad \tfrac{1}{5}, \quad \tfrac{1}{5}$$

The numbers assigned to the simple events are in fact probabilities for they satisfy the conditions listed in the definition of probability (§4.1); namely,

(1) each is greater than or equal to zero and less than or equal to one, and
(2) their sum is 1.

In a similar manner if there are $k$ colors

$$\{color\ 1, color\ 2, \ldots, color\ k\},$$
$$p_1, \quad p_2, \ldots, \quad p_k$$

and we think of the simple events as being equally likely, we have

$$p_1 + p_2 + \ldots + p_k = 1,$$
$$p + p + \ldots + p = kp = 1,$$

or

$$p = \frac{1}{k},$$

and the assignment of probabilities must be

$$\{color\ 1, color\ 2, \ldots, color\ k\}.$$
$$1/k, \quad 1/k, \quad \ldots, \quad 1/k$$

Numbers assigned in this manner clearly satisfy our definition of *probability*.

Thus, any time we wish to model a situation where we consider the simple events to be "equally likely" we can do this by assigning the same probability to each simple event. Then, with $k$ simple events in the sample space, the probability of any simple event is $1/k$. We speak of *equiprobable simple events* only when each simple event of the sample space has the same probability as any other simple event.

In the case where our sample space represents a "choice" by someone — such as a chimpanzee — and each choice (simple event) is as likely to be made as any other, we call the choosing process *simple random sampling*. Further, we need not restrict outselves to situations in which a *choice* is part of the experiment.

> DEFINITION.   *A* **simple random sample** *represents a single occurrence of an experiment whose sample space consists of equiprobable simple events.*

Most everyday uses of the word *random* have somewhere the underlying notion of equiprobable simple events. We use the following expressions interchangeably, thus, we can say that the simple events of the sample are *equiprobable, equally probable, equally likely*, or *sampled simply at random*.

EXAMPLE 1.   Consider the sample space that is the set of all permutations of the letters ABCDEF. There are $6! = 720$ simple events in this sample space. If these are all *equally likely*, what is the probability of the event

$$K = \{ABCDEF, BCDEFA\}?$$

Each simple event has probability $1/720$ so that $P(K) = 2/720$. If the event L contains three simple events, then

$$P(L) = \frac{1}{720} + \frac{1}{720} + \frac{1}{720} = \frac{3}{720}.$$

If the event M has $r$ simple events, then

$$P(M) = \frac{r}{720}.$$

EXAMPLE 2.   A population consists of six individuals — two diseased ($D_1$, $D_2$) and four healthy ($H_1$, $H_2$, $H_3$, $H_4$). Thus, one third are diseased and two thirds healthy. If an individual is chosen *simply at random*, then the sample space is

$$\{D_1,\ D_2,\ H_1,\ H_2,\ H_3,\ H_4\}$$
$$\tfrac{1}{6},\ \tfrac{1}{6},\ \tfrac{1}{6},\ \tfrac{1}{6},\ \tfrac{1}{6},\ \tfrac{1}{6}.$$

The probability that the individual chosen is diseased is the probability of the event $D = \{D_1, D_2\}$, and $P(D) = \tfrac{1}{3}$. The probability that the individual chosen is healthy is that of the event $H = \{H_1, H_2, H_3, H_4\}$, and $P(H) = \tfrac{1}{6} + \tfrac{1}{6} + \tfrac{1}{6} + \tfrac{1}{6} = \tfrac{2}{3}$.
*Assigning probabilities according to simple random sampling translates the population proportions $\tfrac{1}{3}$ and $\tfrac{2}{3}$ into the probabilities $\tfrac{1}{3}$ and $\tfrac{2}{3}$.*

EXAMPLE 3.   In a particular woodlot there are four dead trees, two pine ($P_1$ and $P_2$) and two sweetgum ($G_1$ and $G_2$). Two pairs of woodpeckers nest in the woodlot.

Each pair establishes a nest in one of the dead trees. A tree may harbor only one nest. If one pair has chosen a tree, the other pair must choose one of the three remaining trees. An observer, notices that both nests are in the pine trees. What is the probability of this event in a model in which the woodpeckers choose the trees simply at random?

We have a set of trees $\{P_1, P_2, G_1, G_2\}$, but this set is not the sample space. From Section 3.3 we know that there are $\binom{4}{2} = 6$ possible ways of choosing two things from this set of four. These choices form the sample space or

$$\{G_1G_2, G_1P_1, G_1P_2, G_2P_1, G_2P_2, P_1P_2\}.$$

The sample space contains six simple events. If the woodpecker's choices are simply at random the probability of choosing both pine trees is $\frac{1}{6}$. The probability of choosing one pine and one sweetgum is $\frac{4}{6}$ or $\frac{2}{3}$.

## EXERCISES

1. A sample space consists of seven simple events. These are equiprobable. What is the probability of;
   (a) a simple event?
   (b) an event consisting of two simple events?
   (c) an event consisting of seven simple events?
   (d) the empty event?

2. A sample space which represents a simple random sampling experiment contains eight simple events. What is the probability of:
   (a) a simple event?
   (b) an event consisting of five simple events?
   (c) the empty event?

3. A graduate student (grade P or F) and an undergraduate student (grade A, B, C, D, or F) take an exam. The sample space of possible results is

   $\{PA, PB, PC, PD, PF, FA, FB, FC, FD, FF\}$.

   Suppose the simple events are equally probable. Then what is the probability of the event:
   (a) the graduate student fails?
   (b) the undergraduate's grade is B or better?
   (c) the undergraduate passes and the graduate fails?
   (d) either the graduate passes or the undergraduate gets an A, or both happen?

4. A log lies across a small stream. A fox and 100 deer-mice use the log to cross the stream at night. If the fox arrives first he waits at the log for the prey and eats all mice arriving after him (his capacity is 10 mice, after which he leaves). Suppose all orders of

arrival (simple events) are equally likely. What is the probability that:
(a) 10 mice are eaten?
(b) 5 or fewer mice are eaten?
(c) no mice are eaten?

5. An investigator is studying size differences between male and female turtles of the same species. He has a sample of four males and six females. The turtles are ranked according to increasing size (no two are of the same size). He finds the arrangement

FFMFFFMFMM
small ——————————→ large

If all arrangements (simple events) are equally probable, what is the probability that:
(a) only two males are larger than the largest female?
(b) only three males are larger than the largest female?
(c) four males are larger than the largest female?

6. From four people (initials: J, T, M, S) a committee of two is to be chosen. The sample space for possible committees is

{JT, JM, JS, TM, TS, MS}.

If the committees are equally probable,
(a) what is the probability that J is on the committee?
(b) what is the probability that J and S are on the committee?
(c) what is the probability that either J or S (or both) is on the committee?

7. From ten people, two of whom are J and S, a committee of three is to be selected. If the committees are equally likely answer part (a) and (b) of Exercise 6.

8. A population consists of 100 individuals — 12 diseased and 88 healthy. One individual is chosen.
(a) In the sample space where each simple event is a different person, how many simple events are there?
(b) If the sampling is simply at random what is the probability assigned to any simple event?
(c) Then what is the probability that the individual chosen is diseased? Healthy?
(d) How many simple events are in the event "the individual chosen is healthy"?

9. A population consists of individuals of three types (AA, Aa, aa). The respective numbers of each type are 10, 80, and 160. An individual is chosen simply at random,
(a) what is the probability that he is type AA?
(b) type Aa?
(c) type AA or type aa?
(d) how many simple events are in the event "the individual is type Aa"?

(e)  how many are there in the event "the individual is type aa"?

10.   In a particular woodlot there are seven dead trees — three sweetgum and four pine. Three pairs of woodpeckers nest in the woodlot. Each pair nests in a dead tree and no tree may contain more than one nest. An observer notices that all three nests are in the sweetgum trees. What is the probability of this event in a model in which the three trees are chosen simply at random?

11.   A committee is to consist of two botanists and three zoologists. Suppose there are five botanists (among whom are J and S) and five zoologists (among whom are W, M, and K). If each possible committee is as likely to be chosen as any other, what is the probability that the committee J, S, W, M, K is chosen?

| PATH 3 ☞ §4.4 |   | PATH 4 ☞ §4.4 |   | PATH 5 ☞ §4.4 |

## 4.4   HYPERGEOMETRIC PROBABILITIES, SIMPLE RANDOM SAMPLING WITHOUT REPLACEMENT

Five rats arrive in a shipment to an investigator. Unknown to the recipient, three of the rats are sick, while two are healthy. He needs two rats for an experiment. If he chooses two from the five simply at random, what is the probability that one is healthy and one is sick? From Section 3.3 we know that there are $\binom{5}{2} = 10$ ways of choosing two rats from five. If we let $S_1$, $S_2$, $S_3$ stand for the three sick rats and, similarly, $H_1$, $H_2$ for the two healthy ones, these 10 ways are

$$\{S_1S_2, \ S_1S_3, \ S_1H_1, \ S_1H_2, \ S_2S_3, \ S_2H_1, \ S_2H_2, \ S_3H_1, \ S_3H_2, \ H_1H_2\}.$$

In this sample space, the simple event $S_1S_2$ means that the first and second sick rats are chosen. The order in which the two rats are chosen does not matter; and we could as readily write $S_2S_1$ for the same happening. Also, note that the same rat cannot occur twice in the sample. A rat once chosen is *not replaced* before the choice of the next rat.

*Simply at random* means that any element of the sample space has the same probability as any other. Since there are $\binom{5}{2} = 10$ elements, the probability associated with each simple event is $1/\binom{5}{2} = 1/10$. The subset

$$\{S_1H_1, \ S_1H_2, \ S_2H_1, \ S_2H_2, \ S_3H_1, \ S_3H_2\}$$
$$\tfrac{1}{10}, \quad \tfrac{1}{10}, \quad \tfrac{1}{10}, \quad \tfrac{1}{10}, \quad \tfrac{1}{10}, \quad \tfrac{1}{10}$$

is the event "one sick rat and one healthy rat are chosen." The sum of the probabilities associated with this event is $\tfrac{6}{10}$, which is the desired answer to the question of what is the probability of choosing one each of a sick and a healthy rat.

Let us look at this answer more closely. We can evoke the rule of counting to arrive at this answer. From the rule of counting we know that

$$\begin{bmatrix} \text{The number of} \\ \text{ways of choosing} \\ \text{1 healthy rat} \end{bmatrix} \times \begin{bmatrix} \text{The number of} \\ \text{ways of choosing} \\ \text{1 sick rat} \end{bmatrix} = \begin{bmatrix} \text{The number} \\ \text{of ways of choosing} \\ \text{1 healthy and 1 sick rat} \end{bmatrix}.$$

There are two healthy rats. Our problem requires that one be chosen. This can be done in $\binom{2}{1} = 2$ ways. Also, one sick rat must be chosen and there are $\binom{3}{1}$ ways of choosing a sick rat from three. Hence, the number of ways of choosing one healthy and one sick rat is

$$\binom{2}{1} \times \binom{3}{1} = 2 \times 3 = 6.$$

Thus, the event "one healthy and one sick rat are chosen" consists of six simple events. Since each of these six simple events has a probability of

$$\frac{1}{\binom{5}{2}}$$

associated with it, then as the sum of the six probabilities we have

$$\frac{1}{\binom{5}{2}} + \frac{1}{\binom{5}{2}} + \frac{1}{\binom{5}{2}} + \frac{1}{\binom{5}{2}} + \frac{1}{\binom{5}{2}} + \frac{1}{\binom{5}{2}} = \frac{6}{\binom{5}{2}} = \frac{6}{10},$$

which we can also write as

$$\frac{\binom{2}{1}\binom{3}{1}}{\binom{5}{2}}.$$

This latter manner of writing $\frac{6}{10}$ affords us with insight concerning the answer to a more general problem.

Suppose that the shipment arrives with $N$ rats of which $r$ are healthy ($r$ is obviously less than or equal to $N$). Suppose $n$ rats are chosen at random for an experiment ($n \leq N$). What is the probability that among the $n$ rats chosen, exactly $x$ are healthy? We proceed with the same line of reasoning as before. There are $\binom{N}{n}$ ways of choosing $n$ things from $N$. Hence our sample space contains $\binom{N}{n}$ simple events. *Simply at random* means that the probability of any simple event is

$$\frac{1}{\binom{N}{n}}.$$

Now how many simple events are in the event "exactly $x$ of the $n$ rats are healthy"? We can choose $x$ healthy rats from the $r$ healthy rats in $\binom{r}{x}$ ways, provided that $x$ is less than or equal to $r$. There are $N - r$ sick rats; we must choose $n - x$ sick rats from these. We can do this in $\binom{N - r}{n - x}$ ways, provided that $n - x$ is less than or equal to $N - r$. We have then

$$\binom{r}{x} \times \binom{N - r}{n - x}$$

ways of choosing $x$ healthy and $n - x$ sick rats (remember we are choosing $n$ rats in all so that $x + n - x = n$). Each of these simple events has a probability of

$$\frac{1}{\binom{N}{n}}.$$

Thus, the probability of choosing exactly $x$ healthy rats in a sample of $n$ is

$$p(x) = \frac{\binom{r}{x}\binom{N - r}{n - x}}{\binom{N}{n}}.$$

DEFINITION.    *In any situation where one has $N$ objects of two types and from them one chooses a simple random sample of $n(n \leq N)$ objects without replacement (that is an object once-chosen cannot be chosen again) then $p(x)$ gives the probability of obtaining $x$ objects of one type. Such probabilities are called* **hypergeometric probabilities**, *and $p(x)$ is given by the preceding formula.*

We see in the next section that we need not assume $x \leq r$ and $(n - x) \leq (N - r)$ in order to calculate $p(x)$.

EXAMPLE 1.    The probability of no healthy rats in a simple random sample of two rats picked from three sick and two healthy rats is

$$p(0) = \frac{\binom{2}{0}\binom{3}{2}}{\binom{5}{2}} = \frac{1 \times 3}{10} = \frac{3}{10}.$$

The simple events in the event "no healthy rats are chosen" are $S_1S_2$, $S_1S_3$, $S_2S_3$. The probability of choosing one healthy rat is, as we have seen,

$$p(1) = \frac{\binom{2}{1}\binom{3}{1}}{\binom{5}{2}} = \frac{2 \times 3}{10} = \frac{6}{10},$$

and the probability that both rats chosen are healthy is

$$p(2) = \frac{\binom{2}{2}\binom{3}{0}}{\binom{5}{2}} = \frac{1 \times 1}{10} = \frac{1}{10}.$$

Note that $p(0) + p(1) + p(2) = 1$. The events $x = 0$, $x = 1$, and $x = 2$ are mutually exclusive. A graph of these probabilities is given.

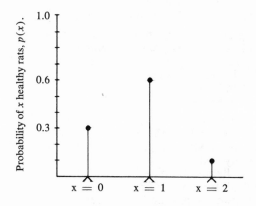

EXAMPLE 2. Four butterflies are marked, and released at Jasper Ridge. There are also 16 unmarked butterflies in the population. An ecologist catches 4 of the 20 butterflies. Using the model where his is a simple random sample, what is the probability that exactly 2 of the butterflies are marked?

Here, $N = 20$, $r = 4$, $N - r = 16$; $n = 4$, $x = 2$, $n - x = 2$. We have

$$p(2) = \frac{\binom{4}{2}\binom{16}{2}}{\binom{20}{4}} = \frac{\dfrac{4 \times 3}{2 \times 1} \times \dfrac{16 \times 15}{2 \times 1}}{\dfrac{20 \times 19 \times 18 \times 17}{4 \times 3 \times 2 \times 1}} = \frac{720}{4845}.$$

Note that there are 4845 simple events in the sample space. The probability that none of the butterflies is marked is

$$p(0) = \frac{\binom{4}{0}\binom{16}{4}}{\binom{20}{4}} = \frac{1 \times \dfrac{16 \times 15 \times 14 \times 13}{4 \times 3 \times 2 \times 1}}{4845} = \frac{1820}{4845}.$$

The other probabilities are

$$p(1) = \frac{2240}{4845}, \qquad p(3) = \frac{64}{4845}, \qquad p(4) = \frac{1}{4845}.$$

Note that

$$p(0) + p(1) + p(2) + p(3) + p(4) = 1.$$

## EXERCISES

1.  From seven rats, three sick and four healthy ones, two rats are chosen simply at random. What is the probability that:
    (a) both rats are sick?
    (b) both are healthy?
    (c) one is healthy and one is sick?

2.  A preparation in a test tube contains 45 pine pollen grains and 5 oak grains. A simple random sample of 2 grains is chosen. What is the probability that:
    (a) both grains are pine?
    (b) both are oak?
    (c) one is pine and one is oak?

3.  The problem is the same as in Exercise 2; however, a simple random sample of three grains is taken. (Leave answers in general form.) What is the probability that:
    (a) all three are pine?
    (b) all three are oak?
    (c) two are pine and one is oak?
    (d) one is pine and two are oak?

4.  There are four rats — two healthy and two sick $(S_1, S_2, H_1, H_2)$. A sample of two rats is chosen.
    (a) How many different samples (combinations or subsets) of two rats are there?
    (b) List these.
    Using the possibilities listed in part (b) as a sample space, list the elements in the following events:
    (c) two healthy rats are chosen;
    (d) one sick and one healthy rat are chosen;
    (e) two sick rats are chosen.

5.  Use the sample space of Exercise 4. Suppose the simple events are equiprobable. Then we have a simple random sampling model.
    (a) Calculate the probability of each of the events listed in parts (c), (d), and (e) of Exercise 4.
    (b) Calculate the probabilities of the same events using the general result for hypergeometric probabilities.

6.  There are four grains of pollen in a preparation — three pine and one oak $(P_1, P_2, P_3, O)$. One grain is chosen simply at random. The sample space of possible one grain samples is then

$$\{P_1, P_2, P_3, O\} \atop \tfrac{1}{4}, \ \tfrac{1}{4}, \ \tfrac{1}{4}, \ \tfrac{1}{4} \ .$$

The event "the grain is pine" is $\{P_1, P_2, P_3\}$. Its probability is $\frac{3}{4}$. The event "the grain is oak" is $\{O\}$, with probability $\frac{1}{4}$. Calculate the probabilities of these events using the general result for hypergeometric probabilities.

7. From 1000 persons of whom 10 are diseased, a sample of 20 is chosen simply at random. Leaving your answers in general form, what is the probability that:
   (a) exactly two diseased individuals are in the sample?
   (b) no diseased individuals are in the sample?
   (c) how many simple events are in the sample space?

8. A molecule contains ten bonds; seven are C bonds and three are U bonds. Three bonds are broken simply at random. What is the probability that:
   (a) all three are of type C?
   (b) two are of type C and one of type U?
   (c) how many simple events are in the sample space?
   (d) how many are in the event "all three are of type C"?

9. In a population of 200 snakes, 50 have been previously marked by an investigator. The remainder are unmarked. Six snakes are collected. In the model where each possible sample of size six has the same probability as any other sample of size six determine the probabilities of the following (leave answers in general form):
   (a) all six snakes were previously marked;
   (b) four snakes are unmarked and two marked;
   (c) how many simple events are in the sample space?

| PATH 3 ☞ §4.5 |   | PATH 4 ☞ §5.1 |   | PATH 5 ☞ §4.5 |

## 4.5 MORE ON HYPERGEOMETRIC PROBABILITIES

Suppose that an investigator has a shipment of three healthy and two sick rats and chooses four of these simply at random. There are $\binom{5}{4} = 5$ simple events in the sample space. If we let $S_1, S_2, H_1, H_2, H_3$ represent the five rats, these are

$$\{S_1S_2H_1H_2,\ S_1S_2H_2H_3,\ S_1S_2H_1H_3,\ S_1H_1H_2H_3,\ S_2H_1H_2H_3\}.$$
$$\tfrac{1}{5}\ ,\quad \tfrac{1}{5}\ ,\quad \tfrac{1}{5}\ ,\quad \tfrac{1}{5}\ ,\quad \tfrac{1}{5}$$

The event "two healthy rats are in the sample" is

$$\{S_1S_2H_1H_2,\ S_1S_2H_2H_3,\ S_1S_2H_1H_3\},$$
$$\tfrac{1}{5}\ ,\quad \tfrac{1}{5}\ ,\quad \tfrac{1}{5}$$

and has probability $\frac{3}{5}$. The event "three healthy rats are in the sample" is

$$\{S_1H_1H_2H_3, \ S_2H_1H_2H_3\}$$
$$\quad \tfrac{1}{5} \qquad , \qquad \tfrac{1}{5}$$

and has probability $\frac{2}{5}$. These probabilities can also be found by considering the hypergeometric probabilities for

$$p(2) = \frac{\binom{3}{2}\binom{2}{2}}{\binom{5}{4}} = \frac{3 \times 1}{5} = \frac{3}{5},$$

and

$$p(3) = \frac{\binom{3}{3}\binom{2}{1}}{\binom{5}{4}} = \frac{1 \times 2}{5} = \frac{2}{5}.$$

But suppose in this example we had been asked to calculate the probability that exactly one of the four rats is healthy. This must be zero for it is not a logical possibility. There are only two sick rats, and consequently there must be at least two healthy rats in each sample of four. If we simply substitute $N = 5$, $n = 4$, $r = 3$, $x = 1$ into our general expression

$$p(x) = \frac{\binom{r}{x}\binom{N-r}{n-x}}{\binom{N}{n}},$$

we obtain

$$p(1) = \frac{\binom{3}{1}\binom{2}{3}}{\binom{5}{4}}.$$

We now show that the definition $\binom{2}{3} = 0$ permits us to obtain the correct answer (as determined from the sample space) by routine application of our general formula, without forcing us to think about each case. To have only one healthy rat we are required to choose three sick rats from two, and this is impossible. Since there are no ways of doing this the symbol $\binom{2}{3}$ equals zero, and

$$p(1) = \frac{\binom{3}{1}\binom{2}{3}}{\binom{5}{4}} = \frac{3 \times 0}{5} = 0.$$

In fact, anytime we have the symbol $\binom{w}{v}$ and $v$ is greater than $w$ we have already defined the expression to be zero (*cf.* Section 3.3); that is,

$$\binom{w}{v} = 0, \qquad \text{if } v > w.$$

In words this says that there is no way of choosing $v$ things from $w$ when $v$ is greater than $w$.

Again suppose we wish to find the probability of selecting three healthy rats in a sample of two. Although it is impossible to find three rats in a sample of two, we can use the general expression to show that the event's probability is zero by

$$p(3) = \frac{\binom{3}{3}\binom{2}{-1}}{\binom{5}{2}}.$$

We previously defined (Section 3.3) the expression $\binom{w}{v}$ in which $v < 0$ as being equal to zero. Thus, $\binom{2}{-1}$ must equal zero and

$$p(3) = \frac{\binom{3}{3} \times 0}{\binom{5}{2}} = 0.$$

With this in mind, we can routinely calculate

$$p(x) = \frac{\binom{r}{x}\binom{N-r}{n-x}}{\binom{N}{n}},$$

even when $x > r$ or $(n - x) > (N - r)$, or $x > n$. We do, however, keep the restriction that the sample size $n$ is less than or equal to $N$ the population size.

EXAMPLE 1.    As in the example in the text there are three healthy and two sick rats. If we draw a simple random sample of size four from these five rats (the same rat can not be drawn twice), then $p(x)$ gives the probability that exactly $x$ healthy rats are in the sample. $p(x)$ is a hypergeometric probability. The hypergeometric probabilities where we have a random sample of four from three healthy and two sick rats are:

$$p(4) = \frac{\binom{3}{4}\binom{2}{0}}{\binom{5}{4}} = \frac{0 \times 1}{5} = 0,$$

$$p(3) = \frac{\binom{3}{3}\binom{2}{1}}{5} = \frac{1 \times 2}{5} = \frac{2}{5},$$

$$p(2) = \frac{\binom{3}{2}\binom{2}{2}}{5} = \frac{3 \times 1}{5} = \frac{3}{5},$$

$$p(1) = \frac{\binom{3}{1}\binom{2}{3}}{5} = \frac{3 \times 0}{5} = 0,$$

$$p(0) = \frac{\binom{3}{0}\binom{2}{4}}{5} = \frac{3 \times 0}{5} = 0.$$

This illustrates that our definitions mean that we can apply the general formula routinely without prior analysis as to whether a particular sample is possible or not.

The important thing to note in this section is that the *basic* knowledge of the probability of a particular event comes from an analysis of the sample space. The general formula that we have developed may appear to be somehow more "mathematical" in nature. Its *only* validity though is in its correspondence with the more fundamental assignment of probability on the sample space.

## EXERCISES

In the following exercises use the general result for hypergeometric probabilities.

1. If $N = 7, r = 4$, and $n = 6$, determine $p(0)$, $p(1)$, $p(4)$, and $p(5)$.

2. If $N = 5, r = 2$, and $n = 3$, determine $p(0)$, $p(3)$, and $p(4)$.

3. If $N = 1000, r = 60$, and $n = 50$, determine $p(51)$, $p(53)$, and $p(54)$.

4. If $N = 2000, r = 100$, and $n = 200$, determine $p(150)$, $p(170)$, and $p(200)$.

5. If $N = 5, r = 3$, and $n = 4$, determine $p(1), p(2), p(3)$, $p(4)$, and $p(5)$.

6. From seven pine pollen and three oak pollen grains a simple random sample of six grains is taken. What is the probability of the event "exactly two pine grains are in the sample"?

7. From 1000 persons, 10 diseased, the rest healthy, a simple random sample of 50 persons is taken. What is the probability that:
   (a) only 35 persons in the sample are healthy?
   (b) eleven diseased individuals are in the sample?

| PATH 3 ☞ §4.6 | | PATH 5 ☞ §4.6 |

## 4.6 THE SUM OF HYPERGEOMETRIC PROBABILITIES

We now show that the hypergeometric probabilities, $p(x)$, for $x = 0, 1, \ldots, n$, total to 1 when added together. Let us consider an example where there are six rats — three healthy and three sick ones. A sample of three rats is taken. Thus, there are $\binom{6}{3} = 20$ possible samples. The number of possible samples with no sick rats is $\binom{3}{0}\binom{3}{3} = 1$; the number with one sick rat is $\binom{3}{1}\binom{3}{2} = 9$; and so forth. A sample of three rats may contain no sick ones, or it may contain exactly one, two, or three sick rats. Hence, the total number of different samples could be determined as follows:

$$\binom{3}{0}\binom{3}{3} + \binom{3}{1}\binom{3}{2} + \binom{3}{2}\binom{3}{1} + \binom{3}{3}\binom{3}{0}$$

$$= 1 + 9 + 9 + 1 = 20 = \binom{6}{3}.$$

In general, suppose there are $N$ things, $r$ of one type and $(N - r)$ of another. Consider any sample of size $n$. It may contain no healthy rats; on the other hand, it may contain exactly one, two, three, . . ., or $n$ healthy rats. It must, however, contain exactly 0 or 1 or 2 or . . . or $n$ healthy rats. Furthermore, no two of these numbers can describe the same sample, since the same sample cannot contain exactly two as well as exactly three healthy rats, etc. It follows then that we can write

$$\begin{bmatrix} \text{The number of} \\ \text{samples of size} \\ n \text{ with 0 healthy} \\ \text{rats} \end{bmatrix} + \begin{bmatrix} \text{The number of} \\ \text{samples of size} \\ n \text{ with exactly} \\ 1 \text{ healthy rat} \end{bmatrix} + \ldots + \begin{bmatrix} \text{The number of} \\ \text{samples of size} \\ n \text{ with exactly} \\ n \text{ healthy rats} \end{bmatrix} = \begin{bmatrix} \text{The num-} \\ \text{ber of} \\ \text{samples} \\ \text{of size } n \end{bmatrix}.$$

Since there are $\binom{N}{n}$ samples of size $n$, we obtain the result

$$\binom{r}{0}\binom{N-r}{n} + \binom{r}{1}\binom{N-r}{n-1} + \ldots + \binom{r}{n}\binom{N-r}{0} = \binom{N}{n}.$$

If we divide both sides of the above equation by $\binom{N}{n}$ we obtain

$$\frac{\binom{r}{0}\binom{N-r}{n}}{\binom{N}{n}} + \frac{\binom{r}{1}\binom{N-r}{n-1}}{\binom{N}{n}} + \ldots + \frac{\binom{r}{n}\binom{N-r}{0}}{\binom{N}{n}} = 1,$$

and since the numbers on the left-hand side are hypergeometric probabilities for $x = 0, 1, \ldots, n$, we see that their sum is in fact equal to 1.

GENERAL STATEMENT.   *For hypergeometric probabilities $p(x)$ with $x = 0, 1, 2, \ldots, n$, the sum of all the $p(x)$ equals one. (See preceding formula.)*

EXAMPLE 1.   Suppose $N = 10, r = 4$, and $n = 3$. Then substituting into the general result we obtain

$$\binom{4}{0}\binom{6}{3} + \binom{4}{1}\binom{6}{2} + \binom{4}{2}\binom{6}{1} + \binom{4}{3}\binom{6}{0} = \binom{10}{3}.$$

The left-hand side of the equation is

$$(1 \times 20) + (4 \times 15) + (6 \times 6) + (4 \times 1)$$
$$= 20 + 60 + 36 + 4 = 120,$$

while the right-hand side of the equation is

$$\binom{10}{3} = \frac{10 \times 9 \times 8}{3 \times 2} = 120.$$

This general illustration has many possible individual realizations. One such is the following. There are $N = 10$ individuals, 4 smokers and 6 nonsmokers. Of all the 120 possible samples of size 3 that exist there are:

$$
\begin{array}{r}
20 \text{ with no smokers} \\
60 \text{ with one smoker} \\
36 \text{ with two smokers} \\
\underline{4} \text{ with three smokers} \\
120 \text{ Total.}
\end{array}
$$

An important special case of this general statement is obtained by setting $r = 1$. This gives

$$\binom{1}{0}\binom{N-1}{n} + \binom{1}{1}\binom{N-1}{n-1} + \binom{1}{2}\binom{N-1}{n-2} + \binom{1}{3}\binom{N-1}{n-3} + \cdots$$
$$+ \binom{1}{n}\binom{N-1}{0} = \binom{N}{n}$$

In the first term there is a factor $\binom{1}{0}$; in the second, $\binom{1}{1}$. Both of these are equal to 1,

$$\binom{1}{0} = \frac{1!}{0!1!} = 1, \qquad \binom{1}{1} = \frac{1!}{1!0!} = 1.$$

For the remaining terms

$$\binom{1}{2} = 0, \qquad \binom{1}{3} = 0, \qquad \ldots, \qquad \binom{1}{n} = 0.$$

Thus, we have, for $r = 1$,

$$\binom{N-1}{n} + \binom{N-1}{n-1} = \binom{N}{n}.$$

**EXERCISES**

1. Verify by calculation that:

(a) $\binom{6}{2} + \binom{6}{1} = \binom{7}{2}$;　　(b) $\binom{8}{3} + \binom{8}{2} = \binom{9}{3}$;

(c) $\binom{2}{1} + \binom{2}{0} = \binom{3}{1}$;　　(d) $\binom{3}{2} + \binom{3}{1} = \binom{4}{2}$;

2. Verify by calculation that:

(a) $\binom{4}{0}\binom{2}{3} + \binom{4}{1}\binom{2}{2} + \binom{4}{2}\binom{2}{1} + \binom{4}{3}\binom{2}{0}$
$$= \binom{6}{3};$$

(b) $\binom{2}{0}\binom{2}{3} + \binom{2}{1}\binom{2}{2} + \binom{2}{2}\binom{2}{1} + \binom{2}{3}\binom{2}{0}$
$$= \binom{4}{3};$$

(c) $\dfrac{\binom{2}{0}\binom{3}{3}}{\binom{5}{3}} + \dfrac{\binom{2}{1}\binom{3}{2}}{\binom{5}{3}} + \dfrac{\binom{2}{2}\binom{3}{1}}{\binom{5}{3}} + \dfrac{\binom{2}{3}\binom{3}{0}}{\binom{5}{3}} = 1$ .

3. Verify by calculation that:

(a) $\binom{3}{0}\binom{6}{5} + \binom{3}{1}\binom{6}{4} + \binom{3}{2}\binom{6}{3} + \binom{3}{3}\binom{6}{2} +$
$$\binom{3}{4}\binom{6}{1} + \binom{3}{5}\binom{6}{0} = \binom{9}{5};$$

(b) $\binom{1000}{2} + \binom{1000}{1} = \binom{1001}{2}$ .

| PATH 3 ☛ §4.7, 4.8 |    | PATH 5 ☛ §5.1 |

## 4.7★ APPLICATIONS OF HYPERGEOMETRIC PROBABILITIES: SMOKING AND LUNG CANCER, DUALITY OF HYPERGEOMETRIC PROBABILITIES

In medical research a problem of major importance is to determine whether or not the risk of developing or dying from a disease (say lung cancer) is the same among two or more subclasses (say smokers and nonsmokers) of a population. One manner of ascertaining this is to take a population, divide it into two groups like smokers and nonsmokers, and to study new cases of lung cancer that subsequently develop in each group. The risk of smokers then would be determined as the ratio of smokers who contract the disease to the total number of smokers; similarly, the risk of nonsmokers would be the number of non-smokers contracting the disease over the total number of nonsmokers. A study of this type in which the population is divided into two or more groups, and new cases of the disease subsequently observed in both groups, is called a *pro-spective* study. Its essential characteristic is that the subclasses of the population are established and the individuals therein observed *prior to* their contracting the disease in question.

However, the risk of developing or dying from any one disease in any one year is small. For this reason prospective studies must include observations of many persons, usually for several years. Most of the observations are of persons who never contract the disease in question. There is another type of study, the *retrospective* or *case control* study in which the necessity of observing large numbers of persons without the disease is obviated. In this kind of study one starts with two groups — one of persons having the disease, the other of persons not having the disease. The persons not having the disease are usually chosen to match those having the disease with respect to characteristics like age, economic status, etc. They are called *controls* or *case controls*. Looking back, "retro-spectively," one then determines the proportion of smokers and nonsmokers (say) among those who died of lung cancer and those who did not. The essential feature of this sort of study is that individuals are observed after having con-tracted the disease in question.

There are several sorts of risks which must be carefully distinguished in medical studies of both of the above types — the prospective and the retrospective study.

> DEFINITION.    **Incidence rate.**    This is the rate at which new cases of the disease occur in the population. It is the number of new cases per number of persons in the population per unit time. It gives the risk of contracting the disease.

> DEFINITION.    **Prevalence rate.**    This is the rate at which the disease occurs in the population. It is the number of people having the disease per number of persons in the population at a given period of time. It gives the risk of having the disease.

Two diseases having the same incidence rate may have markedly different prevalence rates because of the differing durations of the diseases.

> DEFINITION.    **Mortality rate.**    This is the rate at which deaths occur due to the disease. It is the number of persons dying from the disease per number of persons in the population per unit time. It gives the risk of dying from the disease.

With the above background we now develop random models in which smokers and nonsmokers have the *same* risk of dying of lung cancer. Such models can be compared with observations in order to test whether the risk of smokers is higher than the risk of nonsmokers. This point should be emphasized. The random models constructed in this section would apply if there were *no* difference between the mortality rates due to lung cancer of smokers and nonsmokers. Such models of "no difference" can be called *null models*.

Using such null models, differences between the lung cancer mortality rates of smokers and nonsmokers have been demonstrated in many studies. These demonstrations follow a basic pattern typical of much scientific research. For some defined population the numbers of smokers or nonsmokers who die or do not die of lung cancer are recorded. Departures of these observations from the null model are tested statistically to see if the model can serve as a reasonable explanation of the observations. Thus, the null model serves as an hypothesis which is accepted or rejected on the basis of the extent to which it agrees or disagrees with the observations. With these preliminaries in mind let us now develop the following random models.

MODEL I.     There are $N$ individuals, $m$ smokers and $N - m$ non-smokers. Suppose $n$ deaths from lung cancer occur among the $N$ individuals. There are $\binom{N}{n}$ ways for the cancer to strike $n$ individuals of the $N$. These $\binom{N}{n}$ ways are the simple events of our sample space. We consider the model in which each of these has the same probability, that is,

$$\frac{1}{\binom{N}{n}} \, .$$

MODEL II.     There are $N$ individuals, $n$ die from lung cancer, $N - n$ die from other nonrespiratory cancer. There are $m$ smokers among the $N$ individuals. Suppose that $m$ individuals are designated as smokers simply at random among the $N$ individuals. There are $\binom{N}{m}$ ways for the $m$ smokers to be designated among the $N$ dead persons. Let each of these be a simple event in our sample space. There are then $\binom{N}{m}$ simple events in the sample space. We assign each the same probability

$$\frac{1}{\binom{N}{m}} \, .$$

EXAMPLE I.     There are 5 individuals, 2 smokers and 3 nonsmokers. One dies of lung cancer, four do not. Thus, $N = 5$, $m = 2$, $N - m = 3$, and $N - n = 4$. MODEL I: Label the 2 smokers $S_1$, $S_2$; label the 3 nonsmokers $N_1$, $N_2$, $N_3$. One person dies of lung cancer. The sample space contains $\binom{N}{n} = \binom{5}{1} = 5$ simple events. Each indicates the person dying from lung cancer,

$$\{N_1, \ N_2, \ N_3, \ S_1, \ S_2\} \, .$$
$$\tfrac{1}{5}, \ \tfrac{1}{5}, \ \tfrac{1}{5}, \ \tfrac{1}{5}, \ \tfrac{1}{5}$$

The event "no smoker dies from lung cancer" is

$$\{N_1, \ N_2, \ N_3\}$$

and has probability $\tfrac{3}{5}$.

MODEL II: Label the individual dying from lung cancer L; label the others $A_1$, $A_2$, $A_3$, $A_4$. Two people are designated as smokers. The sample space contains $\binom{N}{m} = \binom{5}{2} = 10$ simple events each indicating a possibility for the two smokers:

$$\{LA_1, LA_2, LA_3, LA_4, A_1A_2, A_1A_3, A_1A_4, A_2A_3, A_2A_4, A_3A_4\}.$$
$$\tfrac{1}{10}, \tfrac{1}{10}, \tfrac{1}{10}, \tfrac{1}{10}, \tfrac{1}{10}, \tfrac{1}{10}, \tfrac{1}{10}, \tfrac{1}{10}, \tfrac{1}{10}, \tfrac{1}{10}$$

The event "no person dying of lung cancer smoked" is

$$\{A_1A_2, A_1A_3, A_1A_4, A_2A_3, A_2A_4, A_3A_4\},$$

which also has probability $\tfrac{3}{5}$ agreeing with our result using model I.

In model I any individual (smoker or nonsmoker) has the same probability of dying from lung cancer. To show this choose any individual (say John Smith) and determine the probability of the event "John Smith dies of lung cancer." The number of simple events in this event is

$$\begin{bmatrix} \text{The number of} \\ \text{ways of "choosing} \\ \text{John Smith"} \end{bmatrix} \times \begin{bmatrix} \text{The number of ways of} \\ \text{choosing } (n-1) \text{ of the} \\ \text{remaining } (N-1) \text{ individuals} \\ \text{for death from lung cancer} \end{bmatrix},$$

or

$$\binom{1}{1} \times \binom{N-1}{n-1} = \binom{N-1}{n-1}.$$

Each of the simple events has probability

$$\frac{1}{\binom{N}{n}},$$

and hence the probability that John Smith (or any of the $N$ individuals) dies from lung cancer is

$$\frac{\binom{N-1}{n-1}}{\binom{N}{n}} = \frac{\dfrac{(N-1)!}{(n-1)!(N-n)!}}{\dfrac{N!}{n!(N-n)!}} = \frac{(N-1)!}{N!} \times \frac{n!}{(n-1)!} = \frac{n}{N}.$$

Thus, in model I any individual has the same probability $n/N$ of dying from lung cancer whether he is a smoker or not.

In model II any individual has the same probability $m/N$ of being designated as a smoker, whether he died from lung cancer or not. The number of simple events in the event "John Smith is designated as a smoker" is

$$\begin{bmatrix} \text{The number of} \\ \text{ways of designating} \\ \text{John Smith} \end{bmatrix} \times \begin{bmatrix} \text{The number of ways of} \\ \text{designating } (m-1) \text{ of the} \\ \text{remaining } (N-1) \text{ individuals} \\ \text{as smokers.} \end{bmatrix},$$

or

$$\binom{1}{1} \times \binom{N-1}{m-1} = \binom{N-1}{m-1}.$$

The probability of each simple event is

$$\frac{1}{\binom{N}{m}},$$

so that the probability of "John Smith is a smoker" is

$$\frac{\binom{N-1}{m-1}}{\binom{N}{m}} = \frac{\dfrac{(N-1)!}{(m-1)!(N-m)!}}{\dfrac{N!}{m!(N-m)!}} = \frac{m}{N}.$$

Thus, John Smith (or any individual) has the same probability $m/N$ of being designated as a smoker whether he died from lung cancer or not.

Let us now find the probability $p(x)$ of the event "$x$ smokers die of lung cancer." We show that *this probability is the same in model I and model II.*

In model I the number of simple events in the event "$x$ smokers die of lung cancer" is

$$\left[\begin{array}{l}\text{The number of ways of} \\ \text{choosing } x \text{ of the} \\ m \text{ smokers for death} \\ \text{from lung cancer}\end{array}\right] \times \left[\begin{array}{l}\text{The number of ways of} \\ \text{choosing } (n-x) \text{ of} \\ \text{the } (N-m) \text{ nonsmokers} \\ \text{for death from lung} \\ \text{cancer}\end{array}\right],$$

or

$$\binom{m}{x} \quad \times \quad \binom{N-m}{n-x} \quad = \binom{m}{x}\binom{N-m}{n-x}.$$

Its probability is then

$$p(x) = \frac{\binom{m}{x}\binom{N-m}{n-x}}{\binom{N}{n}}, \qquad (1)$$

which is a hypergeometric probability.

In model II, the event "$x$ smokers die of lung cancer" has

$$\left[\begin{array}{l}\text{The number of ways of} \\ \text{designating } x \text{ of the} \\ n \text{ individuals who died} \\ \text{from lung cancer as} \\ \text{smokers}\end{array}\right] \times \left[\begin{array}{l}\text{The number of ways of} \\ \text{designating } (m-x) \text{ of} \\ \text{the remaining } (N-n) \\ \text{individuals as smokers}\end{array}\right],$$

or

$$\binom{n}{x} \quad \times \quad \binom{N-n}{m-x} \quad = \binom{n}{x}\binom{N-n}{m-x}$$

simple events, each with a probability of

$$\frac{1}{\binom{N}{m}}.$$

Its probability is, thus, (we read "$p$-prime" for $p'$)

$$p'(x) = \frac{\binom{n}{x}\binom{N-n}{m-x}}{\binom{N}{m}},$$

(2)

which is also a hypergeometric probability.

We now show that $p(x) = p'(x)$. By formula (1) we have

$$p(x) = \frac{\dfrac{m!}{x!(m-x)!}\dfrac{(N-m)!}{(n-x)!(N-m-n+x)!}}{\dfrac{N!}{n!(N-n)!}}$$

$$= \frac{\dfrac{n!(N-n)!}{x!(m-x)!(n-x)!(N-m-n+x)!}}{\dfrac{N!}{m!(N-m)!}}$$

Writing $(N-n-m+x)!$ for $(N-m-n+x)!$ and arranging factors, this becomes

$$p(x) = \frac{\dfrac{n!}{x!(n-x)!}\dfrac{(N-n)!}{(m-x)!(N-n-m+x)!}}{\dfrac{N!}{m!(N-m)!}} = \frac{\binom{n}{x}\binom{N-n}{m-x}}{\binom{N}{m}},$$

and from formula (2) we see that this is $p'(x)$. Thus, the probability of the event "$x$ smokers die of lung cancer" is the same in model I as in model II.

EXAMPLE 2.  Suppose $m = 2$, $N - m = 3$, $n = 1$, $N - n = 4$, $N = 5$, and $x = 1$; then

$$p(1) = \frac{\binom{m}{1}\binom{N-m}{n-1}}{\binom{N}{n}} = \frac{\dfrac{2!}{1!1!}\dfrac{3!}{0!3!}}{\dfrac{5!}{1!4!}} = \frac{2}{5},$$

$$p'(1) = \frac{\binom{n}{1}\binom{N-n}{m-1}}{\binom{N}{m}} = \frac{\dfrac{1!}{1!0!}\dfrac{4!}{1!3!}}{\dfrac{5!}{2!3!}} = \frac{4}{10} = \frac{2}{5},$$

and

$$p(1) = p'(1).$$

An important dual aspect of hypergeometric probabilities has been demonstrated and illustrated here in the context of our models of smoking and lung cancer. Let us recapitulate,

The probability of the event "$x$ smokers die of lung cancer" is the same whether we use:

MODEL I and we regard the $n$ persons who die of lung cancer as a simple random sample of size $n$ from a population of $m$ smokers and $(N - m)$ nonsmokers;

or

MODEL II and we regard the $m$ smokers as a simple random sample of size $m$ from a population of $n$ persons dying of lung cancer and $N - n$ not so dying.

The dual nature of hypergeometric probabilities is quite general. For any sample of size $n$ from a population of $m$ positives and $N - m$ negatives we can either:

regard the sampling procedure as that of choosing $n$ individuals simply at random from the $m$ positive and $(N - m)$ negative individuals;

or we can

regard the sampling procedure as that of assigning $m$ positive designations simply at random among a population of $N$ individuals, $n$ in the sample and $(N - n)$ not in the sample.

We have shown that the probabilities $p(x)$ are the same regardless of which model is used.

### EXERCISES

1.  Suppose there are 20 individuals, 17 smokers and 3 nonsmokers. Of these, 4 die from lung cancer, 16 do not.
    (a) Using model I, how many simple events are there in the sample space?
    (b) Using model II, how many simple events are there in the sample space?

2.  Suppose there are 9 individuals, 7 smokers and 2 non-smokers. 5 die from lung cancer, 4 do not.
    (a) Using model I, how many simple events are there in the sample space?
    (b) Using model II, how many simple events are there in the sample space?
    (c) Using model I calculate the probability that "3 individuals are smokers and die from lung cancer"?
    (d) Do the same using model II.

3.  Using the same data as in Exercise 1;
    (a) Determine the probability that "2 persons are

smokers and die from lung cancer", using first model I and secondly model II.

(b) determine the probability that "6 individuals are smokers and die from lung cancer", using both models.

4. There are 4 individuals, 2 smokers, 2 nonsmokers. Three die of lung cancer, one does not:

(a) Enumerate the sample spaces under model I and Model II.

(b) Calculate the respective probabilities of 0, 1, 2, 3 smokers dying from lung cancer.

5. There are 200 persons, of these 120 are smokers. There are 125 deaths due to lung cancer in the 200 individuals. Using model I,

(a) How many simple events are there in the event "M dies of lung cancer," where M is the initial of a particular individual of one of the 200 persons?

(b) What is the probability of this event?

(c) What is the probability that any particular individual dies of lung cancer?

| PATH 3 ☞ §4.8 |     | PATH 5 ☞ §4.8, 6.5, 7.3 |

## 4.8★ APPLICATIONS OF HYPERGEOMETRIC PROBABILITIES: MEASURING FAUNAL SIMILARITIES. A PROBLEM IN ZOOGEOGRAPHY

Different kinds of animals are found in different areas of the world today. This present day geographic distribution of the many kinds of land animals is a result of many interwoven events of the past. Changes in the configuration of land masses, drastic changes in climate (for example, those concomitant with glaciation), evolutionary modification of the animal populations themselves — all of these factors interact in a complex history. A great deal of effort is expended in genetics in studying evolutionary mechanisms, that is, how hereditary changes can occur at the cellular and subcellular (or molecular) level. It is equally important to study how evolution *has* occurred, and an understanding of this can be obtained by studying present day animal distributions.

Zoogeographers have studied present day distributions of animals and have divided the earth into faunal regions. These are regions throughout which members of the same or similar groups of animals are likely to be found, and between which the kinds of animals found are likely to differ.[2] Faunal regions represent the major land centers of evolution during the last 70,000,000 years, the Tertiary era of the geological time-scale. During this time the land masses

---

[2] The faunal regions were first delineated by Alfred R. Wallace who along with Charles Darwin was an early proponent of evolution due to natural selection.

delineated as regions were relatively stable. Between any two such masses isolating barriers such as oceans or mountains resulted in little to no interbreeding between the various populations. Within a region, however, interbreeding, with consequent genetic exchange, was possible for many populations. Thus, evolutionary changes within a given region occurred more or less independently of those in other regions, and we have the simple interpretation that faunal regions represent the major land centers of Tertiary evolution. In its broad outline, fossil evidence corroborates this.

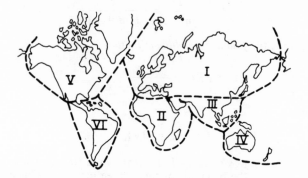

The biogeographic regions of the world: I — Palearctic region; II — Ethiopian (African) region; III — Oriental (Indian) region; IV — Australian region; V — Nearctic region; VI — Neotropical region.

It can be seen that zoogeographical studies are an important means to understanding the past. Nor is such an understanding limited to comparisons of extensive areas like continents. More localized studies contribute to a detailed understanding of how and why animals are found where they are today.

In delimiting different faunal areas — whether on the large scale of a region or on a much smaller scale — zoogeographers need to group together subareas having similar faunas and to separate subareas with dissimilar ones. Various measures of the similarity of different faunas have been utilized. Three are considered here with a simplified example. Suppose we are comparing areas with the following two lists of species:

| Species in Area 1 | Species in Area 2 |
| --- | --- |
| Coyote | Coyote |
| Prairie dog | Mountain lion |
| Antelope | Jumping mouse |
| Mule deer | Beaver |
| | Mule deer |

If we let $m$ be the number of species *in the first area*, then $m = 4$. Similarly let $n$ be the number in the second area, $n = 5$. Let $x$ be the number of species common to both areas, that is, the number in the intersection of the two sets. One measure of similarity is *Simpson's index*

$$S = \frac{x}{m},$$

where the denominator contains the number in the shorter list ($m$ in this case) or the number in either list should both contain the same number of species. Another measure is *Pirlot's index*

$$PT = \frac{2x}{m+n} = \frac{x}{\frac{1}{2}(m+n)}.$$

A third measure is the *faunal resemblance factor*

$$FRF = \frac{x}{m+n-x}.$$

In our example,

$$S = \tfrac{2}{4} = 0.5, \qquad PT = \tfrac{4}{9} = 0.44, \qquad FRF = \tfrac{2}{7} = 0.29.$$

EXAMPLE 1. It is worthwhile to give some examples of the behavior of these three measures. Consider the cases given below:

| Case | Area 1 | Area 2 | | | |
|------|--------|--------|---|---|---|
| I | coyote antelope mule deer | coyote antelope mule deer | $S = \tfrac{3}{3} = 1$; | $PT = \tfrac{6}{6} = 1$; | $FRF = \tfrac{3}{3} = 1$ |
| II | coyote antelope mule deer prairie dog deermouse | coyote antelope | $S = \tfrac{2}{2} = 1$; | $PT = \tfrac{4}{7} = 0.57$; | $FRF = \tfrac{2}{5} = 0.40$ |
| III | coyote antelope mule deer prairie dog | coyote antelope beaver | $S = \tfrac{2}{3} = 0.67$; | $PT = \tfrac{4}{7} = 0.57$; | $FRF = \tfrac{2}{5} = 0.40$ |

Simpson's index, $S$, does not distinguish between cases I and II. Neither the $FRF$ nor Pirlot's index $PT$ distinguishes between cases II and III. Note that (as in case II) $S$ can be 1 even though the faunas differ. ($S$ is always 1 when one fauna is a subset of the other.)

## A Random Model

We now examine the behavior of these indices under a random model. There are surely a variety of models possible, and the one presented here has no exclusive claim for consideration. It does provide an understanding and background that can be of considerable use in interpreting observations. It turns out that the same basic probability model can result from a variety of different biological situations.

We commence by way of an illustration. Suppose there are five species occurring in a coastal area at some time, time period 1. With a subsequent rise in sea level, a part of the original mainland is separated as an island, and the populations on this island become isolated from those on the mainland. By time period 2, three of the original five species survive on the island, while four of the original five survive on the mainland. In how many ways can the survivors

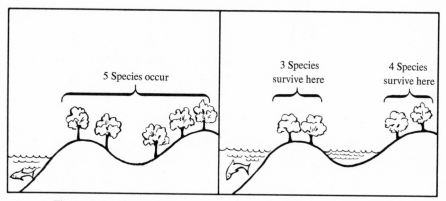

Time period 1: low sea level

Time period 2: high sea level

occur? First there are $\binom{5}{3}$ possibilities for the island's three surviving species. Similarly, there are $\binom{5}{4}$ possibilities for the mainland's survivors. Over-all then there are

$$\binom{5}{3}\binom{5}{4} = 50$$

total possible ways for the survivors to occur. Using the set of these possibilities as our sample space, consider a *simple random sample* from such a space. The probability of each simple event is

$$\frac{1}{\binom{5}{3}\binom{5}{4}} = \frac{1}{50}.$$

Now let us find the number of simple events in the event "exactly two species surviving on the island and the mainland are the same"; that is, "exactly two species are common to the two areas during the second time period." This number can be determined as follows. First, we pick three island survivors and this can be done in $\binom{5}{3}$ ways. Given the three species that survive on the island, we next determine the possibilities for the four species that survive on the mainland. These must be chosen so that two of the four are among those surviving on the island while the remaining two are not. The number of ways of doing this is

$$\begin{bmatrix} \text{The number of ways} \\ \text{of choosing 2 species} \\ \text{from the 3 that survive} \\ \text{on the island} \end{bmatrix} \times \begin{bmatrix} \text{The number of ways} \\ \text{of choosing 2 species} \\ \text{from the 2 that do not} \\ \text{survive on the island} \end{bmatrix}.$$

or

$$\binom{3}{2} \quad \times \quad \binom{2}{2}.$$

This is the number of ways of choosing the mainland species *given a particular choice of the three island survivors*. To determine the total number of ways of picking island and mainland survivors so that "exactly two species are common to the island and mainland" we first pick three island survivors in any of $\binom{5}{3}$ ways. Then we pick four mainland survivors in any of $\binom{3}{2}\binom{2}{2}$ ways. By the rule of counting the total number of ways is

$$\binom{5}{3}\binom{3}{2}\binom{2}{2} = 10 \times 3 \times 1 = 30.$$

This is the number of simple events in the event "exactly two species surviving on the island and the mainland are the same." Since each simple event has the same probability $\frac{1}{50}$, the probability of the above event is

$$\frac{30}{50} = \frac{\binom{5}{3}\binom{3}{2}\binom{2}{2}}{\binom{5}{3}\binom{5}{4}} = \frac{\binom{3}{2}\binom{2}{2}}{\binom{5}{4}} = \frac{3}{5}.$$

After cancelling the $\binom{5}{3}$ factor, which occurs in both the numerator and denominator, the remaining expression is recognizable as a *hypergeometric probability* (Section 4.4). In fact, if we determine the probability of 3 common species for the island and the mainland the result is, following the same argument,

$$\frac{\binom{5}{3}\binom{3}{3}\binom{2}{1}}{\binom{5}{3}\binom{5}{4}} = \frac{\binom{3}{3}\binom{2}{1}}{\binom{5}{4}} = \frac{2}{5}.$$

(We have already calculated these same hypergeometric probabilities in the example of a sample of size 4 from 3 healthy and 2 sick rats in Section 4.5.)

If there are 2 common species, Simpson's index $S$ is $\frac{2}{3}$, and Pirlot's index $PT$ is $\frac{4}{7}$. If there are three common species then $S = 1$ and $PT = \frac{6}{7}$. Note that the event "2 species are common to the two areas" is the same as the event "Simpson's index is $\frac{2}{3}$" or the event "the $PT$ is $\frac{4}{7}$." *For each of these word sentences defines the same subset of the sample space.* Thus, if we seek the probability that $S = \frac{2}{3}$ we are speaking of the probability *of an event in the sample space.* This is simply to reiterate that we speak only of the probabilities of *events.*

We now develop the general model without reference to the terms, such as survival or island, of a specific example. The general model applies to more than one biological situation. Suppose there are $N$ species and that one area contains $m$ of these species, while another contains $n$ of them. Without loss of generality we can say that $m$ is less than or equal to $n$. There are $\binom{N}{m}$ possible species compositions for one area and $\binom{N}{n}$ for the other. The total number of possibilities for the species composition of both areas together is therefore

$$\binom{N}{n}\binom{N}{m}.$$

Regarding the set of these possible combinations as our sample space, consider any random process (purposely left general) that would result in the simple events being equally likely. The probability assigned to each simple event is then

$$\frac{1}{\binom{N}{m}\binom{N}{n}}.$$

The argument follows as before. We need to determine the number of simple events in the event "$x$ species are in common." (This event is the same as the event "$S = x/m$," the event "$PT = 2x/(m + n)$," or the event "$FRF = x/(m + n - x)$.") We first choose the $m$ species for the first area, and this can be done in

$$\binom{N}{m}$$

ways. We next choose the $n$ species for area 2. To choose $x$ of the same species as in area 1, we take $x$ things from $m$, and this can be done in

$$\binom{m}{x}$$

ways. The remaining $(n - x)$ species must be chosen from the $(N - m)$ species not found in area 1. There are

$$\binom{N - m}{n - x}$$

ways of choosing these.  Our rule of counting gives

$$\binom{N}{m}\binom{m}{x}\binom{N-m}{n-x}$$

as the number of simple events in "$x$ species are in common."  Since each simple event has the same probability

$$\frac{1}{\binom{N}{m}\binom{N}{n}},$$

the sum of the probabilities in this event is

$$p(x) = \frac{\binom{N}{m}\binom{m}{x}\binom{N-m}{n-x}}{\binom{N}{m}\binom{N}{n}} = \frac{\binom{m}{x}\binom{N-m}{n-x}}{\binom{N}{n}}, \tag{1}$$

which is simply a hypergeometric probability.  (Note the difference in this sample space and the one previously seen for hypergeometric probabilities in Section 4.4.  This space contains $\binom{N}{m}\binom{N}{n}$ simple events, the former contained $\binom{N}{n}$ simple events.)

If you are worried about the lack of symmetry in the argument we used (that is, choosing first the $m$ in population 1, and then the $n$ for population 2) the same results are obtained if the order is reversed (see Exercise 5 of this section).

EXAMPLE 2.   10 species occur in a given area; 4 and 5 of these, respectively, occur in two subareas.  If the species which occur in these subareas constitute a simple random sample of all possibilities, what is the probability that $S = 0.75$?
First $S = \frac{1}{4} x$ and for $S$ to be 0.75, $x$ must be 3.  We have

$$p(3) = \frac{\binom{4}{3}\binom{6}{2}}{\binom{10}{5}} = \frac{60}{252} = \frac{5}{21}.$$

Thus, the probability that Simpson's index is 0.75 is $\frac{5}{21}$ or just under one fourth.
What is the probability that $S = 1$?  This implies that $x = 4$.  We have

$$p(4) = \frac{\binom{4}{4}\binom{6}{1}}{\binom{10}{5}} = \frac{6}{252} = \frac{1}{42},$$

a quite improbable event.

What is the probability that $PT = 1$?  This is zero, since $m \neq n$ $(4 \neq 5)$. $PT = 2x/(m + n)$ can only be 1 if $m = n$.

The hypergeometric probabilities and their derivations hold for the following three biological models:

(1) There are $N$ species in area 1 and in area 2. In area 1, $(N - m)$ are eliminated. In area 2, $(N - n)$ are eliminated for some reason (e.g., migration, extinction). Suppose the "choice" of those persisting is simply at random from all possible choices. Results are that $m$ species are left in area 1; $n$, in area 2, and the probability of $x$ species in common is given by our general hypergeometric probability given in formula (1) of this section.

(2) There are $N$ species in a homeland area; $m$ species migrate to area 1; $n$ migrate to area 2. The "choice" of those migrating is simply at random from all possible migrating combinations. (Some species may migrate to both areas, the probability that $x$ species do migrate to both areas is given by the general hypergeometric probability referred to in model 1.) This model differs somewhat from the preceding, but the probability model is the same.

(3) There are $m$ species in area 1, and the same $m$ species are in area 2, isolated from area 1. Let us say area 1 is mountain 1, and area 2 is mountain 2. Through mutation and selection some of the species in the first mountain evolve into new species *found on this mountain and no other*. Likewise some of the species on the second mountain evolve into new species *found only on that mountain*. On the first mountain say $y$ species remain stable and $m - y$ change; on the second $z$ remain stable and $m - z$ change. There are then

$$\binom{m}{y}\binom{m}{z}$$

possibilities for the species which do not change. If all possibilities are equally likely what is the probability that $x$ of the species remain in common to the two mountains. The number of simple events in "$x$ are in common to the two mountains" is

$$\binom{m}{y}\binom{y}{x}\binom{m - y}{z - x},$$

the same as in our previous arguments, and

$$p(x) = \frac{\binom{y}{x}\binom{m - y}{z - x}}{\binom{m}{z}}.$$

This again is a hypergeometric probability.

**EXERCISES**

1. Let $m$ be the number of species in area 1; $n$ the number in area 2; $x$ the number common to area 1 and area 2. Calculate Simpson's index, Pirlot's index, and the faunal resemblance factor ($FRF$) for the following cases:
   (a) $n = 10, m = 5,\quad x = 3$;
   (b) $n = 60, m = 5,\quad x = 3$;
   (c) $n = 10, m = 120, x = 6$;
   (d) $n = 70, m = 70,\quad x = 60$;
   (e) $n = 20, m = 20,\quad x = 10$;
   (f) $n = 20, m = 21,\quad x = 0$.

2. In the general random model given in the text

$$p(x) = \frac{\binom{m}{x}\binom{N-m}{n-x}}{\binom{N}{n}}.$$

   Suppose $m = 4, n = 3, N = 5$.
   (a) What is the probability of the event "Simpson's index is 1"?
   (b) Is the event "the $FRF$ is 1" the same event? If not what is its probability?
   (c) What is the probability of the event "2 species occur in both areas"? Is this the same event as "$PT = 0.57$"?

3. Consider the drawing below. There are two mountains.

Time period 1: cold          Time period 2: warm

In time period 1 there are six species of animals occurring in and restricted to the coniferous forest which extends continuously from mountain to mountain. By time period 2 the climate has warmed considerably and only the tops of the two mountains have coniferous forest. On one mountain 3 species survive; on the other 4. If all combinations of surviving species are equally likely, what is the probability that only 0, 1, 2, 3, 4 of the same species, respectively, survive on both mountain tops?

4.  Adjacent mountaintops in the tropics often exhibit markedly different fauna. Animal populations living in a cold and moist climate at high altitudes on one mountain are often isolated from those at similar altitudes on another. Hot tropical terrain at low altitudes between the mountains acts as a barrier to the dispersal of the cold-adapted species.
    Suppose there are three mountains — A, B, C. At high altitudes on these there are, respectively, 4, 5, and 3 species of reptiles and amphibians. The chart below gives the distribution of species on the three mountains. (X means present.)

| Mountain<br>Species | A | B | C |
|:---:|:---:|:---:|:---:|
| 1 | X | X | ... |
| 2 | ... | ... | X |
| 3 | X | X | X |
| 4 | ... | X | X |
| 5 | X | X | ... |
| 6 | X | X | ... |

(a) Calculate Simpson's index, Pirlot's index, and the *FRF* for the three pairs (A, B) (A, C), (B, C). Which mountains are more closely related faunistically?
(b) Taking $N = 6$, use the random model developed in the text and calculate the probabilities it yields for:
   (i) 4 species being common to A and B;
   (ii) 1 species being common to A and C;
   (iii) 2 species being common to B and C.

5.  Of $N$ possible species, area 1 has $m$ species and area 2 has $n$. (The same species may be found in both areas.) There are $\binom{N}{m}\binom{N}{n}$ possible combinations of species in areas 1 and 2 together. Consider the sample space containing all these possibilities and no others, and let them be equally likely. In the text the number of simple events in the event "only $x$ species are common to both areas" was determined as follows. One can choose $m$ species for area 1 in $\binom{N}{m}$ ways, $x$ common species for area 2 in $\binom{m}{x}$ ways, and the $(n - x)$ species found only in area 2 in $\binom{N - m}{n - x}$ ways. Hence, we found

$$p(x) = \frac{\binom{m}{x}\binom{N - m}{n - x}}{\binom{N}{n}}.$$

Show that choosing the $n$ species for area 2 first, and then choosing the $m$ species for area 1 gives the result

$$p'(x) = \frac{\binom{n}{x}\binom{N-n}{m-x}}{\binom{N}{m}}.$$

Write both $p(x)$ and $p'(x)$ in terms of factorials and show that $p(x) = p'(x)$.

| PATH 3 ☞ §4.7 |   | PATH 5 ☞ §4.7, 6.5, 7.3 |

## REFERENCES

### General

GOLDBERG, S., *Probability An Introduction* (Englewood Cliffs, N. J.: Prentice-Hall, Inc., 1960), Ch. 2.

KEMENY, J. G., SNELL, J. L., and THOMPSON, G. L., *Introduction to Finite Mathematics* (Englewood Cliffs, N. J.: Prentice-Hall, Inc., 1956), Ch. 4.
[The authors use a probability of statements approach.]

SCHLAIFER, R., *Probability and Statistics for Business Decisions* (New York: McGraw-Hill Book Company, Inc., 1959).
[In Chapter 1 the axioms of probability are motivated without reference to relative frequencies. The interested student will find it worthwhile to read this treatment.]

For readers with more mathematical background, the following books are invaluable.

FELLER, W., *An Introduction to Probability Theory and Its Applications*, Vol. I., 2nd ed. (New York: John Wiley & Sons, Inc., 1957).

PARZEN, E., *Modern Probability Theory and Its Applications* (New York: John Wiley & Sons, Inc., 1960).

### Optional Section 4.7

CORNFIELD, J., "A Statistical Problem Arising from Retrospective Studies," *Proceedings of the Third Berkeley Symposium on Mathematical Statistics and Probability, Vol. IV*, J. Neyman, Ed. (Berkeley: University of California Press, 1956).

SARTWELL, P. E., Ed., *Maxcy-Rosenau Preventive Medicine and Public Health*, 9th ed. (New York: Appleton-Century-Crofts, Inc., 1965), Section 1.

*Smoking and Health*, Report of the Advisory Committee to the Surgeon General of the Public Health Service. Public Health Service Publication No. 1103.

## Optional Section 4.8

DARLINGTON, P. J., *Zoogeography: The Geographical Distribution of Animals* (New York: John Wiley & Sons, 1957).

DUELLMAN, W. E., "A Biogeographic Account of the Herpetofauna of Michoacán, México" — *University of Kansas Publications, Museum of Natural History*, Vol. 15, No. 14, (1965), pp. 627–709.
[An interesting example and exposition of modern zoogeographic analysis. In Duellman's terminology, Pirlot's index is called the *FRF*.]

HUHEEY, J. E., "A Mathematical Method of Analyzing Biogeographical Data." I. Herpetofauna of Illinois, *The American Midland Naturalist*, Vol. 73 No. 2 (1965), pp. 490–500.

SIMPSON, G. G., "Notes on the Measurement of Faunal Resemblance," *American Journal of Science*, Vol. 258-A (1960), pp. 300–311.

## ODDS, CONDITIONAL PROBABILITY, AND INDEPENDENCE

### 5.1 ODDS

Before passing to the main topics of this chapter we introduce the subject of odds-ratios and odds.

> DEFINITION. *Given a sample space* S *and one of its events* A *with* A′ *the complement of* A *then the* **odds ratio in favor of** A *is given by*
>
> $$\frac{P(A)}{P(A')} = \frac{P(A)}{1 - P(A)},$$
>
> *provided that neither* $P(A)$ *nor* $P(A')$ *is zero.*

For example, consider the following sample space for two coin flips:

$$\{HH, HT, TH, \quad TT\}$$
$$\tfrac{4}{9}, \quad \tfrac{2}{9}, \quad \tfrac{2}{9}, \quad \tfrac{1}{9}$$

The probabilities indicate that the coin is biased to fall heads. In many repetitions of this conceptual experiment two heads would be likely to occur $\frac{4}{9}$ of the time. Let A = {HH}, so that A′ = {HT, TH, TT}. Then $P(A) = \frac{4}{9}$ and $P(A') = \frac{5}{9}$. The odds ratio in favor of A is

$$\frac{P(A)}{P(A')} = \frac{\frac{4}{9}}{\frac{5}{9}} = \frac{4}{5}.$$

For each four times that A does occur there are about five times that it does not. The numerator and denominator of this ratio give the odds favoring the occurrence of A. Thus, the odds in favor of A are 4 to 5. Since we have a ratio, we can also write

$$\tfrac{4}{5} = \tfrac{8}{10} = \tfrac{80}{100}.$$

Thus, we can also say that the odds in favor of A are 8 to 10, or 80 to 100.

The *odds ratio in favor* of A is the ratio of $P(A)$ to $P(A')$. Both A and A′ are events of S. In considering odds we need not restrict ourselves to pairs of complementary events. More generally, we can consider any two events of S.

DEFINITION.    *Given a sample space* S, *and two of its events* A *and* B, $(P(A) > 0, P(B) > 0)$ *then the* **odds ratio of A to B** *is given by*

$$\frac{P(A)}{P(B)}.$$

Thus, in the model of flipping two coins, let A = {HH} and B = {HT}. The odds ratio of A to B is

$$\frac{P(A)}{P(B)} = \frac{\frac{4}{9}}{\frac{2}{9}} = \frac{4}{2} = \frac{2}{1}.$$

For each four times that two heads occur, a head followed by a tail occurs about twice. The odds of A relative to B are 4 to 2 (or 2 to 1). The event A is twice as likely to occur as the event B.

The relative odds of all four simple events may be expressed simultaneously. In doing so it is convenient to choose a simple event with the smallest possible probability (in this case TT with probability $\frac{1}{9}$). We then determine the odds ratios of each simple event to this event: HH to TT, HT to TT, TH to TT, and TT to TT. We obtain, respectively,

$$\frac{\frac{4}{9}}{\frac{1}{9}}, \frac{\frac{2}{9}}{\frac{1}{9}}, \frac{\frac{2}{9}}{\frac{1}{9}}, \frac{\frac{1}{9}}{\frac{1}{9}},$$

or

$$\frac{4}{1}, \frac{2}{1}, \frac{2}{1}, \frac{1}{1}.$$

If desired we can write the relative odds as

$$4:2:2:1.$$

Such odds precisely define how likely one event is relative to another. To say that odds are 4 to 2 means that one event's probability is twice as great as another's probability.

> EXAMPLE 1.   In the sample space for the arrangements of three bank swallows and one tree swallow on a phone wire, suppose each of the events is equally likely (the birds are arranged "simply at random")
>
> {BBBT, BBTB, BTBB, TBBB}
> $\frac{1}{4}$ ,    $\frac{1}{4}$ ,    $\frac{1}{4}$ ,    $\frac{1}{4}$
>
> then the relative odds of the simple events are, of course,
>
> 1:1:1:1.
>
> Consider the event "the tree swallow is not at the extreme left,"
>
> {BBBT, BBTB, BTBB}
> $\frac{1}{4}$ ,    $\frac{1}{4}$ ,    $\frac{1}{4}$

and the event "the tree swallow is at the extreme right,"

$$\{BBBT\}_{\frac{1}{4}}.$$

The odds ratio of the first event to the second is

$$\frac{\frac{3}{4}}{\frac{1}{4}} = \frac{3}{1}.$$

The relative odds are therefore $3:1$.

EXAMPLE 2. Conversely, suppose we have the sample space

$$\{a, b, c\},$$

and are given the odds of its simple events to be

$$3:3:1.$$

We can readily determine the probabilities of the simple events. Let $p$ be the probability of $\{c\}$; then the probability of b (as well as a) is $3p$. The sum of the probabilities must be 1, and we have

$$3p + 3p + p = 1,$$
$$7p = 1,$$
$$p = \tfrac{1}{7}.$$

Hence, the probabilities of the simple events are

$$\tfrac{3}{7}, \tfrac{3}{7}, \tfrac{1}{7}.$$

To convert odds to probabilities, simply total the odds and divide each by the total.

EXAMPLE 3. There are $8 = 2^3$ possible triplets or three-letter sequences of the two letters A and C (A, adenine; C, cytosine). Suppose probabilities are assigned as follows:

$$\{AAA, AAC, ACA, CAA, CCA, CAC, ACC, CCC\}$$
$$0 , \tfrac{1}{12} , \tfrac{1}{12} , \tfrac{1}{12} , \tfrac{2}{12} , \tfrac{2}{12} , \tfrac{2}{12} , \tfrac{3}{12}$$

The event D "the triplet has exactly two C's" has probability $\tfrac{6}{12}$, while the event G "the triplet has just one C" has probability $\tfrac{3}{12}$. The odds of D relative to G are two to one ($6:3$). Two C's are twice as likely to occur as one C. The odds of the event H "the triplet has 3 C's" to the event L "the triplet has just one C" are *even*, that is, $1:1$. One C is as likely to occur as three C's.

In the model of Example 3 the event the "triplet has no C's" is impossible. Since its probability is zero, *the odds of this event to any other are undefined.* Odds are defined only for events with probabilities greater than zero.

## EXERCISES

1. In the sample space

$$\{ a , \; b , \; c , \; d , e \}$$
$$\tfrac{2}{10}, \tfrac{1}{10}, \tfrac{3}{20}, \tfrac{1}{20}, \tfrac{1}{2}$$

(a) give the relative odds of $a:b:c:d:e$;
(b) $\{e\}$ is how many times as likely as $\{d\}$?

2. In the sample space of Exercise 1 let the events be defined as

$$A = \{a, b, c\}, \quad B = \{d, e\}, \quad C = \{c, d\},$$

Give the odds of:
(a) event A to event B;  (b) B to C;
(c) A to C;  (d) A to $(B \cap C)$.

3. In the sample space,

$$\{a, b, c, d, e\} \; .$$

The relative odds of $a:b:c:d:e$ are $7:6:5:4:3$. Find the probability of each simple event in the sample space.

4. In the sample space

$$\{h, \; t, \; r, q\},$$
$$\tfrac{3}{4}, \tfrac{1}{8}, \tfrac{1}{8}, 0$$

let

$$H = \{h\}, \quad T = \{t\}, \quad R = \{r\}, \quad Q = \{q\}.$$
$$A = H \cup T, \quad B = R \cup Q, \quad C = H \cup T \cup R.$$

What are the odds of the event:
(a) H to T;  (b) A to B;  (c) A to C;
(d) R to Q;  (e) $A \cap B$ to Q;  (f) $A \cap B$ to C.

5. (a) In a mating between two black guinea pigs the probability that an offspring is black is $\tfrac{3}{4}$, and that it is white is $\tfrac{1}{4}$. What are the black:white odds?
(b) In a mating of a black-rough-haired guinea pig with a white-smooth-haired guinea pig the hair of the progeny is black-rough, black-smooth, white-rough, or white-smooth. The relative odds of these events are respectively, $9:3:3:1$. If the sample space contains only these four simple events what is the probability assigned to each? What are the odds of the event "an offspring is black-haired" to the event "an offspring is white-haired"?

6. A garden pea plant which is tall, and in which the ripe seed (pea) is yellow and round is crossed with

another which is tall and has yellow round seeds. The progeny fall into the following $2^3 = 8$ categories:

| Progeny | Odds |
|---|---|
| tall, yellow, round | 27 |
| tall, yellow, wrinkled | 9 |
| tall, green, round | 9 |
| tall, green, wrinkled | 3 |
| dwarf, yellow, round | 9 |
| dwarf, yellow, wrinkled | 3 |
| dwarf, green, round | 3 |
| dwarf, green, wrinkled | 1 |

(a) Assign probabilities on the sample space consistent with the odds given.
(b) What is the probability that a plant either is tall or has wrinkled seeds?

| PATH 4 ☞ §5.2 |   | PATH 5 ☞ §5.2 |

## 5.2  CONDITIONAL PROBABILITY OF AN EVENT

Consider again the results of two flips of a coin (biased to heads), with the sample space

$$\{HH, HT, TH, TT\}$$
$$\tfrac{4}{9} , \tfrac{2}{9} , \tfrac{2}{9} , \tfrac{1}{9}$$

Suppose one knows that at least one tail has occurred. What, then, is the probability that at least one head occurs? In other words what is the probability that a second event occurs *given* that the first has occurred?

To say that at least one tail has occurred is to say that either HT or TH or TT has occurred. Thus, the event which is known to have occurred is

$$A = \{HT, TH, TT\}$$
$$\tfrac{2}{9} , \tfrac{2}{9} , \tfrac{1}{9}$$

and has probability $\tfrac{5}{9}$. One may now think of this event as a *new sample space*, with a (new) probability of 1 since it is of certain occurrence.

The old probabilities must then be adjusted. Within this event, the relative odds of the simple events are 2 :2 :1. A natural way to assign probabilities in the "new" sample space is one which preserves these relative odds.

In order to preserve odds and have the new probabilities add to 1 we simply divide each original probability by $P(A) = \tfrac{5}{9}$, the event probability. We have $\tfrac{2}{9} + \tfrac{2}{9} + \tfrac{1}{9} = \tfrac{5}{9}$. Dividing each probability on the left-hand side by $\tfrac{5}{9}$, we obtain

$$\{HT, TH, TT\}$$
$$\tfrac{2}{5} , \tfrac{2}{5} , \tfrac{1}{5}$$

We thus have a new sample space whose probabilities add to 1; $\frac{2}{5} + \frac{2}{5} + \frac{1}{5} = 1$. Such a division always gives a new set of probabilities totaling one, with the same odds as before. Now, if we look at this new sample space the event "at least one coin falls heads" is

$$\{HT, TH\}$$
$$\frac{2}{5} \, , \, \frac{2}{5}$$

and thus the probability that at least one coin falls heads given that at least one coin is tails is $\frac{4}{5}$.

In most problems, it is not convenient actually to define a new sample space and fortunately this procedure is not necessary. We can carry out all our calculations in terms of the original sample space without explicit reference to the new one. For example, suppose event B is $\{HH, HT, TH\}$, "at least one coin falls heads." *To say that B occurs given A is simply to say that both A and B occur;* that is, $A \cap B$ occurs. Thus, we have

$$A = \{HT, TH, TT\}, \qquad P(A) = \tfrac{5}{9},$$
$$B = \{HH, HT, TH\}, \qquad P(B) = \tfrac{8}{9},$$
$$A \cap B = \{HT, TH\} \atop \frac{2}{9} \, , \, \frac{2}{9} \, , \qquad P(A \cap B) = \tfrac{4}{9}.$$

But $A \cap B$ is the event B *in terms of the new sample space A.* To put this probability in terms of the new space, we divide by the probability of the event which is known to have occurred. This event is A, and $P(A) = \frac{5}{9}$. We have

$$\frac{\frac{4}{9}}{\frac{5}{9}} = \frac{4}{5},$$

which is the answer already obtained. This is "the probability of B given A." We denote this probability by $P(B|A)$. If we speak in terms of the events of the original sample space we see that

$$P(B|A) = \frac{P(A \cap B)}{P(A)}.$$

What we have done is to *illustrate the naturalness* of the following definition.

DEFINITION.      *Given a sample space, let A and B be any two of its events. The probability of event B given that event A has occurred is (provided that $P(A) \neq 0$),*

$$P(B|A) = \frac{P(A \cap B)}{P(A)},$$

*and it is called the* **conditional probability of B given A.** *For $P(A) = 0$, this probability is not defined.*

EXAMPLE 1. In the diagram below, events A and B are represented by circles while the rectangle represents the entire sample space S.

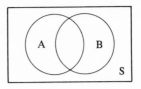

The representation is diagrammatic, and the actual areas indicated are not related to the probabilities of the designated events. Suppose that $P(A) = \frac{1}{3}$, $P(B) = \frac{1}{4}$, $P(A \cap B) = \frac{1}{5}$. To say that A has occurred, means that a simple event in A has occurred. To find the probability of B given A, consider A as a new sample space.

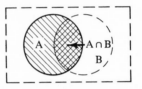

To have B occur in this new space means that $A \cap B$ occurs. Considering A as a sample space, $P(A)$ must now equal one. To accomplish this (and preserve odds) we take the probabilities from the original space S and divide each by $P(A) = \frac{1}{3}$. Thus, the probability of B given A is seen to be the probability of $A \cap B$ divided by the probability of A

$$\frac{P(A \cap B)}{P(A)} = \frac{\frac{1}{5}}{\frac{1}{3}} = \frac{3}{5}.$$

EXAMPLE 2. Again consider the first diagram of Example 1 where S is the sample space, and A and B two of its events. Suppose $P(A) = 0$. Since A is impossible, we can never think of it as having occurred, nor of it as being of certain occurrence. When $P(A) = 0$ the conditional probability of B given A is *not defined*. Further, should we try to calculate routinely using

$$P(B|A) = \frac{P(A \cap B)}{P(A)}$$

we run immediately into the problem of division by zero, and are stopped.

EXAMPLE 3. A psychological experimenter is studying

how intelligent people respond to routine and boring tasks. A graduate student (the subject) is asked to flip a coin twice, record the two results, and repeat this 500 times (for a total of 1000 flips). The psychologist then leaves the room. The graduate student cuts his work in half as follows. He flips a coin and records the results of the first toss, instead of flipping again he turns the coin over (mentally) and records the opposite result. The only possible observations are then heads-tails and tails-heads.

If $p$ is the probability that the coin falls heads when tossed, the sample space is

$$\{HH, HT, \ \ TH \ , TT\}$$
$$0 \ , \ p \ , 1 - p, \ 0$$

The event exactly one head occurs in two "tosses" is

$$\{HT, \ TH \ \}$$
$$p \ , 1 - p$$

and has probability $1 = p + 1 - p$. Thus, in the 500 "double" flips exactly 500 heads occur no matter what the value of $p$. (The student automatically records a head for every tail and tail for every head.) The event "a head occurs on the first toss" is

$$Hl = \{HH, HT\}$$
$$0 \ , \ p$$

and has probability $p$. Hence, only the heads in the actual flip reflect $p$, which is natural enough. Some other events are:

"a tail occurs on the second toss" $= T2 = \{HT, TT\}$,
$$p \ , \ 0$$

"head first *and* tails second" $= H1 \cap T2 = \{HT\}$;
$$p$$

"a head occurs second" $= H2 = \{HH, \ TH \ \}$;
$$0 \ , 1 - p$$

"head first and head second" $= H1 \cap H2 = \{HH\}$.
$$0$$

If a head occurs first, a tails must occur second. The conditional probability of T2 given H1 is

$$P(T2|H1) = \frac{P(H1 \cap T2)}{P(H1)} = \frac{p}{p} = 1.$$

Also, if a tails occurs second, a head must occur first

$$P(H1|T2) = \frac{P(H1 \cap T2)}{P(T2)} = \frac{p}{p} = 1.$$

If a head occurs first, a second head cannot occur. The conditional probability of H2 given H1 is

$$P(H2|H1) = \frac{P(H1 \cap H2)}{P(H1)} = \frac{0}{p} = 0.$$

On the other hand the conditional probability of a head first *given* that two heads occur is *meaningless* for two heads cannot occur

$$P(H1|H1 \cap H2) \text{ is undefined,}$$

since $P(H1 \cap H2) = 0$. An event with probability zero cannot occur.

EXAMPLE 4.   Two local populations of salamanders each contain two types of animals — dark-backed and light-backed. We choose a population and take one individual from it.  Suppose the sample space is

$$\{1D, 2D, 1L, 2L\}$$
$$\tfrac{2}{6}, \tfrac{1}{6}, \tfrac{1}{6}, \tfrac{2}{6},$$

where the simple event 2D indicates that a dark individual is chosen from population 2; 1L, "a light individual from population 1"; etc.  Consider the events

$L = \{1L, 2L\}$    "a light-backed animal is chosen";
  $\tfrac{1}{6}, \tfrac{2}{6}$

$D = \{1D, 2D\}$    "a dark-backed animal is chosen";
  $\tfrac{2}{6}, \tfrac{1}{6}$

$A = \{1D, 1L\}$    "population 1 is sampled";
  $\tfrac{2}{6}, \tfrac{1}{6}$

$B = \{2D, 2L\}$    "population 2 is sampled";
  $\tfrac{1}{6}, \tfrac{2}{6}$

$A \cap L = \{1L\}$    "a light-backed animal is chosen
  $\tfrac{1}{6}$          from population 1";

$B \cap L = \{2L\}$    "a light-backed animal is chosen
  $\tfrac{2}{6}$          from population 2";

$D \cap L = \varnothing$    "the animal chosen is light-backed
              and dark-backed".

The probability that a light-backed animal is chosen *given* that population 1 is sampled is

$$P(L|A) = \frac{P(A \cap L)}{P(A)} = \frac{\tfrac{1}{6}}{\tfrac{1}{2}} = \frac{1}{3}.$$

The probability that population 2 was sampled *given* that the individual found is light-backed is

$$P(B|L) = \frac{P(B \cap L)}{P(L)} = \frac{\tfrac{2}{6}}{\tfrac{1}{2}} = \frac{2}{3}.$$

The probability that the animal chosen is light-backed *given* that it is dark-backed is

$$P(L|D) = \frac{P(L \cap D)}{P(D)} = \frac{0}{\tfrac{2}{3}} = 0.$$

The situation modeled here is that where:
(1) Each population is as likely to be chosen as the other.
(2) Population 1 contains two dark-backed animals for each light-backed while population 2 contains one dark-backed for every two light-backed.
(3) Once a population is chosen any animal in it is as likely to be chosen as any other.
The reasoning leading to the assignment is instructive. The event "population 1 is chosen" has probability $\frac{1}{2}$

$$\frac{\{1D, 1L\}}{a, b}, \quad a + b = \tfrac{1}{2}.$$

Since there are twice as many dark as light animals in population 1, 1D should be twice as likely as 1L; that is, $a = 2b$. Then

$$2b + b = \tfrac{1}{2},$$
$$3b = \tfrac{1}{2},$$
$$b = \tfrac{1}{6} \quad \text{and} \quad a = \tfrac{2}{6}.$$

Analogous reasoning applies to the simple events in "population 2 is chosen," and gives the over-all assignment

$$\frac{\{1D, 2D, 1L, 2L\}}{\tfrac{2}{6}, \tfrac{1}{6}, \tfrac{1}{6}, \tfrac{2}{6}}.$$

In Chapter 6 we consider many examples of this nature.

## EXERCISES

1. Given the probability model

$$\frac{\{a, b, c, d, e\}}{\tfrac{1}{2}, \tfrac{1}{4}, \tfrac{1}{8}, \tfrac{1}{16}, \tfrac{1}{16}},$$

   consider the events

   $H = \{a, b, c\}; \quad M = \{a, c, d\}; \quad N = \{d, e\}.$

   Calculate: $P(H|M)$; $P(H|N)$; $P(M|N)$; $P(N|N)$; and $P(M|H)$.

2. Suppose A and B are events of the sample space S. Suppose $P(A) = \tfrac{1}{4}$. $P(B) = \tfrac{1}{3}$.
   (a) If $P(A \cap B) = \tfrac{1}{10}$, determine $P(B|A)$ and $P(A|B)$.
   (b) If $P(A \cap B) = \tfrac{1}{4}$ what are $P(B|A)$ and $P(A|B)$?
   (c) If A and B are mutually exclusive, what are $P(B|A)$ and $P(A|B)$?

3. Given a sample space $S$ let E and Y be two of its events. Let $Y = \{a, b\}$ and $E \cap Y = \{a\}$.
   (a) If $P(Y) = \tfrac{1}{3}$ and $P(E|Y) = \tfrac{1}{10}$, determine the probabilities of the simple events $\{a\}$ and $\{b\}$.

(Hint:  $P(E|Y) = P(E \cap Y)/P(Y)$,  so that $P(E \cap Y) = P(E|Y)P(Y) = P\{a\}$.)

(b) If $P(Y) = r$ and $P(E|Y) = s$, determine the probability of the simple event $\{b\}$.

4. A small population consists of two males and one female. The female only mates once, and only one fertilized egg results from the mating. Suppose each male is equally likely to mate with the female. If the first male mates with the female the probability is $\frac{1}{4}$ that the egg does not develop, but dies; if the second male mates the probability is 1 that the egg does develop. Consider the sample space

$$\{1d, 1n, 2d, 2n\}$$
$$\tfrac{3}{8}, \tfrac{1}{8}, \tfrac{1}{2}, 0$$

where $\{1d\}$ is the simple event "male one mates and the egg develops"; $\{1n\}$ is the event "male 1 mates and the egg does not develop;" etc. Show that the conditional probabilities are as stated.

5. In a population of caribou, the probability that an animal is sickly is $\frac{1}{10}$. If an animal is sickly, its probability of being eaten by wolves is $\frac{1}{4}$; if it is not sickly but is healthy, its probability of being eaten is $\frac{1}{100}$. Consider the sample space

$$\{he, se, hn, sn\}$$

whose simple events denote that an individual is "healthy and eaten" $\{he\}$, "sickly and eaten" $\{se\}$, "healthy and not eaten" $\{hn\}$, and "sickly and not eaten" $\{sn\}$.

(a) Assign probabilities on the sample space so that the probability model embodies the given facts. (Hints: The event "sickly" is $Y = \{se, sn\}$. The event "eaten" is $E = \{he, se\}$; $E \cap Y = \{se\}$. Use the method of Exercise 3, etc.)

(b) Determine the probability of the event "an individual caribou is not eaten by wolves."

| PATH 4 ☛ §5.3 |    | PATH 5 ☛ §5.3 |

## 5.3  INDEPENDENT EVENTS

In this section we introduce an important definition, that of independent events. Informally, the notion is that the occurrence or nonoccurrence of one event does not change the probability of occurrence of the other. We now give a precise definition of this notion.

DEFINITION.    *Given a sample space and two of its events* A *and* B, *then the events* A *and* B *are said to be* **independent**, *if*

$$P(A)P(B) = P(A \cap B)$$

*In this definition either* $P(A)$ *or* $P(B)$ *may be zero.*

From Section 5.2 we know that if $P(A) \neq 0$, then the conditional probability of B given A is

$$\frac{P(A \cap B)}{P(A)} = P(B|A).$$

Thus, we have

$$P(A \cap B) = P(A)P(B|A).$$

This formula is easy to remember. In order for A and B both to occur, we can think first of A occurring, and then of B occurring given that A has occurred. The probability that A and B occur together is then equal to the probability of A times the probability of B given A.

From the definition of independence we see that if A and B are independent

$$P(A \cap B) = P(A)P(B).$$

If in addition $P(A) \neq 0$, then

$$\frac{P(A \cap B)}{P(A)} = P(B),$$

or

$$P(B|A) = P(B).$$

In other words, if A and B are independent then the probability of B given A is the same as the probability of B. Here the knowledge that A has occurred does not affect the probability of the occurrence of A. Similarly, if A and B are independent and $P(B) \neq 0$, then

$$\frac{P(A \cap B)}{P(B)} = P(A),$$

and

$$P(A|B) = P(A).$$

When events are independent the occurrence of one event does not change the probability that the other will occur.

As an example we can consider the two-coin-flip model (biased in favor of heads). We have the sample space

$$\{HH, HT, TH, TT\}$$
$$\tfrac{4}{9}, \tfrac{2}{9}, \tfrac{2}{9}, \tfrac{1}{9}.$$

Think of the events

$$H_1 = \{HH, HT\}$$

"a head occurs on the first toss," and

$$H_2 = \{HH, TH\}$$

"a head occurs on the second toss." Here $P(H_1) = P(H_2) = \frac{6}{9} = \frac{2}{3}$. The intersection of these events is "two heads occur"

$$H_1 \cap H_2 = \{HH\}, \qquad P(H_1 \cap H_2) = \frac{4}{9}.$$

$H_1$ and $H_2$ are independent events, since

$$P(H_1)P(H_2) = P(H_1 \cap H_2),$$

or

$$\tfrac{2}{3} \times \tfrac{2}{3} = \tfrac{4}{9}.$$

The probability of a head on the second toss given that a head occurred on the first toss is

$$P(H_2|H_1) = \frac{P(H_1 \cap H_2)}{P(H_1)} = \frac{\frac{4}{9}}{\frac{6}{9}} = \frac{2}{3},$$

and $P(H_2|H_1) = P(H_2)$ as it must since $H_1$ and $H_2$ are independent. Similarly, $P(H_1|H_2) = P(H_1)$. After further examples, we discuss the somewhat more complicated question of the independence of more than two events.

EXAMPLE 1.   Let S be a sample space with A, B and C three of its events. Suppose that $P(A) = \frac{1}{3}$, $P(B) = \frac{1}{4}$, $P(C) = \frac{1}{5}$, while $P(A \cap B) = \frac{1}{14}$, $P(A \cap C) = \frac{1}{15}$ with $P(B|C) = \frac{1}{6}$. Then A and B are not independent, for

$$P(A)P(B) = \tfrac{1}{12}, \qquad \text{and} \qquad P(A \cap B) = \tfrac{1}{14}.$$

B and C are not independent, for $P(B|C) = \frac{1}{6}$ which implies that

$$P(B \cap C) = \tfrac{1}{6} \times \tfrac{1}{5} = \tfrac{1}{30}, \qquad \text{while } P(B)P(C) = \tfrac{1}{20}.$$

On the other hand, A and C are independent since

$$P(A)P(C) = \tfrac{1}{15} = P(A \cap C).$$

EXAMPLE 2.   In the diagram below A and B are mutually exclusive events.

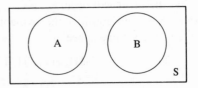

Since $A \cap B = \varnothing$, $P(A \cap B) = 0$. Thus, for A and B to be independent we must have

$$P(A)P(B) = 0,$$

and hence either $P(A)$ or $P(B)$ or both must be zero. Two mutually exclusive events are independent only if one or both of the events is impossible.

When there are *more than two* events, the notion of independence is somewhat more complicated. For example, three events A, B, C are said to be *mutually independent* if *all* of the following are true:

(1)  $P(A)P(B)P(C) = P(A \cap B \cap C)$;
(2)      $P(A)P(B) = P(A \cap B)$;
(3)      $P(A)P(C) = P(A \cap C)$;
(4)      $P(B)P(C) = P(B \cap C)$.

If any one of these does not hold then A, B, and C are *not* mutually independent. If (1) is not true but (2), (3) and (4) are true, the events are *pairwise independent;* however, they are not mutually independent.

We have the following general definitions.

DEFINITION.    *Suppose we have a sample space and any number N of its events. These events are* **mutually independent** *if for every combination of any r of these N events it is true that the probability of the intersection of the r events is equal to the product of the probabilities of the r events.*

Thus, for any two of the $N$ events (say A, B) it must be true that

$$P(A)P(B) = P(A \cap B),$$

for any three of the $N$ events (say A, B, C) it must be true that

$$P(A)P(B)P(C) = P(A \cap B \cap C),$$

and for any four of the $N$ events (say A, B, C, D) it must be true that

$$P(A)P(B)P(C)P(D) = P(A \cap B \cap C \cap D),$$

and so forth.

The definition of pairwise independence can be similarly stated.

DEFINITION.    *Given a sample space and any number N of its events. These events are* **pairwise independent** *if for every combination of any 2 of the N events it is true that the probability of the intersection of the two events is equal to the product of the probabilities of the two events.*

Thus, if A and B are any two of the $N$ events, it must be true that

$$P(A)P(B) = P(A \cap B).$$

If events are mutually independent they are also pairwise independent, but pairwise independent events need not be mutually independent. In this book if three or more events are said to be independent, this is understood to mean mutually independent.

EXAMPLE 3. *Mutually independent events.* In the sample space for three-coin-flips

$$\{\text{HHH, HHT, THH, HTH, TTH, THT, HTT, TTT}\}$$
$$\tfrac{1}{27}, \quad \tfrac{2}{27}, \quad \tfrac{2}{27}, \quad \tfrac{2}{27}, \quad \tfrac{4}{27}, \quad \tfrac{4}{27}, \quad \tfrac{4}{27}, \quad \tfrac{8}{27}$$

The events "the first coin falls heads," "the second coin falls tails," "the third coin falls heads" are

$$A = \{\text{HHH, HHT, HTH, HTT}\}, \qquad P(A) = \tfrac{1}{3};$$
$$B = \{\text{HTH, TTH, HTT, TTT}\}, \qquad P(B) = \tfrac{2}{3};$$
$$C = \{\text{HHH, THH, HTH, TTH}\}, \qquad P(C) = \tfrac{1}{3}.$$

We have also

$$A \cap B = \{\text{HTH, HTT}\} \qquad P(A \cap B) = \tfrac{2}{9};$$
$$A \cap C = \{\text{HTH, HHH}\}, \qquad P(A \cap C) = \tfrac{1}{9};$$
$$B \cap C = \{\text{HTH, TTH}\}, \qquad P(B \cap C) = \tfrac{2}{9};$$

and in addition

$$A \cap B \cap C = \{\text{HTH}\}, \qquad P(A \cap B \cap C) = \tfrac{2}{27}.$$

Here A, B, and C are mutually independent.

EXAMPLE 4. *Events pairwise independent but not mutually independent.* In a laboratory of molecular biology an investigator has nine preparations of RNA fragments each containing a fragment consisting of two bases as follows (the bases are A, C, G or U for adenine, cytosine, guanine, and uracil, respectively).

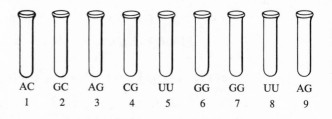

| AC | GC | AG | CG | UU | GG | GG | UU | AG |
| 1 | 2 | 3 | 4 | 5 | 6 | 7 | 8 | 9 |

The identity of the fragments is not known to the investigator. Constructing the model where one of the nine preparations is chosen simply at random, one defines a sample space for the *kind* of fragment chosen as

$$\{\text{AC, GC, CG, AG, GG, UU}\}.$$
$$\tfrac{1}{9}, \tfrac{1}{9}, \tfrac{1}{9}, \tfrac{2}{9}, \tfrac{2}{9}, \tfrac{2}{9}$$

The event "the fragment chosen contains adenine" represented by A is

$$A = \{AC, AG\}, \qquad P(A) = \tfrac{1}{3}.$$

Similarly, the events "the fragment contains guanine" G, "the fragment contains cytosine" C are, respectively,

$$G = \{GC, AG, CG, GG\}, \qquad P(G) = \tfrac{2}{3};$$
$$C = \{AC, GC, CG\}, \qquad P(C) = \tfrac{1}{3}.$$

We also find that $P(A \cap C) = \tfrac{1}{9}$, $P(A \cap G) = \tfrac{2}{9}$, $P(C \cap G) = \tfrac{2}{9}$. Thus,

$$P(A)P(C) = P(A \cap C),$$
$$P(A)P(G) = P(A \cap G),$$
$$P(C)P(G) = P(C \cap G).$$

However, the events A, C, and G are not mutually independent for the fragment cannot simultaneously contain an A, a C, and a G. We have $A \cap C \cap G = \varnothing$. Thus, $P(A \cap C \cap G) = 0$, which is not equal to $P(A)P(B)P(C)$. Although the events are pairwise independent they are not mutually independent. Thus, if the fragment is known to contain an A, the probability that it contains C or G is unchanged from the probability without such knowledge. However, if a fragment contains both an A and G, this clearly tells us it cannot contain a C.


## EXERCISES

1. Given the probability model

$$\{a, b, c, d, e\}$$
$$\tfrac{1}{16}, \tfrac{1}{16}, \tfrac{2}{16}, \tfrac{3}{16}, \tfrac{9}{16},$$

let

$A = \{a, b, c\}$, $B = \{b, c, d\}$, $C = \{b, c, e\}$, $D = \{d, e\}$, $E = \{c, e\}$.

Which of the following pairs of events are independent?
(a) A, B; (b) A, C; (c) A, D; (d) D, E; (e) C, D; (f) B, C.

2. Given a sample space S. Let A, B, and C be three of its events with probabilities $P(A) = \tfrac{1}{4}$, $P(B) = \tfrac{1}{8}$, $P(C) = \tfrac{1}{2}$. In which of the following three cases are A, B, C (i) mutually independent; (ii) pairwise independent; (iii) neither?
(a) $P(A \cap B \cap C) = 0$, while $P(A \cap B) = 0$, $P(A \cap C) = 0$, $P(B \cap C) = 0$.
(b) $P(A \cap B \cap C) = \tfrac{1}{64}$ while $P(A \cap B) = \tfrac{1}{32}$, $P(A \cap C) = \tfrac{1}{8}$, $P(B \cap C) = \tfrac{1}{16}$.
(c) $P(A \cap B \cap C) = \tfrac{1}{32}$, while $P(A \cap B) = \tfrac{1}{32}$, $P(A \cap C) = \tfrac{1}{8}$, $P(B \cap C) = \tfrac{1}{16}$.

3. Given the sample space S = {a, b, c, d, e, f, g, h}, consider the three events

   $A = \{a, d, g, e\}, \quad B = \{b, d, g, f\}, \quad C = \{c, e, g, f\}.$

   Suppose A, B, C are mutually independent. Also, suppose $P(A) = P(B) = P(C) = \frac{1}{3}$. Find the probability of each simple event of S. (Hint:

   $$P(A \cap B \cap C)$$

   must be $\frac{1}{27}$, hence {g} has probability $\frac{1}{27}$, and so forth.)

4. Two bees are trained to distinguish between the two shapes • and **X**. A particular experimental situation is modeled as follows:

   $$\{\bullet\textbf{X}, \textbf{X}\bullet, \bullet\bullet, \textbf{XX}\}$$
   $$p_1, \ p_2, \ p_3, \ p_4$$

   where

   {•**X**} means the first bee chose •, the second **X**;

   {**X**•} means the first bee chose **X**, the second •; etc.

   Suppose $p_1 = \frac{8}{15}, p_2 = \frac{1}{15}, p_3 = \frac{4}{15}$, and $p_4 = \frac{2}{15}$.
   (a) Are the events "the first bee chose •" and "the second bee chose **X**" independent?
   (b) What is the probability that "the second bee chooses •"? That "the second bee chooses • given that the first bee chose **X**"?
   (c) Are the events "the second bee chooses •" and "the second bee chooses **X**" independent?

5. In the sample space of Exercise 4 let
   $p_1 = \frac{8}{15}, p_2 = \frac{2}{15}, p_3 = \frac{4}{15}, p_4 = \frac{1}{15}.$
   (a) What is the probability that the second bee chooses **X** given that the first bee chose **X**? What is the probability that the second bee chooses **X**? Is this the same, greater, or less than the conditional probability?
   (b) Is the event {••, •**X**, **X**•} independent of the event {•**X**, **X**•, **XX**}?

6. In the sample space of Exercise 4, let $p_1 = p_2 = p_3 = p_4 = \frac{1}{4}$. Consider the events

   $A = \{\bullet\textbf{X}, \bullet\bullet\}, \qquad$ "the first bee chooses •";

   $B = \{\textbf{X}\bullet, \bullet\bullet\}, \qquad$ "the second bee chooses •";

   $C = \{\textbf{XX}, \bullet\bullet\}, \qquad$ "the two bees make the same choice"

   Show that (A, B), (A, C), (B, C) are pairwise independent but that A, B, and C are not mutually independent.

7. Given a sample space S, suppose an event A is independent of itself; that is, $P(A)P(A) = P(A \cap A)$. What does this tell us about $P(A)$?

## REFERENCES

### General

GOLDBERG, S., *Probability An Introduction* (Englewood Cliffs, N. J.: Prentice-Hall, Inc., 1960), Ch. 2.

KEMENY, J. G., SNELL, J. L., and THOMPSON, G. L., *Introduction to Finite Mathematics* (Englewood Cliffs, N. J.: Prentice-Hall, Inc., 1956), Ch. 4.

MOSTELLER, F., ROURKE, R. E. K., and THOMAS, G. B., *Probability with Statistical Applications* (Reading, Mass.: Addison-Wesley Publishing Company, Inc., 1961), Ch. 3.

# USE OF TREE DIAGRAMS TO ASSIGN PROBABILITIES

## 6.1  COMBINING SAMPLE SPACES USING TREE DIAGRAMS

Of two local populations of moths population A has 2 dark-colored moths for each white moth, while population B has one dark moth for each two white individuals. A zoologist collects a moth. This can be viewed as a combination of two experiments:
(1) the zoologist finds a population;
(2) he then collects a moth.
The individual sample space for the first experiment is

$$\{A, B\},$$

in which the simple event $\{A\}$ means population A is found. The space for the second experiment is

$$\{D, W\},$$

in which the simple event $\{D\}$ means a dark moth is found. A combined space for both together is

$$\{AD, AW, BD, BW\},$$

in which the simple event $\{AD\}$ indicates that a dark moth is collected from population A.
We can diagram the combination of sample spaces as a *tree diagram*.

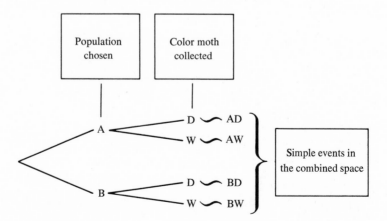

in which, for example, the path

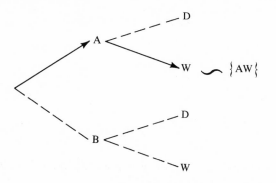

means that population A is found and then a white moth collected. *Each path through the tree diagram represents a simple event in the combined space.*
Consider the event "population A is found." In the combined space this is

$$A = \{AD, AW\}.$$

In the tree diagram, this event consists of *all paths through A;* namely,

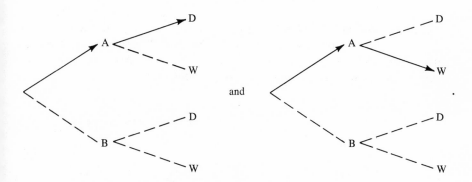

and

.

Similarly, the event "a white moth is collected" is

$$W = \{AW, BW\},$$

and this corresponds to *all paths through the letter W;* namely,

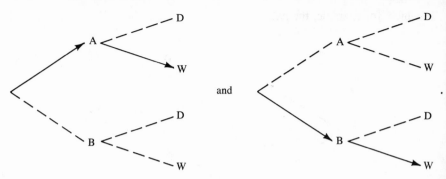

The event "population A is found" *and* "a white moth collected" is A ∩ W = {AW} and corresponds to the single path

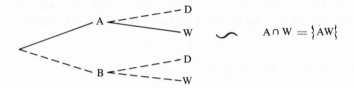

which goes through A *and* W. In a like manner if we consider the two events "a dark moth is collected" D = {AD, BD}, and "population B is found" B = {BD, BW}, then we can see that *each path in the tree corresponds to an intersection of events in the combined space* as follows:

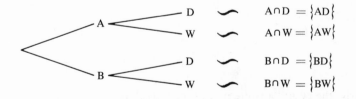

Thus, a line through A and D corresponds to the *event* A ∩ D in the combined space. There is a simple relation between a tree diagram and the events in the combined sample space. Following the path through B and W is like saying that B *and* W have occurred in the combined space. In words this means that "population B is chosen" *and* "a white moth is found." A tree diagram is a visual extension of the basic rule of counting. In a tree diagram we simply list all the possibilities for each happening and connect the possibilities. There must be as many paths as possibilities.

EXAMPLE 1. If three coins are flipped, and the sample space for any one coin is {H, T}, the combined sample space is

{HHH, HHT, HTH, HTT, THH, THT, TTH, TTT}.

A tree diagram for this experiment is

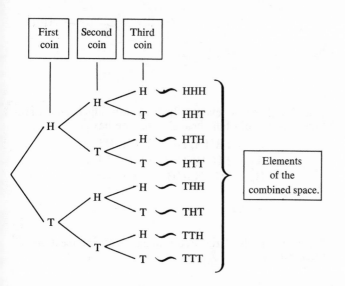

The event "the second coin falls heads" is {HHH, HHT, THH, THT} = H₂. It consists of all four paths through an H in the second column or

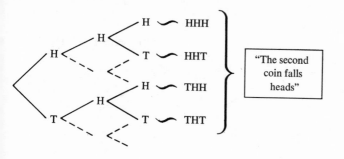

Similarly, the event "the last two coins are heads" consists of the paths

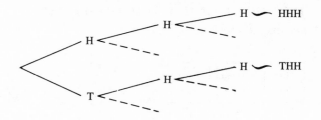

If we let $H_1$ be the event "the first coin falls heads"; $H_2$, "the second coin falls heads"; etc., we have

$$H_1 = \{HHH, HHT, HTH, HTT\},$$
$$T_1 = \{THH, THT, TTH, TTT\},$$
$$H_2 = \{HHH, HHT, THH, THT\},$$

.
.
.

Thus each path of the tree represents an intersection of three events.

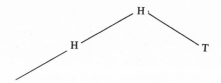

represents $H_1 \cap H_2 \cap T_3$,

and

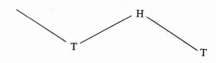

represents $T_1 \cap H_2 \cap T_3$.

**EXERCISES**

1. Consider the tree diagram below.

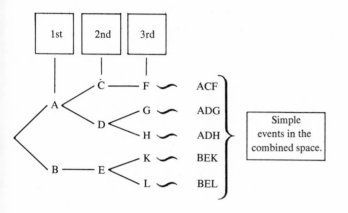

All questions pertain to the combined sample space.
(a) How many simple events are in the event A defined by "A occurs in the first experiment?"
(b) How many in the event B defined by "B occurs in the first experiment"?
(c) Darken the paths corresponding to the event "G, D, or both occur."

2. Use the same tree diagram as Exercise 1. All events of the combined space are labeled as follows:

A = "A occurs" = {ACF, ADG, ADH},
B = "B occurs" = {BEK, BEL},

⋮          ⋮

List the simple events in the following:
(a) A ∩ D;       (b) A ∩ D ∩ G;       (c) A ∩ B;
(d) E ∩ K;       (e) B ∩ E ∩ K;       (f) B ∪ D;
(g) D ∪ G;       (h) C ∪ E.

3. Draw the paths through the tree diagram corresponding to the events in parts (a)–(h) of Exercise 2.

4. A graduate student receives grades of pass (P) or fail (F). An undergraduate can receive a grade of A, B, C, D, or F. There are two graduates and one undergraduate. Using a tree diagram determine a combined sample space for the grades of all three individuals (e.g., one simple event of the combined space is PPA).

| PATH 4 ☞ §6.2 |    | PATH 5 ☞ §6.2 |

## 6.2  ASSIGNING PROBABILITIES USING TREE DIAGRAMS

In three local populations of moths, the first contains all dark-colored individuals; the second, two dark moths for each light one; the third, one dark for each three light individuals. As before in Section 6.1, the collection of a moth can be modeled as the following two experiments in sequence:

(1) the zoologist finds a population (*simply at random*);

(2) the zoologist collects a moth (also *simply at random*).

The first experiment has as its sample space

$$\{A, B, C\}, \atop \frac{1}{3}, \frac{1}{3}, \frac{1}{3}$$

where $\{A\}$ is the simple event "the first population is chosen," etc. The probabilities for the second experiment vary depending on the population found. There are no light-colored moths in population A. If this population has been chosen the sample space is

$$\{D, L\}. \atop 1, 0$$

If population A has been chosen the probability is 1 that a dark moth will be collected. On the other hand, if population B or C is found, the probabilities will be, respectively,

$$\{D, L\}, \qquad \{D, L\}. \atop \frac{2}{3}, \frac{1}{3} \qquad \frac{1}{4}, \frac{3}{4}$$

The probabilities of collecting a dark-colored moth are conditional probabilities. They vary with the population found.

It is possible to *assign* probabilities on the *combined space* so that these conditional probabilities are realized. We can do this using a tree diagram where we write the probability of choosing a population on the branch leading to that population. On the branches leading from it, we write the conditional probabilities of dark or light moths.

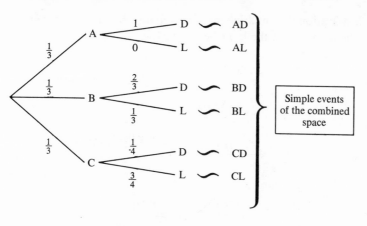

For example, the probability of finding population B is $\frac{1}{3}$. If population B is chosen, then there is a probability of $\frac{2}{3}$ of finding a dark moth. We can now assign probabilities on the combined space as follows.

GENERAL STATEMENT.     *Multiply all the probabilities along a path leading to the event in the combined space, and assign this product to be the probability of this event.*[1]

Thus, the probability of event {AD} "population A is chosen and a dark moth is collected" is

$$\tfrac{1}{3} \times 1 = \tfrac{1}{3}.$$

On the other hand, the probability of "population B is chosen and a light-colored moth is collected" is

$$\tfrac{1}{3} \times \tfrac{1}{3} = \tfrac{1}{9}.$$

The probabilities assigned on the combined space are

$$\{AD, AL, BD, BL, CD, CL\},$$
$$\tfrac{1}{3} \;,\; 0 \;,\; \tfrac{2}{9} \;,\; \tfrac{1}{9} \;,\; \tfrac{1}{12} \;,\; \tfrac{3}{12}$$

which add up to 1 or

$$\tfrac{12}{36} + 0 + \tfrac{8}{36} + \tfrac{4}{36} + \tfrac{3}{36} + \tfrac{9}{36} = 1.$$

---

[1] This general statement is given in detail in the next section.

The justification for multiplying along paths becomes apparent when we identify the numbers on the branches, as below.

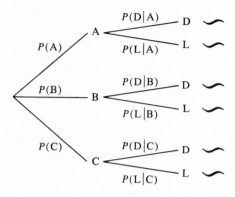

$$A \cap D = \{AD\}; \ P(A)P(D|A) = P(A \cap D)$$
$$A \cap L = \{AL\}; \ P(A)P(L|A) = P(A \cap L)$$
$$B \cap D = \{BD\}; \ P(B)P(D|B) = P(B \cap D)$$
$$B \cap L = \{BL\}; \ P(B)P(L|B) = P(B \cap L)$$
$$C \cap D = \{CD\}; \ P(C)P(D|C) = P(C \cap D)$$
$$C \cap L = \{CL\}; \ P(C)P(L|C) = P(C \cap L)$$

The multiplication rule simply makes use of the fact that if X and Y are events of the *same* sample space, then

$$P(X)P(Y|X) = P(X \cap Y).$$

In the tree diagram all the events depicted are events of the same space, that is, the combined sample space. For example, the event "population C is chosen" is

$$C = \{CL, CD\} \quad \text{and} \quad P(C) = \tfrac{1}{3}.$$
$$\underset{\tfrac{3}{12}, \ \tfrac{1}{12}}{}$$

Also the probability of finding a dark moth given that C is chosen is

$$P(D|C) = \frac{P(D \cap C)}{P(C)} = \frac{\tfrac{1}{12}}{\tfrac{1}{3}} = \tfrac{1}{4}.$$

EXAMPLE 1. We can arrive at hypergeometric probabilities using the notion of repeated experiments and tree diagrams. Repeating the illustration of Section 4.4, consider 5 rats, 2 healthy and 3 sick ones. What is the probability that exactly one of two rats chosen is sick when the two are a simple random sample of the five. We can look upon this as a combination of two experiments:

(1) the first rat is chosen;
(2) the second rat is chosen.

The sample space for the first experiment is

$$\{H, S\}$$
$$\tfrac{2}{5}, \tfrac{3}{5}$$

If a healthy rat is chosen, 1 healthy and 3 sick rats remain for the second choice. If a sick rat is chosen, 2 healthy and 2 sick rats remain. The sample spaces for the second choice are

$$\{H, S\}$$
$$\tfrac{1}{4}, \tfrac{3}{4}$$

if the first rat is healthy, and

$$\{H, S\}$$
$$\tfrac{1}{2}, \tfrac{1}{2}$$

if the first rat is sick. The complete tree diagram is

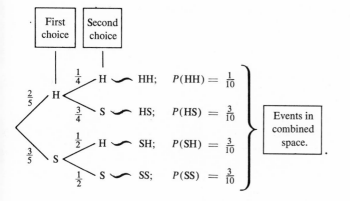

The probability that both rats are healthy is $\tfrac{1}{10}$, that exactly one is healthy is $\tfrac{3}{10} + \tfrac{3}{10} = \tfrac{6}{10}$, and that none is healthy, $\tfrac{3}{10}$.

These are simply hypergeometric probabilities

$$p(2) = \frac{\binom{3}{0}\binom{2}{2}}{\binom{5}{2}} = \frac{1}{10}; \qquad p(1) = \frac{\binom{3}{1}\binom{2}{1}}{\binom{5}{2}} = \frac{6}{10};$$

$$p(0) = \frac{\binom{3}{2}\binom{2}{0}}{\binom{5}{2}} = \frac{3}{10}.$$

EXAMPLE 2. In any tree diagram the branch numbers are conditional probabilities given the event signified by the point to the left of the branch. Consider this tree:

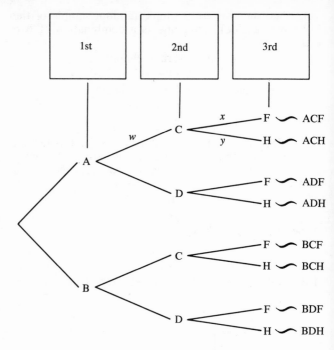

The branch number $x$ is the conditional probability of "F occurring in the third experiment" given that "A occurred in the first" *and* "C occurred in the second." Thus,

$$P(F|A \cap C) = x.$$

The events involved are, of course,

$$A = \{ACF, ACH, ADF, ADH\},$$
$$C = \{ACF, ACH, BCF, BCH\},$$
$$A \cap C = \{ACF, ACH\}.$$

Similarly, if

$$H = \{ACH, ADH, BCH, BDH\},$$

or the event "H occurs in the third experiment" then

$$P(H|A \cap C) = y.$$

The branch number $w$ is $P(C|A)$.

**EXERCISES**

1.  Consider the tree diagram

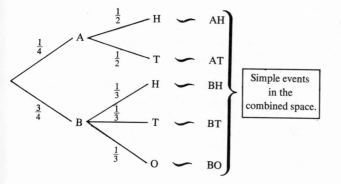

Let A = {AH, AT}; B = {BH, BT, BO}; T = {AT, BT};....

Determine the following probabilities:

(a) $P(H)$;          (b) $P(A \cap T)$;        (c) $P(H|A)$;
(d) $P(H|B)$;        (e) $P(B \cap T)$;        (f) $P(T)$;
(g) $P(A)$;          (h) $P(B)$;               (i) $P(A|B)$.

2.  There are two urns — urn 1 contains four red balls and two black balls and urn 2 contains three red balls and one black ball. Experiment (1): An urn is chosen simply at random. Experiment (2): A ball is then chosen from the urn simply at random.

    (a) Determine a combined sample space for the two experiments.

    (b) What is the probability that the ball chosen is black?

    (c) What is the probability that the ball is black if urn 1 is chosen?

3.  The problem is the same as in Exercise 2, except that urn 1 contains 10 red balls and one black ball while urn 2 contains all black balls.

    (a) What is the probability that the ball chosen is black?

    (b) What is the probability that it is red?

4.  There are two populations of moths. The first contains one dark moth for each light-colored individual. The second, five dark moths for each light-colored individual.

    (1) A population is found. (Both are equally likely to be found.)

    (2) A moth is collected simply at random.

    (a) Determine the combined sample space for the two experiments.

(b) What is the probability that the moth collected is dark?

5. There are three populations of moths. In the first there are three dark moths for every light-colored one. In the second, the moths are all dark; in the third, all are light-colored. A zoologist is twice as likely to find the first population as either of the others. (The second and third populations are equally likely to be found). Once a population is found any moth is as likely to be collected as any other. Use a tree diagram and determine the probability that:
(a) a dark moth is collected.
(b) the first population is found.
(c) the first population is found and a dark moth collected.

| PATH 4 ☞ §6.3 |   | PATH 5 ☞ §6.3 |

## 6.3 GENERAL RULES FOR TREE DIAGRAMS

Consider a tree diagram for combining $k$ experiments. Call any direct line between two of its points a *branch*. A *path* through the tree diagram consists of $k$ branches connecting the beginning point of the diagram with an end point of the diagram. To each path there corresponds a simple event of the combined sample space.

GENERAL STATEMENT.     *The tree diagram can be used to assign probabilities on the combined sample space if:*
(1) *to each branch we assign a number p such that*
     (a) $0 \leqslant p \leqslant 1$;
     (b) *the sum of the numbers assigned to all the branches that originate at the same point is 1; and*
(2) *for each path we multiply the numbers assigned to the branches that form the path and assign this product to the corresponding simple event of the combined sample space.*

A valid assignment of probabilities on the combined space is always obtained by following rules (1) and (2).

EXAMPLE 1.  In the tree diagram below, the branch numbers have been assigned in accordance with the rules just given.

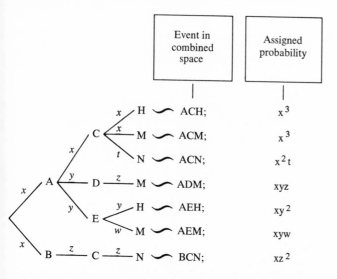

| Event in combined space | Assigned probability |
|---|---|
| ACH; | $x^3$ |
| ACM; | $x^3$ |
| ACN; | $x^2 t$ |
| ADM; | $xyz$ |
| AEH; | $xy^2$ |
| AEM; | $xyw$ |
| BCN; | $xz^2$ |

From part (1) of our rule $x$, $y$, $z$, $w$, and $t$ are each greater than or equal to zero and less than or equal to 1.  From part (2) of the rule we know that the sum of the branch numbers from a single point must be 1.

$$2x = 1,\ x + 2y = 1,\ 2x + t = 1,\ z = 1,\ y + w = 1.$$

Thus,

$$x = \tfrac{1}{2},\ y = \tfrac{1}{4},\ t = 0,\ w = \tfrac{3}{4}$$

and the assignment is

$$\{\text{ACH, ACM, ACN, ADM, AEH, AEM, BCN}\}$$
$$\tfrac{1}{8},\quad \tfrac{1}{8},\quad 0,\quad \tfrac{1}{8},\quad \tfrac{1}{32},\quad \tfrac{3}{32},\quad \tfrac{1}{2}.$$

Consider the tree:

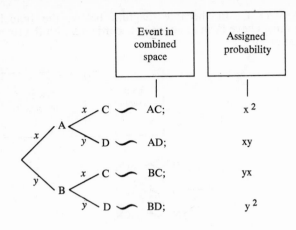

We know that $0 \leq x \leq 1$, $0 \leq y \leq 1$, and $x + y = 1$. We also know the probabilities on the simple events of the combined space in terms of $x$ and $y$. Here $x$ can be any number in its range, and the assignment is valid according to our rule.

EXAMPLE 2. This example indicates the utility of tree diagrams in answering complex questions. Consider the model below for the circulation of the element phosphorus in a simple pasture ecosystem.

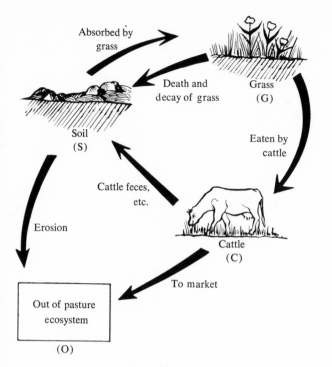

We now construct a simple probability model. Suppose that:

(1) *Whenever* an atom of phosphorus is in the *soil* at the beginning of the day, then the sample space giving its location at the end of the day is

$$\{S, \; G, \; O\}$$
$$\tfrac{3}{5}, \; \tfrac{3}{10}, \; \tfrac{1}{10}.$$

(In this case if O occurs the molecule has been lost to the pasture by erosion).

(2) *Whenever* an atom of phosphorus is in the *grass* at the beginning of the day, then its probable location at the end of the day is given by the sample space

$$\{S, \; G, \; C\}$$
$$\tfrac{1}{10}, \; \tfrac{4}{10}, \; \tfrac{1}{2},$$

so that the probability is $\tfrac{1}{2}$ that the atom of phosphorus will be eaten by cattle.

(3) Similarly, whenever the atom of phosphorus starts in cattle,

$$\{S, \; C, \; O\}$$
$$\tfrac{3}{4}, \; \tfrac{1}{5}, \; \tfrac{1}{20}$$

is the sample space for its location at the end of the day. (Note the high probability $\tfrac{3}{4}$ of the ingested phosphorus being returned to the soil via feces).

(4) Finally if an atom of phosphorus is outside the pasture it stays outside, so that a sample space for its location at the end of the day is

$$\{O\}_1.$$

We now ask: If an atom of phosphorus starts in the soil. what is the probability that it will be outside the system in three days? We can construct the following tree diagram:

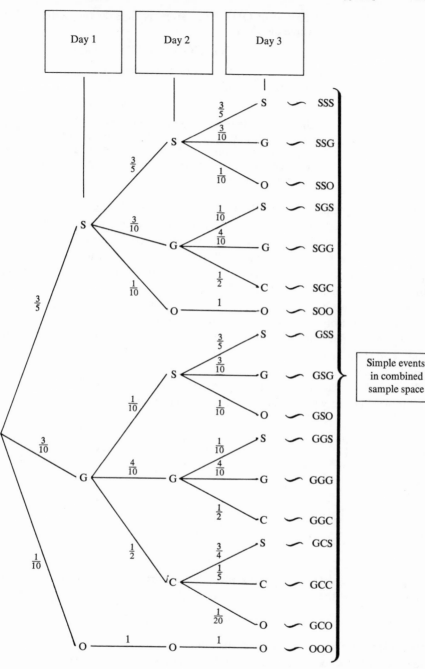

The event OUT "the atom is outside the system after three days" is

$$\{SOO, SSO, GSO, GCO, OOO\},$$
$$\tfrac{3}{50}, \tfrac{9}{250}, \tfrac{3}{1000}, \tfrac{3}{400}, \tfrac{1}{10}$$

and its probability is

$$P(\text{OUT}) = \tfrac{3}{50} + \tfrac{9}{250} + \tfrac{3}{1000} + \tfrac{3}{400} + \tfrac{1}{10} = \tfrac{413}{2000}.$$

In this simple model the probable loss of phosphorus due to erosion is very high, and the system is not at all balanced. The example illustrates the considerable utility of tree diagrams in determining the answer to rather complex problems.

We have not yet proved the validity of the rules given in this section; that is, we have not proved that the numbers assigned on the combined sample space satisfy the definition of probability given in Section 4.1. That they do so is indicated below. The paragraphs which follow can easily be omitted on first reading. It is suggested that the reader do this and go directly to the exercises at the end of this section.

Suppose that we have $k$ experiments to combine using the tree diagram rules given in this section. In doing so, suppose that we assign the number $y$ to a simple event of the combined sample space. To satisfy the definition of probability one must have $0 \leqslant y \leqslant 1$. Also the numbers assigned on the combined sample space must total 1.

We first show that $0 \leqslant y \leqslant 1$. Suppose that the path below corresponds to the simple event to which $y$ has been assigned given by

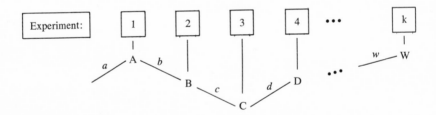

The number $y$ is determined using the general rules for tree diagrams. From rule (2) we know that

$$y = abcd \ldots w.$$

From rule (1) we know that none of the numbers $a, b, c, d, \ldots, w$ is greater than one or less than zero. Hence, their product $y$ cannot be greater than one or less than zero.

Next we must show that the numbers assigned to the simple events of the combined sample space total 1. We prove this for a 2-experiment tree diagram.

Consider the general 2-experiment tree diagram below:

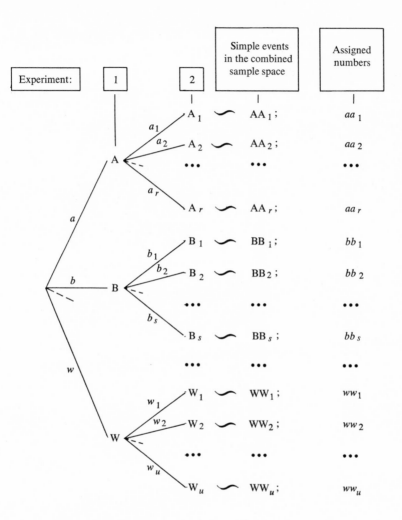

From rule (1) we know that $a + b + \ldots + w = 1$ and also that

$$a_1 + a_2 + \ldots + a_r = 1; \qquad b_1 + b_2 + \ldots + b_s = 1;$$
$$\ldots; \qquad w_1 + w_2 + \ldots + w_u = 1.$$

If we add the numbers assigned to the simple events of the combined space, we obtain

$$aa_1 + aa_2 + \ldots + aa_r + bb_1 + bb_2 + \ldots + bb_s + \ldots + ww_1 + ww_2 +$$
$$\ldots + ww_u$$

$$= a(a_1 + a_2 + \ldots + a_r) + b(b_1 + b_2 + \ldots + b_s) + \ldots + w(w_1 + w_2 + \ldots + w_u)$$
$$= a + b + \ldots + w$$
$$= 1.$$

We have now proved the following:

(I) In a $k$-experiment tree, if $y$ is a number assigned to a simple event of the combined sample space, then $0 \leqslant y \leqslant 1$.

(II) In a 2-experiment tree, the sum of the numbers assigned on the combined sample space is 1.

To complete the proof that the tree diagram rules give a valid assignment of probabilities it is necessary to generalize statement (II) to a $k$-experiment tree. We do not prove that this can be done, but we give an indication of the way that it can be done.

We can write any 3-experiment tree as a 2-experiment tree by simply combining the first two experiments and treating these as a single experiment. For example, consider the two tree diagrams below. Diagram I is a 3-experiment tree. In Diagram II, the first and second experiments have been combined as a single experiment and the result is a 2-experiment tree. *Both diagrams give the same assignment of probabilities on the combined sample space for the three experiments.*

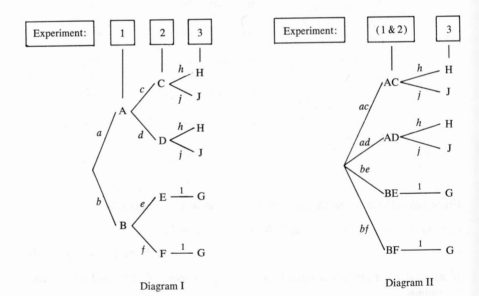

Diagram I                         Diagram II

From the 2-experiment proof already given we know that $ac + ad + be + bf = 1$. Thus, the branch numbers in the first column of Diagram II total 1.

Diagram II consists of only two experiments. Using the 2-experiment result we have that

$$ach + acj + adh + adj + bej + be + bf = 1.$$

In brief, we have shown for this 3-experiment example that the numbers assigned on the combined space using the tree diagram rules total 1. There is nothing special about this example and the result is generally true.

One could continue to apply this method of reasoning indefinitely. A 4-experiment tree can be regarded as a 2-experiment tree by combining the first three experiments as a single experiment. Using the 3-experiment result, one is assured that the branch numbers in the first column of the 2-experiment tree total 1. One then uses the 2-experiment rule and proves that the numbers assigned by the 4-experiment tree total 1. This gives a 4-experiment rule. One can then consider a 5-experiment tree as a 2-experiment tree, and again repeat the process, and so forth.

This proof is reminiscent of the one used in Section 1.2 to extend the rule of counting. Both that proof and this one can be given formally using mathematical induction. The reader familiar with this method of proof may wish to apply it here. However, for the remainder of this book we simply accept the fact that the rules of this section give a valid assignment of probabilities on the combined sample space.

## EXERCISES

1.  The following is a path through a tree diagram:

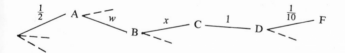

(a) What is the probability assigned to the simple event ABCDF of the combined space?
(b) If $w = 0$, what is the probability?
(c) If $w = \frac{1}{2}$ and $x = \frac{1}{3}$, what is the probability?

2.  Consider the tree diagram

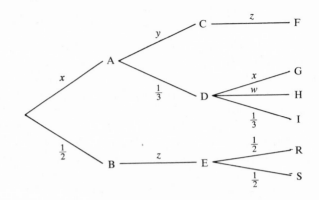

(a) If the branch probabilities are validly assigned what must be the value of $x$?
(b) Of $w$, $y$, and $z$?
(c) List the simple events of the combined space with the probability assigned to each.

3.  Consider the tree diagram

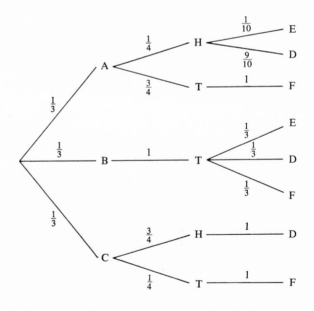

(a) Determine the assignment of probabilities on the combined space.
(b) Show that their sum is 1.

4. In the combined space of Exercise 3 define events as follows:

A = "A occurs on the first experiment"
$$= \{AHE, AHD, ATF\};$$
F = "F occurs on the third experiment"
$$= \{CTF, ATF, BTF\};$$

.   .
.   .
.   .

What are the probabilities of the following events:
(a) $A \cap T \cap F$;   (b) $A \cap H$;   (c) $B \cap E$;
(d) $B \cup E$;   (e) H;   (f) B?

5. In the pasture ecosystem model of Example 2 of this section assign the following probabilities: Whenever an atom of phosphorus is in the soil at the beginning of the day, the sample space giving its location at the end of the day is

$$\begin{matrix} \{S, G, O\} \\ s, \; r, \; v \end{matrix}, \quad \text{with } s + r + v = 1.$$

Similarly, whenever an atom is in the grass at the beginning of the day the corresponding sample space is

$$\begin{matrix} \{S, G, C\} \\ u, \; w, \; y \end{matrix}, \quad \text{with } u + w + y = 1.$$

And whenever in the cattle, the corresponding sample space is

$$\begin{matrix} \{S, C, O\} \\ z, \; t, m \end{matrix}, \quad \text{with } z + t + m = 1.$$

If the atom is outside it stays outside, and the sample space is

$$\begin{matrix} \{O\} \\ 1 \end{matrix}.$$

(a) If an atom starts in the soil, use a tree diagram to determine the sample space for its probable location after two days. (Thus the simple event GC has probability $ry$.)
(b) What is the probability that the atom is still in the pasture ecosystem after two days?
(c) What is the probability that it is either in the soil or in grass after two days?
(d) What is the probability that it is in the soil at the end of the first day?
(e) What is the probability that it is in the soil at the end of the first day and outside the system at the end of the second?

6. The problem is the same as in Exercise 5. If an atom starts in the grass, what is the probability that it is outside the system in two days?

7. The problem is the same as in Exercise 5. If an atom starts outside the system, what is the probability that it is outside the system after ten days?

8. The problem is the same as Exercise 5. What is the probability that the atom is still in the pasture ecosystem after three days?

| PATH 4 ☞ §6.4 |    | PATH 5 ☞ §6.4 |

## 6.4 INDEPENDENT EXPERIMENTS

We have already defined *independent events* for any number of events of the same sample space. We now consider the meaning of *independent experiments*. Briefly put, experiments are independent if the outcome of any one experiment does not affect the probability of an outcome of any other. However, we give a mathematical definition for independent experiments. We speak only of independence with reference to events of a single sample space, and we now see that the definition of independent experiments has precise meaning in terms of the *events* of the *combined sample space*.

To return to coin flipping, suppose that two coins are tossed, each falling heads or tails. Construct the model in which the probability that the first coin falls heads is $a$, and the probability that the second coin falls heads is $b$. Add the condition that the outcome for the first coin does not affect the probability of any outcome for the second coin, and vice versa. This condition gives us *independent tosses* (or experiments). In other words

GENERAL STATEMENT.    *Any event of the combined space which describes only an outcome of the first coin must be independent of any event of the combined space describing only an outcome of the second coin.*

DEFINITION.    *The two tosses (experiments) are* **independent** *if and only if the preceding general statement is true.*

Individual sample spaces for each toss are

$$\{H, \quad T\ \} \qquad \text{and} \qquad \{H, \quad T\ \}.$$
$$a, 1 - a \qquad\qquad\qquad b\ , 1 - b$$
$$\text{first} \qquad\qquad\qquad \text{second}$$

The combined sample space is

$$\{HH, HT, TH, TT\},$$

and we now consider the assignment of probabilities to its simple events.

Let the event $H_1$ be "a head occurs on the first toss," while $T_2$ is "a tail occurs on the second toss," and so forth. These events are

$$H_1 = \{HH, HT\}, \quad T_1 = \{TH, TT\}, \quad H_2 = \{HH, TH\}, \quad T_2 = \{HT, TT\}.$$

The outcomes of the first and second tosses are independent, if and only if

$$P(H_1)P(H_2) = P(H_1 \cap H_2),$$
$$P(H_1)P(T_2) = P(H_1 \cap T_2),$$
$$P(T_1)P(H_2) = P(T_1 \cap H_2),$$
$$P(T_1)P(T_2) = P(T_1 \cap T_2).$$

In this example we know the probability of a head on the first toss is $a$, thus we know that the event $H_1 = \{HH, HT\}$ in the combined space must have probability $a$. Analogously we know that $P(T_2) = (1 - b)$. Hence, since the tosses are independent, we must have

$$P(H_1)P(T_2) = P(H_1 \cap T_2) = a(1 - b).$$

Since

$$H_1 \cap T_2 = \{HT\},$$

HT in the combined space must have probability $a(1 - b)$. Pursuing this reasoning the assignment in the combined space must be

$$\{HH, \quad HT\ , \quad TH\ , \quad TT \quad \}.$$
$$ab\ , a(1 - b), (1 - a)b, (1 - a)(1 - b)$$

Using a tree diagram

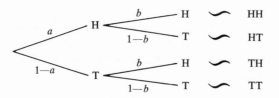

it is particularly easy to construct a model of independent experiments. No matter what the outcome of one coin, the conditional probabilities of the other are unaffected. The probability that the second coin falls heads is $b$, given any outcome for the first coin. The probabilities assigned using the tree rule are

$$\{HH, \quad HT\ , \quad TH\ , \quad TT \quad \}$$
$$ab\ , a(1 - b), (1 - a)b, (1 - a)(1 - b)$$

as before, and the two tosses are independent.

The notion of independent experiments is not limited to two experiments. To say that three experiments are independent is to say the following. Suppose that A is any event of the combined space such that A is defined only in terms of the outcome of the first individual experiment. For example, in three-coin tosses let A be "the first coin falls tails" then A = {THH, THT, TTH, TTT}. Similarly let B and C be events of the combined space describing only outcomes of the second and third individual experiments, respectively. Note that A, B, and C are all events of the combined space. Then the three simple experiments are independent if, for any A, B and C so defined, A, B, and C are mutually independent events. A similar definition is readily applied to any number, say $k$, of simple experiments.

> DEFINITION.    *Let* $A_1$, $A_2$, . . ., $A_k$ *be events of the combined space defined analogously to* A, B, *and* C *above (e.g.,* $A_k$ *is defined in terms of the kth individual experiment). Then the k simple experiments are* **independent** *if for every possible combination like* $A_1$, . . . , $A_k$ *defined in the above manner, the* $A_1$, . . . , $A_k$ *are mutually independent events.*

No matter how many experiments are involved, a glance at the tree diagram reveals whether they are independent or not. We can see this as follows. Call each set of branches emanating from a single point, as these branches do, a *cluster*.

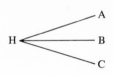

Two clusters are identical if their branches lead to the same events with the same branch probabilities. For example, the two clusters in the tree diagram given below on the left are not identical; however, the two clusters in the diagram on the right are identical.

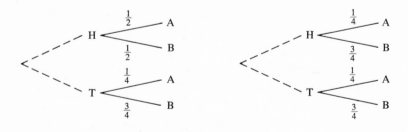

Or again, in the diagrams below the three clusters in the diagram on the left are identical, while the two clusters in the diagram on the right are not.

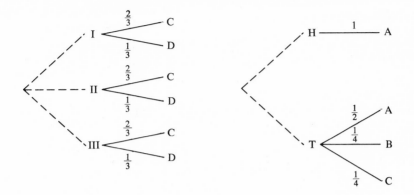

Finally, we note that in the diagram below the two clusters are identical.

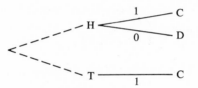

To have a branch with a probability of 0 is the same as having no branch at all. In the following diagram the second experiment does not have identical clusters.

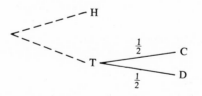

To say that clusters are identical for a given experiment implies that *each* point in a given column gives rise to a cluster which is identical to any other cluster in that column.

Any one of the experiments combined in the tree diagram is represented by some number of clusters arranged vertically in a column. For example,

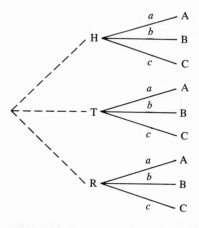

If all the clusters in a given column of the tree diagram are identical, then the experiment corresponding to that column is independent of any preceding experiment, and of any experiment representing a combination of the preceding ones. The reasoning behind this statement is as follows. A cluster represents a conditional sample space, each branch corresponding to a simple event. Each branch probability gives the conditional probability of that simple event. Pick any experiment, and call it the "current" one. It has a certain number of clusters. If these are identical, the conditional probability of any simple event in the current experiment is unchanged from cluster to cluster. This implies that the conditional probability of any simple event of the current experiment is the same regardless of the previous outcomes. Hence, the current experiment is independent of any of the previous experiments as well as any combination of them.

If the clusters in the column are not identical, conditional probabilities differ and the current experiment is not independent of all the previous ones. With the above explanation in mind we state the following without a full proof.

GENERAL STATEMENT.    *If all the clusters in a given column are identical and if this is true for all columns in the tree diagram, then all the experiments represented are mutually independent. If all the clusters in any given column are not identical, then all the experiments are not mutually independent.*

EXAMPLE 1.   Suppose that a die is thrown, and a coin is tossed independently.  Consider the tree diagram.

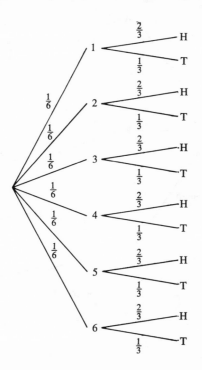

Considering the events of the combined space, we have two independent experiments since the conditional probabilities of H and T do not change, that of H is always $\frac{2}{3}$ and that of T is always $\frac{1}{3}$.

EXAMPLE 2.   In the tree diagrams which follow, diagram I represents independent experiments.  In its first column there is only one cluster, and the first column automatically consists of "identical clusters."  The three clusters in the second column are identical, and so also are the six clusters in the third column.

Diagram II, on the other hand, does not represent independent experiments, except in a special case.  If the probability given by $d$ in the second column has a value other than 1, then the clusters in that column are not identical.  However, if $d = 1$, then the clusters in that column are identical.  In that case the experiments represented by diagram II would be independent.

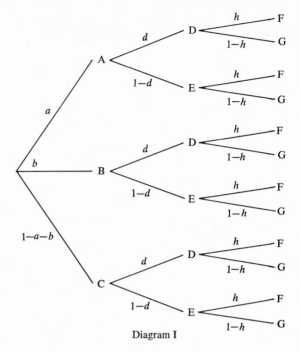

Diagram I

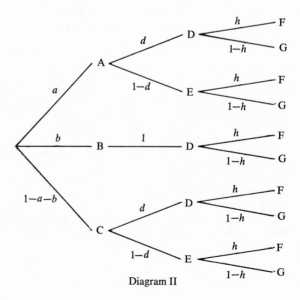

Diagram II

## EXERCISES

1. Three coins are flipped. Two are fairly balanced, but one tends to fall heads. The tree diagram is shown.

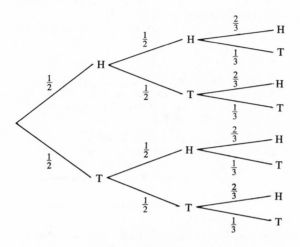

Are the experiments independent? How do you know this without examining the individual events of the combined sample space?

2. In the following diagram we combine three experiments, with their possible outcomes arranged in three columns.

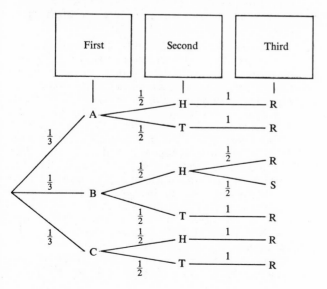

(a) Are the three experiments mutually independent?

(b) Is the second experiment independent of the first?

(c) Is the third experiment independent of the second?

3. On three successive days a bee is given a "choice" of two colors — white (W) and blue (B). The individual sample spaces are

$$\underset{\substack{\frac{4}{5},\ \frac{1}{5}}}{\{W, B\}}, \qquad \underset{\substack{\frac{2}{3},\ \frac{1}{3}}}{\{W, B\}}, \qquad \underset{\substack{\frac{1}{2},\ \frac{1}{2}}}{\{W, B\}}.$$

first day     second day     third day

Suppose the three experiments are independent. Determine the combined sample space and its assignment of probabilities. (For example, the simple event WWW has probability $\frac{4}{15}$.)

4. For the sample space of Exercise 3, determine the probabilities of the events:

(a) The bee chooses white on all three days.

(b) The bee chooses white on the first two days and blue on the third.

(c) The bee chooses white on any two days, and blue on the remaining day.

5. The problem is the same as in Exercise 3 except that the individual sample spaces are

$$\underset{\substack{\frac{1}{2},\ \frac{1}{2}}}{\{W, B\}}, \qquad \underset{\substack{\frac{1}{2},\ \frac{1}{2}}}{\{W, B\}}, \qquad \underset{\substack{\frac{1}{2},\ \frac{1}{2}}}{\{W, B\}}.$$

first day     second day     third day

Determine the probabilities of the events below:

(a) the bee chooses white on all three days;

(b) the bee chooses white on any two days, and blue on the remaining day;

(c) the bee chooses white on only one of the three days.

6. A brooding *herring gull* leaves its nest containing three eggs. Before its return, a zoologist prepares a false nest 1 foot from the real one. In the false nest there are three wooden dummies painted to look like eggs. He is studying the birds' ability to recognize its own eggs. (1) The bird returns and the nest it first chooses is observed. (2) Three actions are recorded at the chosen nest: (i) A bird may only approach the nest (A); (ii) it may approach and make an "intention movement" but not sit on the eggs (B). The breast feathers are fluffed and the legs bent as if preparatory to sitting on the eggs; and (iii) it actually sits on the eggs and incubates them (C).

Construct a model with the following properties: The probability that the bird chooses the nest with the wooden eggs is $\frac{3}{7}$. If the false nest is chosen then $P(A) = \frac{1}{3}$, $P(B) = \frac{1}{3}$, and $P(C) = \frac{1}{3}$. If the real nest is chosen then $P(A) = \frac{3}{8}$, $P(B) = \frac{1}{8}$, and $P(C) = \frac{1}{2}$.

7. The problem is the same as that of Exercise 6. Construct a model in which the probability that the bird chooses the nest with the wooden eggs is $\frac{1}{2}$, and no matter which nest is chosen $P(A) = \frac{9}{20}$, $P(B) = \frac{1}{10}$, and $P(C) = \frac{9}{20}$.

| PATH 4 ☞ §1.3 |   | PATH 5 ☞ §7.1 |

## 6.5★ APPLICATIONS OF TREE DIAGRAMS: A PROBLEM IN POPULATION GENETICS, HARDY-WEINBERG PROBABILITIES

Suppose a sexually reproducing population contains $N$ maies and $K$ females. The total size of the population is $N + K = T$. Each individual carries two genes. Each gene can take one of two forms — A or a. The two genes together constitute that individual's *genotype* — AA, Aa, or aa. The genotype Aa is the same as aA.

At mating the male and the female each contributes one of its genes to the offspring. Thus, for example, if a male of genotype Aa mates with a female of genotype AA, possible genotypes for the offspring are AA and Aa.

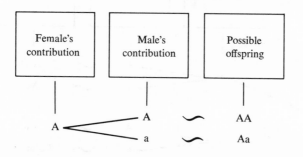

Each individual in the population carries two genes. These may be AA, Aa, or aa. Consider all the male genes. There are $2N$ of these since there are $N$ males. A certain number $r$ of these $2N$ genes are A; the proportion of these is $p = r/(2N)$ the *gene frequency of* A in the males. The remaining genes are of type a. The proportion of these is $1 - p = q$, the *gene frequency* of a in the males. For example, if there are 100 males, there are 200 genes A or a. If $r = 50$ are A, then $p = \frac{50}{200} = \frac{1}{4}$, and $q = \frac{3}{4}$. There are $K$ females. In a similar way we define $p'$ as the gene frequency of A in females, with $q'$ being the gene frequency of a.

It should be noted that we can have the same *gene frequencies* even though the proportions of genotypes differ. For example, in 100 males we might have

50 AA; 0 Aa; and 50 aa, in which case $p = 0.5$. We might also have 25 AA, 50 Aa, and 25 aa, in which case also $p = 0.5$.

We have a *random mating* if the determination of the *genotype* of an offspring is as follows:

(1) A gene is selected *simply at random* from all male genes in the population.
(2) A gene is selected *simply at random* from all female genes in the population.
(3) The two experiments are independent.

In the first experiment there are $2N$ male genes in the sample space. Since the selection is simply at random each has probability $1/(2N)$. There are $r$ genes of type A. This then is the number of simple events in the event "the gene chosen is type A." The probability of this event is $r/(2N) = p$. *Note that the simple random sampling assignment translates the gene frequency p into a probability.* Similarly, the probability of the event "the gene chosen is a" is $1 - p = q$.

Exactly analogous reasoning holds for the second experiment, the selection of a gene from a female. There are $2K$ simple events in the sample space; the probability of the event "the gene chosen is A" is $p'$, and that of "the gene chosen is a" is $q'$: Since the two experiments are independent we have the following tree diagram:

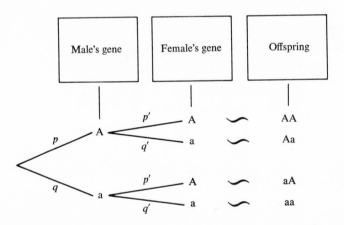

Recall that the genotype Aa is the same as aA. The probabilities of the geno-types in the offspring are:

$$P(\text{AA}) = pp'; \qquad P(\text{Aa}) = pq' + qp'; \qquad P(\text{aa}) = qq'. \qquad (1)$$

These probabilities are called Hardy-Weinberg probabilities.[2] If the gene fre-

---

[2] In 1908 W. Weinberg, a German physician, and G. H. Hardy, an English mathematician, independently published the result given in this section the *Hardy-Weinberg* model or law. Hardy was a pure mathematician whose contributions in pure mathematics are well-known. Hardy once wrote that he had never done anything useful. For biologists, the association of his name with the Hardy-Weinberg model belies this statement.

quency of males is the same as that of females (that is, $p = p'$), the probabilities become

$$P(AA) = p^2; \qquad P(Aa) = 2pq; \qquad P(aa) = q^2.$$

The model indicates that the *genotypic probabilities* for the offspring depend only on the gene frequencies of the parents; this is shown clearly in the results.

EXAMPLE 1. Using the independent random mating model just studied, let us examine the situation of two populations. In the first population the numbers of individuals of the three genotypes are

|         | AA  | Aa  | aa  |
|---------|-----|-----|-----|
| Males   | 600 | 0   | 400 |
| Females | 400 | 400 | 200 |

In the second population they are

|         | AA  | Aa  | aa  |
|---------|-----|-----|-----|
| Males   | 400 | 400 | 200 |
| Females | 200 | 800 | 0   |

The populations have varying numbers of the different genotypes. However, the gene frequency of A is $\frac{6}{10}$ in both males and females of each population. Since the gene frequencies are the same, the genotypic probabilities in the offspring are the same for the two populations, namely,

$$P(AA) = \tfrac{36}{100}; \qquad P(Aa) = \tfrac{48}{100}; \qquad P(aa) = \tfrac{16}{100}.$$

In independent random matings these probabilities depend on the gene frequencies $p$ and $p'$, not directly on the genotypic frequencies.

We now show that in order to obtain Hardy-Weinberg probabilities the sex ratio of the offspring may vary and not all of the offspring need survive to breed. However, the sex determination and survival must be independent of genotype. To do this we add two experiments to the preceding. In order to determine *a random mating producing an offspring who lives to breed in the next generation* we set up the following reference model (see also Exercise 6 of this section):

(1) A gene is selected simply at random from all male genes in the population.
(2) A gene is selected simply at random from all female genes in the population.
(3) The sex of the offspring is determined in some manner. Whatever the manner, the probability that the offspring is male is $m$, and the probability that the offspring is female is $n$ ($m + n = 1$).
(4) The survival of the offspring is determined by a number of factors. Whatever the factors, the probability that the offspring survives to mature and

breed is $u$. The probability that the offspring dies before breeding is $w$ $(u + w = 1)$.

(5) These four experiments are independent.

The specification of independence is crucial. Also note that there would be about four male offspring to every female if $m = \frac{4}{5}$. The sex ratio is not assumed to be 1. The tree diagram is as shown.

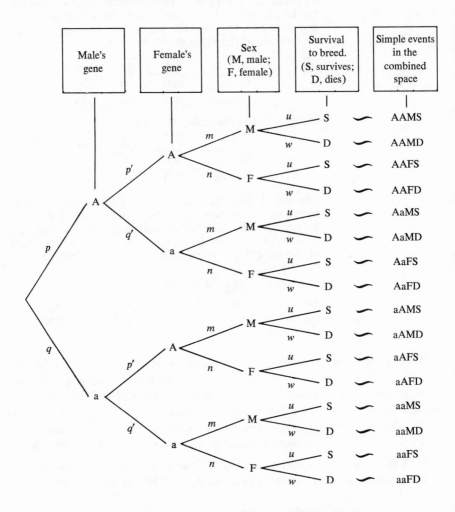

Consider the event X equals "the offspring is a surviving male" or

$$X = \{AAMS, \ AaMS, \ aAMS, \ aaMS\}$$
$$pp'mu, \ pq'mu, \ qp'mu, \ qq'mu$$

We have its probability

$$P(X) = pp'mu + pq'mu + qp'mu + qq'mu$$
$$= (pp' + pq' + qp' + qq')mu.$$

Since the sum of the terms inside the parentheses is equal to 1 (see Exercise 3) we have

$$P(X) = mu.$$

The event "the offspring is AA *and* a surviving male" is

$$\{AAMS\}.$$
$$pp'mu$$

The conditional probability of being AA given that the offspring is a surviving male is

$$P(AA|X) = \frac{pp'mu}{mu} = pp'.$$

In a similar way we obtain the conditional probabilities

$$P(Aa|X) = pq' + qp', \qquad P(aa|X) = qq'.$$

These are the same probabilities as in formula (1). They are the Hardy-Weinberg probabilities. The same results apply for females. As long as sex determination and survival are independent of genotype the Hardy-Weinberg probabilities are obtained for both surviving males and surviving females. If a genotype had preferential survival there would be natural selection in the population for that genotype over the others. More offspring of the favored genotype would survive to breed and form the next generation. To say that survival is independent of genotype is to say that there is no natural selection occurring.

Let us now consider *evolution* in a large random mating population with survival and sex determination as in our model. For our immediate purposes, we can define evolution as a change in gene frequency in a population with the passage of time or generations.

We indicated earlier how the assumption of simple random sampling translated the genotypic frequencies into probabilities. Now we need to reverse the process, we wish to translate the *Hardy-Weinberg probabilities* back into *population frequencies*. To do this we can envision a very large population with a large number of males and females. Then with a large number of independent random matings the genotypic frequencies in the offspring are very nearly the same as the genotypic probabilities.

Let us start with a large population with the gene frequencies $p$ and $p'$ for males and females, respectively. The first generation of *offspring surviving to breed* from independent random matings will have the same genotypic frequencies for males and females:

$$AA :pp'; \quad Aa :pq' + qp'; \quad aa :qq'.$$

Since the genotypic frequencies are the same for males and females, so are the gene frequencies. Call the new gene frequency of A, $p_1$. In fact,

$$p_1 = \frac{p + p'}{2}$$

(see Exercise 3). The gene frequency of a is $1 - p_1 = q_1$. Assume a large number of males and females survive to breed. Now let these offspring produce a new generation. Both male and female offspring of this generation surviving to breed will have genotypic frequencies

$$AA :p_1^2; \quad Aa :2p_1q_1; \quad aa :q_1^2.$$

With these genotypic frequencies the gene frequency is $p_1$ (Exercise 2) for both males and females. Consequently, a third generation produced from the second generation offspring will also have genotypic frequencies

$$AA :p_1^2; \quad Aa :2p_1q_1; \quad aa :q_1^2.$$

A fourth generation will likewise have the same genotypic frequencies, thus so will the fifth, and so forth. Any subsequent generation will have these relative frequencies (always assuming a large number of males and females survive to breed).

The genotypic (and gene) frequencies have become stabilized for all subsequent generations. *Genotypic frequencies which remain stable in the ratio*

$$p_1^2 :2p_1q_1 :q_1^2$$

*from generation to generation are said to be in* **Hardy-Weinberg equilibrium.** We can now give the following basic result in population genetics.

THE HARDY-WEINBERG MODEL (LAW).    *In a large population with independent random mating where sex determination and survival are independent of genotype, the Hardy-Weinberg equilibrium is established and the gene frequency does not change. Further, the equilibrium is established by at least the second generation.*

We have seen that this occurs whatever the sex ratio of males to females (as long as the number of each is large). It also occurs whatever the initial genotypic frequencies of males and of females.

Viewing evolution as a change in gene frequencies in a population, a large population with independent random mating and survival independent of genotypes exhibits no evolutionary change. This is the main conclusion to be drawn from the Hardy-Weinberg model.

## EXERCISES

1. In a large independent random mating population with sex determination and survival independent of genotype, under what conditions is the Hardy-Weinberg equilibrium established by the first generation.

2. If genotypic frequencies are

$$AA:p^2, \qquad Aa:2pq, \qquad aa:q^2,$$

   show that the gene frequency of A is $p$.

3. If genotypic frequencies are
   AA:$pp'$,     Aa:$pq' + qp'$,     aa:$qq'$.
   What is the gene frequency of A? If $p_1$ is the gene frequency of A, then $p_1 = pp' + \frac{1}{2}pq' + \frac{1}{2}qp'$. (*Hint:* Try to obtain terms which collapse, e.g.,

$$\tfrac{1}{2}pp' + \tfrac{1}{2}pq' = \tfrac{1}{2}(pp' + pq') = \tfrac{1}{2}p(p' + q') = \tfrac{1}{2}p$$

   since $p' + q' = 1$.)

4. If $p' + q' = 1$ and $p + q = 1$, show that

$$pp' + pq' + p'q + qq' = 1.$$

5. Consider the sample space and assigned probabilities given in the text by the tree diagram on page 182. List the simple events in the following events: (remember genotype Aa = aA)

   AA = "the offspring is genotype AA,"
   Aa = "the offspring is genotype Aa,"
   aa = "the offspring is genotype aa,"
   X = "the offspring is a surviving male,"
   Y = "the offspring is a surviving female."

   Determine the following conditional probabilities:

$$P(AA|X); \qquad P(Aa|X); \qquad P(aa|X);$$
$$P(AA|Y); \qquad P(Aa|Y); \qquad P(aa|Y).$$

6. You may not have been satisfied with the definition of random mating given in our model. If not, perhaps the model in this exercise will satisfy you. (This exercise may be time consuming.)
   Suppose a population contains $N$ breeding males and $K$ breeding females. The total size of the population is $N + K = T$. Suppose

   $D$ is the number of males of genotype AA;
   $H$ is the number of males of genotype Aa;
   $R$ is the number of males of genotype aa.

   Since each male has one (and only one) of the three genotypes

$$D + H + R = N.$$

The frequencies of the three genotypes for males are

$$d = D/N; \quad h = H/N; \quad r = R/N.$$

Note that $d + h + r = 1$. The number of A genes among the males is $2D + H$, since each genotype AA has two A genes. Similarly the number of a genes is $H + 2R$. The gene frequency of A is

$$p = \frac{2D + H}{2N} = d + \frac{1}{2}h.$$

Similarly let $D'$, $N'$, $R'$ be the numbers of females of genotypes AA, Aa, aa, respectively. The genotypic frequencies for females are then

$$d', \quad h', \quad r',$$

and the gene frequency of A for females is

$$p' = d' + \tfrac{1}{2}h'.$$

Consider the following model. A mating is a random mating if
(1) The determination of a male is simply at random from all males.
(2) The determination of a gene from that male is simply at random from both his genes.
(3) The determination of a female is simply at random from all females.
(4) The determination of a gene from that female is simply at random from both her genes.
(5) The four experiments are independent.
Work out a tree diagram for this combined experiment and show that the Hardy-Weinberg genotypic probabilities hold.

| PATH 4 🖝 §2.6 |   | PATH 5 🖝 §4.7, 4.8, 6.5, 7.3 |

## 6.6★ APPLICATIONS OF TREE DIAGRAMS:
## CHROMOSOME AND GENE MODELS IN HEREDITY.
## PART II.[3] MONOHYBRID AND DIHYBRID CROSSES

A *gene* is some portion of a DNA molecule. In general genetic research it is some unknown sequence of nucleotides whose existence is inferred by observing characteristics (e.g., eye color, hair texture) of several generations of individuals. Genes were first discovered in this way. In molecular terms a *gene* can be defined as some sequence of nucleotides controlling the synthesis of a

---

[3] Part I of chromosome and gene models in heredity is Section 1.3. The reader should review that section before proceeding with this section.

single polypeptide chain or protein.[4] There are many genes in a single DNA chain.

Genes occur in pairs, one on each member of a pair of chromosomes. Also a gene can often occur in two forms[5] — an active form A, and an inactive form a. With such a gene three kinds of individuals are possible. Those with an active gene on both chromosomes of a pair are of type AA; those with inactive genes on each chromosome are aa; and those with one active and one inactive gene another type Aa. When germ cells are formed each contains only one member of the pair. Thus, an Aa individual can form two kinds of germ cells, A and a; however, aa and AA individuals can produce only germ cells of types a and A, respectively.

The diagram is of a pair of chromosomes in each of the three types of individuals possible with a single gene with two forms A and a. A is the active form, and a the inactive form. The types of germ cells (sperm if male, eggs if female) possible for each individual are given.

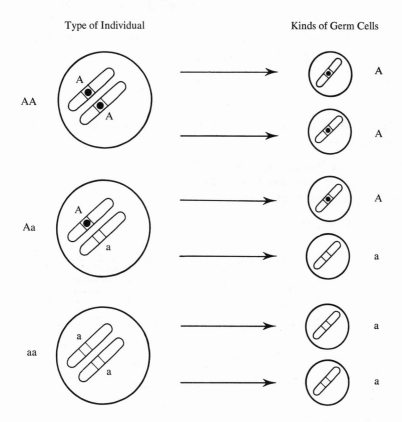

  Type of Individual
  Kinds of Germ Cells

AA

Aa

aa

A

A

A

a

a

a

---

[4] A protein is a chain of amino acids. How a nucleic acid can control protein synthesis is briefly indicated in Section 2.6. However this is not needed for understanding the present section.

[5] Genes may also occur in more than two forms.

### A Monohybrid Cross

We can now consider probability models for various kinds of matings. Suppose that an Aa male mates with an Aa female. Such a mating is known as a *monohybrid cross* (*mono*- because we consider only one gene). In this particular mating each individual can produce two kinds of germ cells — A and a.

The male produces many sperm of these two types. Define a sample space whose simple events indicate which type of sperm, A or a, fertilizes the egg. Consider the probability of either as $\frac{1}{2}$ or

$$\begin{matrix} \{a, A\} \\ \frac{1}{2}, \ \frac{1}{2} \end{matrix}.$$

The two types of sperm are the result of cell division, and should occur in about equal numbers, hence this assignment of probabilities. Although often reasonable, this assignment is not a necessary one. For example, the two types of sperm might exhibit different survival rates, or different motile abilities, and the probabilities would be correspondingly altered.

Consider also the same sample space for females wherein the simple event $\{a\}$ indicates that the egg which is fertilized is type a or

$$\begin{matrix} \{a, A\} \\ \frac{1}{2}, \ \frac{1}{2} \end{matrix}.$$

The fertilization of an egg in a monohybrid cross can be regarded as a combined experiment in which:

(1) A sperm cell is chosen, $P(A) = P(a) = \frac{1}{2}$.
(2) An egg cell is chosen, $P(A) = P(a) = \frac{1}{2}$.
(3) The two experiments are independent.

The tree diagram is of a simple sort.

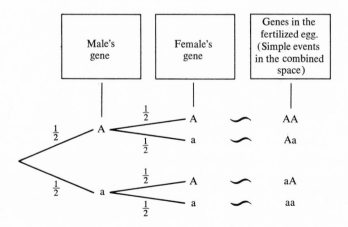

We have the combined sample space

$$\{AA, Aa, aA, aa\} \atop \tfrac{1}{4}, \tfrac{1}{4}, \tfrac{1}{4}, \tfrac{1}{4}.$$

The event "the individual has one gene of each type" is

$$\{Aa, aA\} \atop \tfrac{1}{4}, \tfrac{1}{4},$$

and has probability $\tfrac{1}{2}$. Since aA and Aa individuals are genetically indistinguishable, we use the slightly modified sample space.

$$\{AA, Aa, aa\} \atop \tfrac{1}{4}, \tfrac{1}{2}, \tfrac{1}{4}.$$

Each simple event of this sample space is known as the *genotype* of the individual.

   Although there are three genotypes, these may not all differ in external appearance, that is, in *phenotype*. For example, suppose the active gene A controls the synthesis of a compound causing the individual to be tall. It may be that two active genes AA synthesize more of the compound than the cell needs to accomplish this, and that one active gene alone can produce a sufficient amount. If such is the case, all individuals with one or two A's are tall. Only an aa individual does not synthesize enough of the compound and consequently does not grow tall. The genotypes AA and Aa have the same *phenotype* tall, while aa has the *phenotype* short. In this case the active gene A is said to be *dominant* to the inactive gene a, which is *recessive*. Any time a genotype Aa produces the same effect as AA, A is said to be dominant.

   In the monohybrid cross if A is dominant then the event "an individual has the dominant phenotype" is D or

$$D = \{AA, Aa\}, \qquad P(D) = \tfrac{3}{4}. \atop \tfrac{1}{4}, \tfrac{1}{2},$$

Similarly the event "an individual has the recessive phenotype" is R,

$$R = \{aa\}, \qquad P(R) = \tfrac{1}{4}. \atop \tfrac{1}{4},$$

The odds of D to R are 3 :1 (*cf.*, Section 5.1). These are classical odds in genetics. With many progeny under a monohybrid cross model three times as many dominant phenotypes occur as do recessive.

   It is common to find one gene of a pair to be dominant, but this is not always the case. For example, a single active gene may have some effect on phenotype, but not as much as two active genes together. In this case each genotype has a distinctive phenotype. The gene A is said to exhibit *incomplete dominance*. For example, if A controls tallness, the three phenotypes might be tall (AA), medium (Aa), and short (aa). With incomplete dominance the phenotypic odds are the same as the genotypic odds, 1 : 2 :1.

EXAMPLE 1. Suppose a tall pea plant when crossed with another tall pea plant produced many plants of which $\frac{3}{4}$ are tall, $\frac{1}{4}$ short. A model agreeing with these results is the following. There is a single gene with a dominant form T and a recessive t. The mating would be Tt × Tt and the sample space for the progeny

$$\{TT, Tt, tt\}$$
$$\tfrac{1}{4}, \tfrac{1}{2}, \tfrac{1}{4} \quad .$$

The event the plant is tall is T = $\{TT, Tt\}$, and $P(T) = \frac{3}{4}$.

EXAMPLE 2. Suppose a tall pea plant when crossed with a short pea plant produces many plants, all tall. A model agreeing with these results is that of a single gene as in Example 1. The mating would be TT × tt, and the sample space for the progeny

$$\{Tt\}$$
$$1 \quad .$$

EXAMPLE 3. Suppose in repeated matings of a red bull with a white cow all the offspring are roan-colored. Two of the roan offspring mate with each other and produce 1 white, 2 roan, and 1 red individuals. A possible explanation of these results is given by the following model. There is a single gene with two forms — W, active and w, inactive; W is incompletely dominant to w. The first mating would be

WW × ww;    progeny: $\{Ww\}$
$$1 \quad .$$

The second would be

Ww × Ww;    progeny: $\{WW, Ww, ww\}$
$$\tfrac{1}{4}, \tfrac{1}{2}, \tfrac{1}{4} \quad .$$

## A Dihybrid Cross

Suppose there are two genes, each with an active and inactive form — Y and y, both of which we refer to as the Y-gene, and Z and z, both referred to as the Z-gene. The two genes are located on different pairs of chromosomes — one long, one short. A diagram of the two pairs of an individual with genotype YyZz is shown.

|  | Active genes | Inactive genes |
|---|---|---|
| Long chromosomes | Y | y |
| Short chromosomes | Z | z |

Cell of individual with genotype YyZz

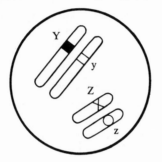

An individual of this genotype can produce $2^2 = 4$ kinds of germ cells.

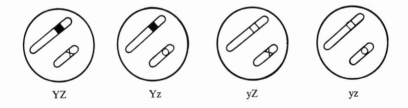

| YZ | Yz | yZ | yz |

Consider a mating of a male of genotype YyZz with a female of type YyZz. Such a mating is called a *dihybrid cross* (*di* because two genes are involved).

We consider the case in which Y is dominant to y, and Z is dominant to z, and suppose that we are only interested in the relative odds of the phenotypes. In order to simplify the problem, we divide it into two simple ones. We first consider the long chromosome pair and the Y-gene alone (without the Z-gene). From our results on the monohybrid cross, we find the sample space for the genotypes to be

$$T_1 = \{YY, Yy, yy\}.$$
$$\tfrac{1}{4}, \tfrac{1}{2}, \tfrac{1}{4}$$

If we let D be the event "an individual has the dominant phenotype" and let R be the event "an individual has the recessive phenotype," then the sample space for phenotypes is

$$S = \{D, R\}.$$
$$\tfrac{3}{4}, \tfrac{1}{4}$$

Now if we consider the short chromosome pair and the Z-gene alone, we arrive at the following sample space for the genotypes

$$T_2 = \{ZZ, Zz, zz\}.$$
$$\tfrac{1}{4}, \tfrac{1}{2}, \tfrac{1}{4}$$

and for the phenotypes obtain the same sample space as for the Y-gene

$$S = \{D, R\}.$$
$$\tfrac{3}{4}, \tfrac{1}{4}$$

We can now construct a model of a dihybrid cross.

A dihybrid cross model can be considered as two independent monohybrid crosses with the following stipulations:

(1) A long chromosome pair is chosen for the offspring; that is, a dominant or recessive phenotype based on the Y-gene found on this pair is chosen according to S, so $P(D) = \tfrac{3}{4}$ and $P(R) = \tfrac{1}{4}$.

(2) A short chromosome pair is chosen; that is, a dominant or recessive phenotype based on the Z-gene is chosen also according to S.

(3) The two experiments are independent.

The tree diagram for the combined experiment is

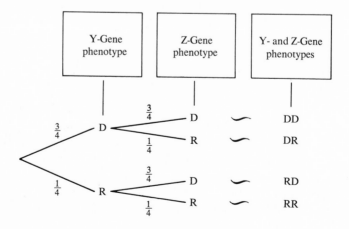

The sample space is

$$\{DD, DR, RD, RR\}$$
$$\tfrac{9}{16}, \tfrac{3}{16}, \tfrac{3}{16}, \tfrac{1}{16},$$

and the phenotypic odds are 9 :3 :3 :1, which again are classical odds in genetics.

EXAMPLE 4. In guinea pigs a black male with a rough coat of hair is mated with a white female with a smooth coat of hair. In ɪ ɪny matings the offspring occur in approximately the f lowing ratios:

black, with rough coat 9;   black, with smooth coat 3;
white, with rough coat 3;   white, with smooth coat 1.

A possible model explaining these results is that there are two genes each with two forms:

black (B) dominant to white (b);   rough (H) dominant to smooth (h).

The model is that of a dihybrid cross with sample space

$$\left\{\begin{matrix} \text{black-} & \text{black-} & \text{white-} & \text{white-} \\ \text{rough,} & \text{smooth,} & \text{rough,} & \text{smooth} \end{matrix}\right\}$$
$$\tfrac{9}{16}, \quad \tfrac{3}{16}, \quad \tfrac{3}{16}, \quad \tfrac{1}{16}.$$

If we wish the relative *genotypic* odds for a dihybrid cross model we must consider the two sample spaces already given for genotypes $T_1$ and $T_2$ (see beginning paragraphs on dihybrid crosses). Again the dihybrid cross can be thought of as two independent monohybrid crosses. The tree diagram is as shown.

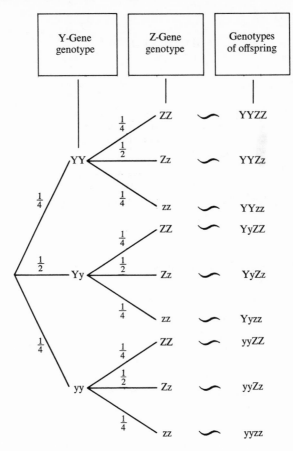

The combined sample space is

$$\{YyZz, YYZz, YyZZ, Yyzz, yyZz, YYZZ, YYzz, yyZZ, yyzz\},$$
$$\tfrac{4}{16} \ , \quad \tfrac{2}{16} \ , \quad \tfrac{2}{16} \ , \quad \tfrac{2}{16} \ , \quad \tfrac{2}{16} \ , \quad \tfrac{1}{16} \ , \quad \tfrac{1}{16} \ , \quad \tfrac{1}{16} \ , \quad \tfrac{1}{16}$$

and the genotypic odds for the dihybrid cross are

$$4:2:2:2:2:1:1:1:1.$$

Again, these are classical genotypic odds.

### EXERCISES

1.  A female fruitfly (*Drosophila*) with long wings mates with a male whose wings are barely developed, vestigial wings. There are 1000 offspring, all with long wings. One of these male offspring then mates

with one of the female offspring. Of 1000 offspring 755 have long wings and 245 have vestigial wings. Give a model consistent with these results.

2.  A male fruitfly with vestigial wings mates with a female with vestigial wings. There are 900 offspring, all with vestigial wings. Two of these offspring mate. There are 1000 offspring all with vestigial wings. Give a model consistent with these results as well as with those of Exercise 1.

3.  A female fruitfly with long wings mates with a male with vestigial wings. There are 950 offspring all with long wings. One of these offspring then mates with a fruitfly with vestigial wings. There are 1000 offspring — 510 have normal wings; 490 vestigial wings. Give a model consistent with these results as well as with the results of Exercises 1 and 2.

4.  A male guinea pig with rough hair mates with a female with smooth hair. There are four offspring — two, with smooth hair; two, with rough hair. Give a model consistent with these results as well as with those in Example 4 of this section.

5.  A male fruitfly with long wings and gray-body color is crossed with a female also with long wings and gray-body color. There are over a thousand offspring. These occur in approximately the ratios

$$9 \quad : \quad 3 \quad : \quad 3 \quad : \quad 1 \quad .$$

| long wings, gray body | : | long wings, ebony body | : | vestigial wings, gray body | : | vestigial wings, ebony body |

(a) Give a model which is consistent with these results.

(b) Do you think ebony body is dominant to gray body?

6.  In the fruitfly long wings is dominant to vestigial wings, and gray body color is dominant to ebony body color. A male fly with long wings and gray body color is mated with a female with vestigial wings and ebony body color. There are 1000 offspring. About $\frac{1}{4}$ of these have long wings and gray body color. About $\frac{1}{4}$ have long wings and ebony bodies. Close to $\frac{1}{4}$ have vestigial wings and gray bodies and the remainder have vestigial wings and ebony bodies. Construct a model consistent with these results.

7.  The genes are the same as in Exercise 5. The mating is of another male with long wings and gray body with another female with vestigial wings and ebony body color. There are 900 offspring. All have long wings and gray body color. Construct a model consistent with these results.

8.  *A Trihybrid Cross.*    Suppose there are three genes
    A, B, C, each with two forms — A and a, B and b,
    C and c.  Suppose in each case the active gene (capital
    letter) is dominant to the inactive form.  Each gene is
    located on a different pair of chromosomes.  A dia-
    gram of a cell of an individual of genotype AaBbCc
    is shown.

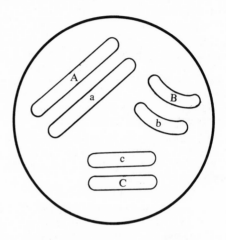

    Two individuals each with this genotype mate.  Let
    D stand for the dominant phenotype, R for the reces-
    sive.  View the determination of a phenotype by one
    of the genes as an experiment with sample space

$$\{\underset{\frac{3}{4},\ \frac{1}{4}}{D, R}\}.$$

    With three independent experiments like this, deter-
    mine the probabilities of phenotypes like DDD (dom-
    inant for all three genes); DDR (dominant for A
    and B, recessive for C); and so forth.

9.  The problem is the same as Exercise 5.  This time
    view the determination of genotype of a single gene
    as experiments with sample spaces, respectively, like:

$$\underset{\frac{1}{4},\ \frac{1}{2},\ \frac{1}{4}}{\{AA, Aa, aa\}} ; \qquad \underset{\frac{1}{4},\ \frac{1}{2},\ \frac{1}{4}}{\{BB, Bb, bb\}} ; \qquad \underset{\frac{1}{4},\ \frac{1}{2},\ \frac{1}{4}}{\{CC, Cc, cc\}} .$$

    (a) If the three experiments are independent, deter-
    mine the combined sample space and the probabilities
    of its simple events.
    (b) Two simple events of the combined space are
    AaBbCc and aabbcc.  What are the odds of the
    former event to the latter?
    (c) What are the odds of the event {aaBBCC} to
    the event {AAbbcc}?

### 6.7★ APPLICATIONS OF TREE DIAGRAMS: CHROMOSOME AND GENE MODELS IN HEREDITY. PART III[6]. LINKAGE, CROSSING OVER, AND CHROMOSOME MAPPING

#### Linkage

Two genes found on the same chromosome are said to be *linked*. Consider two genes, each with two forms — E and e both referred to as the E-gene; C and c, both referred as to the C-gene. Suppose we have an individual of genotype eeCC whose genes are arranged on a chromosome pair like:

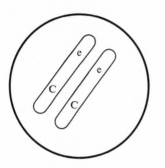

The only kind of germ cell this individual can produce is

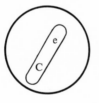

Suppose another individual has the pair of chromosomes:

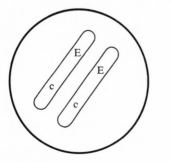

---

[6] Part II is the preceding section.

The only kind of germ cell it can produce is

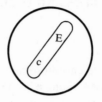

The genotypes of these two individuals are CCee and ccEE, respectively. Their mating can only produce a fertilized egg like

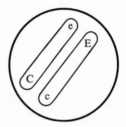

All of the offspring are CcEe with genes arranged as above. Any one of these offspring can itself produce two kinds of germ cell.

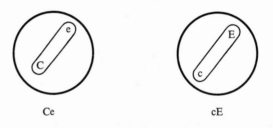

Ce                    cE

A mating of two such offspring can be modeled in a way similar to that of the monohybrid cross, since there is only a single chromosome pair. Thus;

(1) A sperm cell is chosen, $P(Ce) = P(cE) = \frac{1}{2}$;

(2) An egg cell is chosen, $P(Ce) = P(cE) = \frac{1}{2}$;

(3) The two experiments are independent.

The tree diagram is a simple one.

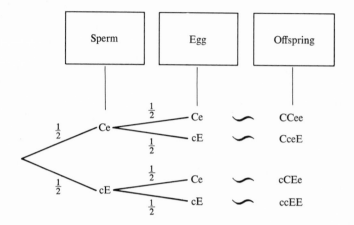

Since CceE is indistinguishable from cCEe, the resulting sample space for the genotypes of the progeny is

$$\{CceE, CCee, ccEE\}$$
$$\tfrac{1}{2}, \quad \tfrac{1}{4}, \quad \tfrac{1}{4}$$

Suppose C (normal eye) is dominant to c (claret eye), and E (normal body) is dominant to e (ebony body).[7] Each genotype is a distinctive phenotype and the sample space can be written as

$$\{normal\ eye\text{-}normal\ body,\ normal\ eye\text{-}ebony\ body,\ claret\ eye\text{-}normal\ body\}$$
$$\tfrac{1}{2}, \qquad \tfrac{1}{4}, \qquad \tfrac{1}{4}$$

The phenotypic odds for this cross with linked genes are 2 :1 :1.

Note how different these odds would be if the C-genes and the E-genes were on different chromosomes. We would start with individuals of the same genotypes (CCee and EEcc); however, in this case the genes would be on separate chromosomes. First, we would have the mating

---

[7] These are characteristics of the fruitfly *Drosophila melanogaster*, a favorite organism for genetic research. The genes indicated are, in fact, linked.

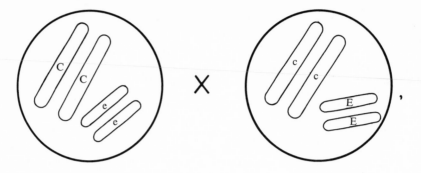

all of whose offspring would be

A mating of two of these offspring could be modeled with our simple dihybrid cross and the phenotypic odds would be the classic ones of 9 :3 :3 :1. The sample space for phenotypes would be

$$\{normal\text{-}normal, normal\text{-}ebony, claret\text{-}normal, claret\text{-}ebony\}$$
$$\tfrac{9}{16} \quad , \quad \tfrac{3}{16} \quad , \quad \tfrac{3}{16} \quad , \quad \tfrac{1}{16}$$

With both genes on the same chromosome pair the odds are 2 :1 :1. On separate chromosomes the odds are 9 :3 :3 :1. These contrast strikingly with the 2 :1 :1 odds in the case where the genes are linked. The models differ, and properly designed experiments can tell whether certain genes are on the same chromosome or not.

### Crossing Over

In all the models we have considered thus far each chromosome of a pair remains intact during meiosis. However, chromosomes can break and rejoin during the formation of germ cells. We now illustrate this by means of two linked genes (E and e, C and c) which occur on a single pair of chromosomes:

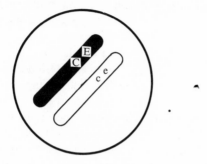

If the chromosomes remain intact, then the only kinds of germ cells that this individual can produce are

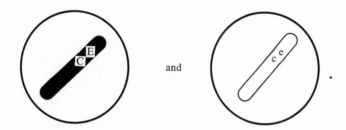

and

However, during meiosis, chromosomes can break and rejoin. If this happens then the following germ cells can also occur

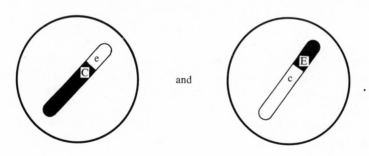

and

In each of these a break occurred and a portion of one chromosome was exchanged with the corresponding portion of the other. This phenomenon is known as *crossing over*. With the occurrence of crossing over the above individual could produce any of the four types of germ cells pictured, namely, CE, ce, Ce, or cE.

At this point we briefly digress to consider some details of meiosis. When a cell undergoes meiosis more than one cell division occurs. First the cell divides. Then each of the two resulting cells divides giving rise to four germ cells in all. Thus each cell undergoing meiosis produces four germ cells. In males all four germ cells typically become functional sperm; however, in females typically only one of the four cells becomes an egg capable of developing into an individual. The other three cells, known as *polar bodies*, do not produce mature eggs.

In a cell about to undergo meiosis, the two members of a chromosome pair become closely associated. Each member of a pair is seen to have a structure known as the *centromere*. In the diagram below the centromeres are shown as circles near the middle of each chromosome.

Prior to cell division, each chromosome *splits* into two *chromatids*. The centromere, however, does not split. Thus the two chromatids derived from the same chromosome remain attached by the undivided centromere. The two chromatids so-attached can be called *sister chromatids*. Sister chromatids presumably contain the same DNA sequences and hence the same genetic information.

Chromatids are often seen to be intertwined, as in the diagram below. Here the two dark chromatids are sisters. So also are the two light chromatids.

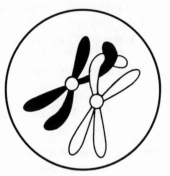

A result associated with this intertwining is the breakage and rejoining of *nonsister* chromatids. In the diagram below breakage and rejoining have occurred. This is the phenomenon referred to as *crossing over*.

Suppose breakage and rejoining have occurred as in the above diagram. Then, after the meiotic cell divisions, the following germ cells are produced:

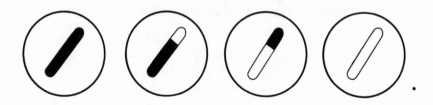

(Note that in females only one of these would be a functional egg.)

Important points to note are that if crossing over occurs it does so prior to any meiotic cell division, and that only two nonsister chromatids are affected by each crossover. Thus a single crossover affects only half of the four cells. More than one crossover may occur and all the chromatids may be affected; but each crossover affects only two of the four germ cells.

Consider an individual of genotype CcEe like the one for which crossing over has been illustrated (individual I). Here the CE genes are on the same chromosome. We model the situation where only one crossover occurs.

In the sample space

$$\{A, \quad B \quad \},$$
$$p, 1 - p$$

the simple event A denotes that a crossover occurs between genes C and E. Correspondingly, B denotes that no such crossover occurs. The probability that a crossover does occur is $p$.

Given that a crossover occurs between genes C and E then four types of germ cells are produced. *Here we model the situation where any one of these types is as likely to mature and produce an offspring as any other.* The sample space then is

$$\{CE, Ce, cE, ce\}.$$
$$\tfrac{1}{4}, \tfrac{1}{4}, \tfrac{1}{4}, \tfrac{1}{4}$$

The probabilities on this space represent conditional *probabilities given a crossover.* If no crossover occurs then only two types can be produced. Here we use the model

$$\{CE, ce\}.$$
$$\tfrac{1}{2}, \tfrac{1}{2}$$

The probabilities on this space represent probabilities given that no crossover occurs.

A combined sample space for the production of mature germ cells is readily determined using a tree diagram. In this combined space each simple event describes the genes of a germ cell which reaches maturity. A simple event also indicates the occurrence or nonoccurrence of crossing over. Thus the simple event A(ce) means that a germ cell which matures has genes c and e and that crossing over occurred. The probability of this simple event is $\tfrac{1}{4}p$.

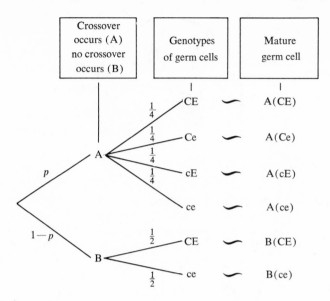

The event "the germ cell has genes CE" is

$$\{A(CE), \ B(CE)\}$$
$$\tfrac{1}{4}p \quad , \tfrac{1}{2} - \tfrac{1}{2}p$$

and has probability $\tfrac{1}{2} - \tfrac{1}{4}p$. The event "a germ cell shows the effects of crossing over" is

$$\{A(Ce), \ A(cE)\}$$
$$\tfrac{1}{4}p \quad , \quad \tfrac{1}{4}p$$

and has probability $\tfrac{1}{2}p$. The probability that a germ cell shows the effects of crossing over is half the probability that a crossover occurs.

To model germ cell production of this individual we can use the slightly simpler sample space below:

$$\{ \ CE \ , Ce, cE, \quad ce \ \}.$$
$$\tfrac{1}{2} - \tfrac{1}{4}p, \ \tfrac{1}{4}p, \ \tfrac{1}{4}p, \tfrac{1}{2} - \tfrac{1}{4}p$$

To observe crossover effects one can make a suitable mating. For example, suppose we have an individual (II) whose genotype is ccee.

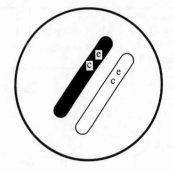

Even with crossing over this individual can only produce ce germ cells.

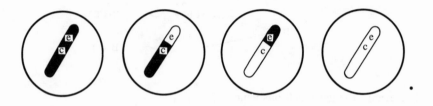

A sample space for its germ cell production is

$$\{ce\}_1.$$

A mating of individual II with individual I can be modeled as two independent experiments using the tree diagram:

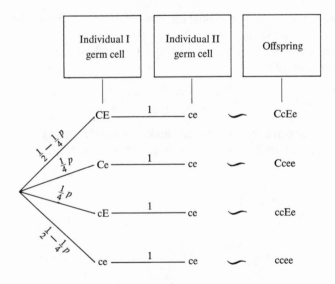

The event that an offspring exhibits crossing over is

$$\frac{\{Ccee,\ ccEe\}}{\frac{1}{4}p\ ,\ \frac{1}{4}p},$$

and the probability of observing the crossover effects in the offspring is $\frac{1}{2}p$, one half the crossover probability.

### Mapping Genes on Chromosomes

Information on frequencies of crossover classes can provide a means of mapping the relative locations of genes on chromosomes.

Suppose three genes D, G, R are linked. Each gene is some nucleotide sequence in some portion of a long DNA molecule. Let us construct the following simple model. Between and within each gene a number of some kind of chemical bonds[8] are found. We diagram the DNA in the chromosome indicating bonds as X's (the numbers of bonds are for illustration not realism).

. . . X X X X X X X X X X X X X X X X X X X X X X X X X X X X X X X X X X X X X . . .

       D               G             R

In this particular diagram we have arbitrarily shown 6 bonds between D and G, 9 bonds between G and R, and 18 bonds between D and R.

We again work with a *single crossover model*. Suppose that the probability of a crossover occurring is $p$, and that there are $N$ bonds susceptible of breakage. We do not need to estimate $p$ nor capital $N$. Given that a crossover occurs, suppose that any bond is as likely to be the site of crossover as any other. Thus the conditional probability of crossover at any particular bond is $1/N$.

We can let A denote that a crossover takes place, $P(A) = p$. Similarly, we can let B denote that no crossover occurs, $P(B) = 1 - p$. There are $N$ different bonds at which a crossover might occur. Given that a crossover does occur each of these bonds has probability $1/N$ of being the site of breakage. The $N$ bonds are denoted by $1, 2, \ldots, N$, respectively.

---

[8] The nature and kind of bonds is purposely left vague. The bonds need not be those between individual nucleotides. Perhaps the bonds occur only between certain groups of nucleotides. Whatever the case a large number of breakable bonds occur.

We have the tree diagram.

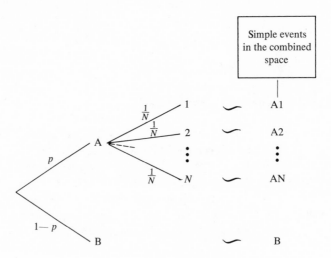

In the combined sample space the event A2 means that a crossover occurred at bond number 2.

Let DG be the event "a crossover occurs somewhere between D and G." Similarly, define the events DG and GR. There are six bonds between genes D and G, and the event DG contains 6 simple events. Its probability is accordingly

$$P(DG) = 6p/N.$$

Similarly,

$$P(DR) = 18p/N, \qquad P(GR) = 9p/N.$$

We do not know $N$, thus we do not know these probabilities. However, we do know the odds of these events under the model:

$$DG : DR : GR$$
$$6 : 18 : 9$$

or

$$2 : 6 : 3 \ .$$

Suppose we examine many offspring. For every two crossovers between genes D and G we should find about six between genes D and R and about three between G and R. In the model presented the crossover probability is proportional to the number of breakable bonds between the two genes. However, DNA may be spiraled and twisted along the length of the chromosome. As a result it may or may not be that chromosome segments of similar length contain the same numbers of breakable bonds. To the extent that they do, the probability of breaking within a segment would increase proportionally with its length. Thus crossover probabilities give indications of the relative distances separating genes in chromosomes. With suitably designed experiments, odds of crossovers between various pairs of genes can be estimated. The relative distances of genes in the chromosome can then be mapped. Thus in the above example, gene G must lie between genes D and R since the odds of a break between D and R are about equal to the sum of the odds of crossovers between D and G and between G and R. This method of mapping has been used with considerable success.

### EXERCISES

1. A hypothetical organism has two genes each with two forms — C and c, G and g. Suppose C (curly) is dominant to c (straight), and G (green) to g (yellow). A curly-yellow individual mates with a straight-green individual. There are 100 offspring, all curly and green. Two of these offspring mate. Their offspring are 52 curly-green; 22 curly-yellow; 26 straight-green.
   (a) Give a model which could explain these results.
   (b) Do you think the genes are on the same chromosome?

2. The problem is the same as in Exercise 1; however, suppose the results of the second mating were 72 curly-green; 23 curly-yellow; 26 straight-green; and 7 straight-yellow.
   (a) Give a model possibly explaining these results.
   (b) Do you think the genes are on the same chromosome?

3. A hypothetical organism has three genes each with two forms: H and h, L and l, M and m. H (hairy) is dominant to h (smooth); L (light) is dominant to l (dark); and M (marked) is dominant to m (unmarked). The three genes are on the same chromosome. A hairy-light male mates with a smooth-dark female. The offspring are 90 hairy-light; 9 hairy-dark; 11 smooth-light; 90 smooth-dark.
   (a) Give a model consistent with these results.
   (b) Supposing that the crossover probability were $\frac{1}{5}$, what would be the odds of the events above?

4. The problem is the same as in Exercise 3. This time a hairy-marked male mates with a smooth-unmarked female. The offspring are 5 hairy-marked; 7 hairy-unmarked; 5 smooth-marked; 3 smooth-unmarked.·
   (a) Give a model consistent with these results.
   (b) If the crossover probability were $\frac{3}{25}$, what would be the odds of the events above?

(c) Suppose that the crossover probabilities are as follows: H and L, $\frac{1}{5}$; H and M, $\frac{3}{25}$; L and M, $\frac{8}{25}$. Which gene do you think occurs between the other two.

5. A diagram of a DNA strand with chemical bonds indicated as X's is given below. (The numbers of bonds are for illustration, not realism.) There are three genes indicated.

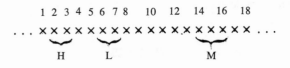

18 bonds are indicated. However, all the bonds do not have the same probability of breaking. Let $p$ be the probability that a break occurs in these 18 bonds. Given that a break occurs in these 18, the probability is $\frac{1}{2}$ that it occurs at bond 4. The probability that it occurs at any other bond is $\frac{1}{34}$. In this model:

(a) what is the probability of a break between H and L?

(b) between H and M?

(c) between L and M?

(d) what are the odds of these three events?

(e) The model in the text considered a DNA strand whose breakable bonds had equal probabilities of breaking. Suppose that the odds in part (d) were interpreted as if this model were true; namely, that each bond has probability $\frac{1}{18}$ of breaking. Would you still conclude that L lies between H and M? Would L seem to be closer to H or to M?

| PATH 4 ☛ §6.5 |

## REFERENCES

### General

KEMENY, J. G., SNELL, J. L., and THOMPSON, G. L., *Introduction to Finite Mathematics* (Englewood Cliffs, N. J.: Prentice-Hall, Inc., 1956), Ch. 1, 6.

### Optional Section 6.5

FALCONER, D. S., *Introduction to Quantitative Genetics* (New York: The Ronald Press Company, 1960).

LI, C. C., *Population Genetics* (Chicago: The University of Chicago Press, 1955).

LI, C. C., *Human Genetics* (New York: McGraw-Hill Book Company, Inc., 1961).

### Optional Sections 6.6, 6.7

ELLIOTT, A. M., *Zoology*, 3rd ed. (New York: Appleton-Century Crofts, 1963), Ch. 25.

ELLIOTT, A. M., and RAY, C., *Biology*, 2nd ed. (New York: Appleton-Century-Crofts, 1960), Ch. 30.

KING, R. C., *Genetics* (New York: Oxford University Press, 1965), Ch. 5, 9.

SRB, A. M., OWEN, R. D., and EDGAR, R. S., *General Genetics*, 2nd ed. (San Francisco: W. H. Freeman and Company), Ch. 1, 2, 3.

WATSON, J. D., *Molecular Biology of the Gene* (New York: W. A. Benjamin, Inc., 1965), Ch. 1. [Chapter 1 is very readable.]

# BINOMIAL PROBABILITIES

## 7.1 BINOMIAL PROBABILITIES

Four rivers empty into the ocean. Salmon captured, tagged, and released in one of these subsequently migrate and return in several years to breed in one of the rivers. A biologist hypothesizes that each fish chooses among the four rivers simply at random; in which case the probability of choosing the home river B is $\frac{1}{4}$. If three fish return and make their choices independently, what is the probability that two return to the home river B while one returns to another river?

We can use a tree diagram to aid in this problem. Let B indicate that river B is chosen. Let B' indicate that B is not chosen; that is, one of the other three rivers is chosen. Then we have the following tree diagram.

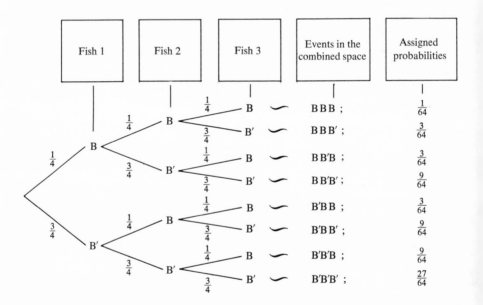

The event "exactly two fish choose the home river B" is

$$\{BBB',\ BB'B,\ B'BB\}\ .$$

$$\tfrac{3}{64}\ ,\quad \tfrac{3}{64}\ ,\quad \tfrac{3}{64}$$

Its probability is $\frac{9}{64}$. Also the event "exactly one fish chooses river B" is

$$\{BB'B',\ B'BB',\ B'B'B\}\ ,$$
$$\frac{9}{64}\ ,\quad \frac{9}{64}\ ,\quad \frac{9}{64}$$

and its probability is $\frac{27}{64}$, a much more probable event if the biologist's conjecture is true.

If $x$ denotes the number of returns to the home river, the values of $p(x)$, the probability of $x$ returns to the home river, are:

$$p(0) = \frac{27}{64};\quad p(1) = \frac{27}{64};\quad p(2) = \frac{9}{64};\quad p(3) = \frac{1}{64}.$$

These probabilities are examples of binomial probabilities, the topic of this section. Each of the above probabilities can be written in the following form:

$$p(x) = \binom{3}{x}\left(\frac{1}{4}\right)^{x}\left(\frac{3}{4}\right)^{3-x},\ x = 0, 1, 2, 3.$$

For example,

$$p(0) = \binom{3}{0}\left(\frac{1}{4}\right)^{0}\left(\frac{3}{4}\right)^{3} = \frac{27}{64},$$

and

$$p(1) = \binom{3}{1}\left(\frac{1}{4}\right)^{1}\left(\frac{3}{4}\right)^{2} = 3 \times \frac{9}{64} = \frac{27}{64}.$$

Probabilities which can be written in this form are *binomial probabilities*.

In this example we have satisfied three conditions:

(1) We have a fixed number "3" of repetitions of a dichotomous "either-or" experiment; that is, the sample space for an individual experiment has exactly two simple events

$$\{B,\ B'\}.$$

(The fish either chooses the home river B, or does not.)

(2) The probability of one alternative is the same for the three individual sample spaces:

| Fish 1 | Fish 2 | Fish 3 |
|--------|--------|--------|
| $\{B, B'\};$ | $\{B, B'\};$ | $\{B, B'\}$ |
| $\frac{1}{4}, \frac{3}{4}$ | $\frac{1}{4}, \frac{3}{4}$ | $\frac{1}{4}, \frac{3}{4}$ |

(The probability that any fish chooses the home river is $\frac{1}{4}$.)

(3) The three experiments are independent. (The fishes' choices are made independently.)

These three conditions can be stated in more general terms.

GENERAL STATEMENT.    (1) *Suppose that we have a fixed number n of repetitions of a dichotomous experiment whose sample space is*

$$\{S, F\}$$

S *for "success"*; F *for "failure"*.

(2) *Suppose that the probability of success* $P(S) = p$, *is the same for each of the n individual sample spaces*

$$\begin{array}{cccc}
\text{Experiment:} & 1 & 2 & n \\
& \{S, \quad F \}, & \{S, \quad F \},..., & \{S, \quad F \} \\
& p, 1 - p & p, 1 - p & p, 1 - p
\end{array}.$$

(3) *Finally, suppose that the n experiments are independent.*
*If these three conditions are met then the probability of exactly x successes in n experiments is a binomial probability and is given by*

$$p(x) = \binom{n}{x} p^x q^{n-x}$$

$$x = 0, 1, 2, ..., n; q = 1 - p. \tag{1}$$

Combining the *n* individual experiments, we have the tree diagram below.

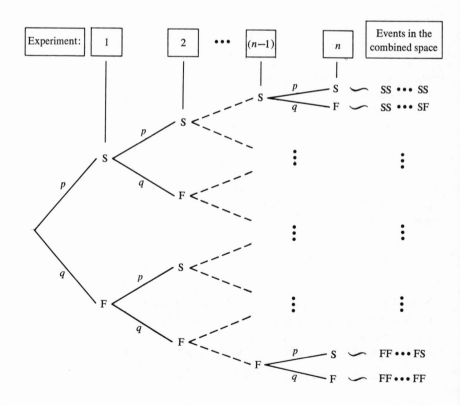

We now show that the probability of $x$ successes in $n$ experiments is given by the binomial probability in formula (1). To do this we begin by finding the probability that the first $x$ experiments are successes and the last $n - x$ experiments are failures. This event is a single path through the tree. We pass through $x$ S's and then through $(n - x)$ F's.

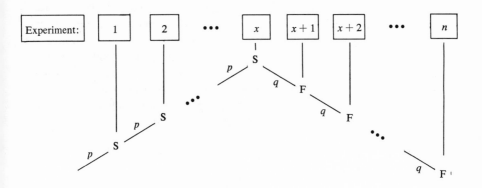

The probability associated with this path is

$$\underbrace{pp \cdots p}_{x\ p\text{'s}}\ \underbrace{qq \cdots q}_{(n-x)\ q\text{'s}} = p^x q^{n-x}.$$

This is the probability associated with the following simple event of the combined space

$$\underbrace{SS \cdots S}_{x\ S\text{'s}}\ \underbrace{FF \cdots F}_{(n-x)\ F\text{'s}}.$$

Correspondingly, if the first $(n - x)$ experiments are failures and the last $x$ experiments are successes, we have the path below.

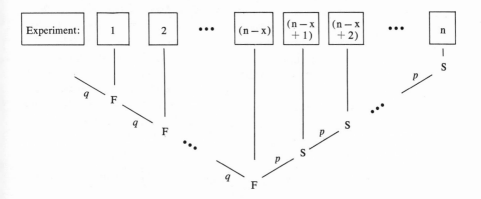

The probability associated with this path is

$$q^{n-x}p^x = p^x q^{n-x}.$$

This is the same as for the previous path. In fact *the order of the S's and F's along the path is quite immaterial.* As long as there are $x$ S's and $(n - x)$ F's then the path probability must be $p^x q^{n-x}$.

Now we can determine the probability of the event "exactly $x$ successes occur in $n$ repetitions." Any arrangement of $x$ S's and $(n - x)$ F's is a simple event in this event. Any such simple event corresponds to a tree diagram path in which there are $x$ S's and $(n - x)$ F's. The probability of any simple event in this event is the product of $x$ $p$'s and $(n - x)$ $q$'s (in some order) and must be equal to $p^x q^{n-x}$. Therefore each simple event in the event "exactly $x$ successes occur in $n$ repetitions" has the same probability $p^x q^{n-x}$. Suppose that the number of simple events in this event is $k$. Then the sum of the probabilities of the $k$ simple events is

$$p(x) = p^x q^{n-x} + p^x q^{n-x} + \dots + p^x q^{n-x}$$
$$= p^x q^{n-x}(1 + 1 + \dots + 1)$$

Since there are $k$ simple events in the event "$x$ successes occur in $n$ repetitions" there are $k$ ones in the parentheses and

$$p(x) = p^x q^{n-x}k. \tag{2}$$

Now we must determine $k$. This is the number of paths through $x$ S's and $(n - x)$ F's; and this is simply the number of permutations of $x$ S's and $(n - x)$ F's or

$$\frac{n!}{x!(n - x)!} = \binom{n}{x}.$$

Substituting this value of $k$ into formula (2) we have

$$p(x) = \binom{n}{x}p^x q^{n-x}, \quad x = 0, 1, 2, \dots, n.$$

Probabilities of this form are binomial probabilities.

*Binomial probabilities occur in a rather natural context. The notion of independent repetitions of the same (dichotomous) experiment under identical conditions is a common notion in biology. The three conditions given earlier give a precise model of this situation.* If these three conditions are met then the probability of $x$ successes in $n$ experiments is a binomial probability. Before concluding, we should note an important fact. Although conditions (1), (2), and (3) of the general statement of this section are sufficient to assure binomial probabilities, they are not necessary. Example 4 and Exercise 6 of this section show that binomial probabilities can arise even though conditions (2) and (3) fail.

Finally, the reader who is familiar with the binomial expansion should recall that

$$(p + q)^n = \binom{n}{0}p^0 q^n + \binom{n}{1}p^1 q^{n-1} + \binom{n}{2}p^2 q^{n-2} + \dots + \binom{n}{n}p^n q^0, \quad n = 0, 1, 2, \dots$$

Binomial probabilities occur as the terms in the binomial expansion of $(p + q)^n$. Since $p + q = 1$, the sum of the terms is 1.

EXAMPLE 1.  Binomial probabilities arise from the notion of independent repetitions of the same (dichotomous) experiment. Suppose four rats are given a dose of a drug. After two days the number dead is observed. We model the situation in which each rat has the same probability $p$ of dying. The four individual sample spaces are (D, dead; $L$, living)

$$\begin{array}{cccc} \text{Rat 1} & \text{Rat 2} & \text{Rat 3} & \text{Rat 4} \\ \{D, L\}, & \{D, L\}, & \{D, L\}, & \{D, L\} \\ p, 1 - p & p, 1 - p & p, 1 - p & p, 1 - p \end{array}.$$

We have four dichotomous experiments with the same probability of dying. Hence conditions (1) and (2) are met. If the four experiments are independent then condition (3) is met. Then $p(x)$ the probability that $x$ rats die is a binomial probability. Letting $q = 1 - p$ we have

$$p(4) = \binom{4}{4} p^4 = p^4; \qquad p(3) = \binom{4}{3} p^3 q = 4p^3 q;$$

$$p(2) = \binom{4}{2} p^2 q^2 = 6p^2 q^2;$$

$$p(1) = \binom{4}{1} pq^3 = 4pq^3; \qquad p(0) = \binom{4}{0} q^4 = q^4.$$

Suppose $p = \frac{1}{2}$. Then the probability that two rats die is

$$6 \times \tfrac{1}{4} \times \tfrac{1}{4} = \tfrac{6}{16} = \tfrac{3}{8}.$$

The binomial model might fail to apply for a variety of reasons. The drug may be administered in food and two of the four rats may eat more than the others and have a higher probability of dying. $P(D)$ would not be the same over the four experiments. Or an undetected infectious disease might occur in the laboratory. If one rat dies of this disease the probability that the others also die may be increased. Thus the deaths would not be independent. Both these departures from the binomial situation are readily understandable only because we have precisely stated a model for independently repeated dichotomous experiments under identical conditions.

EXAMPLE 2.  On two consecutive days an experiment is conducted in which a bee has a choice of alighting on a blue cardboard square or on a white one. The sample space for the experiment on either day is $\{B, W\}$, where B indicates that the bee lands on the blue square, while W indicates that he lands on the white square. This sample space has two simple events so that condition (1) is satisfied. Next suppose that condition (2) is satisfied;

that is, that $P(B)$ is the same for the two days

Day 1          Day 2
{B, W},         {B, W}
$p, 1 - p$       $p, 1 - p$

Finally suppose that condition (3) is satisfied; that is, that the three experiments are independent. Using conditions (1), (2), and (3) and letting $q = 1 - p$ the tree diagram must be as below.

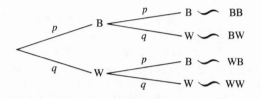

The combined sample space and its assigned probabilities are

{BB, BW, WB, WW}

$p^2$, $pq$, $pq$, $q^2$

The events "blue is chosen on the first day" and "blue is chosen on the second day" are, respectively,

$B_1 = \{BB, BW\}$,     $B_2 = \{BB, WB\}$.

Thus,

$$P(B_1) = p^2 + pq = p(p + q) = p.$$

Similarly,

$$P(B_2) = p^2 + pq = p.$$

The probabilities that blue is chosen twice, once, or no times, are, respectively,

$p(2) = p^2$;     $p(1) = 2pq$;     $p(0) = q^2$.

These are binomial probabilities.

EXAMPLE 3.   In the three parts of this example an attempt is made to illustrate the meaning of each of the three conditions given in the text. The illustration in Example 2 is continued.

(a) Suppose that the probability that the bee chooses blue on the first day is $\frac{1}{2}$. Also now suppose that whatever color is chosen on the first day, the opposite color is chosen on the second. The tree diagram is as follows.

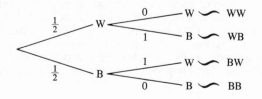

Here the combined space with its probabilities is

$$\{BB, BW, WB, WW\}$$
$$0 , \tfrac{1}{2} , \tfrac{1}{2} , 0 .$$

The events "blue is chosen on the first day" and "blue is chosen on the second day" are the same as in Example 2. We have

$$P(B_1) = 0 + \tfrac{1}{2} = \tfrac{1}{2}; \qquad P(B_2) = 0 + \tfrac{1}{2} = \tfrac{1}{2}.$$

The sample spaces for each day must then be

Day 1        Day 2
$\{B, W\}$ .   $\{B, W\}$
$\tfrac{1}{2}, \tfrac{1}{2}$ ,    $\tfrac{1}{2}, \tfrac{1}{2}$

These are dichotomous experiments with constant probabilities over the days. Hence conditions (1) and (2) are satisfied. However, the probabilities that blue is chosen twice, once, or no times, are, respectively,

$$p(2) = 0; \qquad p(1) = 1; \qquad p(0) = 0.$$

These are not binomial probabilities. A glance at the above tree diagram shows that the experiments are not independent. Thus condition (3) is not met. For example, $P(B_1 \cap B_2) = 0$ but $P(B_1) P(B_2) = \tfrac{1}{4}$.

(b) Consider the tree diagram below.

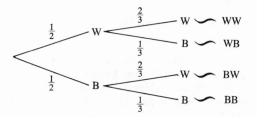

Here the experiments are independent, so that condition (3) is met. Also, there are two alternatives on each of two days so that condition (1) is met. Condition (2) is not met.

The combined sample space is

$$\{BB, BW, WB, WW\}$$
$$\tfrac{1}{6}, \tfrac{2}{6} , \tfrac{1}{6} , \tfrac{2}{6} .$$

The events $B_1$ and $B_2$ are as defined in Example 2. Here $P(B_1) = \tfrac{1}{2}$ and $P(B_2) = \tfrac{1}{3}$. The individual sample spaces must be

Day 1        Day 2
$\{B, W\}$ .   $\{B, W\}$ .
$\tfrac{1}{2}, \tfrac{1}{2}$ ,    $\tfrac{1}{3}, \tfrac{2}{3}$

The probability that the bee chooses blue is not constant. The probabilities,

$$p(2) = \tfrac{1}{6}, \qquad p(1) = \tfrac{3}{6}, \qquad p(0) = \tfrac{2}{6}$$

are not binomial probabilities. If $p(2) = p^2$ and $p(0) = q^2$ then $p(1)$ would have to be

$$p(1) = 2pq = 2\sqrt{\frac{1}{6}\frac{2}{6}} = \frac{1}{3}\sqrt{2}.$$

(c) Suppose that the bee is given a choice of three colors: blue, white, and yellow. Suppose that the sample spaces for each day are

| Day 1 | Day 2 |
|-------|-------|
| {B, W, Y} | {B, W, Y} |
| $\frac{1}{3}$, $\frac{1}{3}$, $\frac{1}{3}$ | $\frac{1}{3}$, $\frac{1}{3}$, $\frac{1}{3}$ |

If the experiments are independent then condition (3) is met. Condition (2) is met since the probability of B is constant. However, the experiments have more than two outcomes so that condition (1) is not met.

If, however, we consider the events B and B' (blue and not blue) we would have

| Day 1 | Day 2 |
|-------|-------|
| {B, B'} | {B, B'} |
| $\frac{1}{3}$, $\frac{2}{3}$ | $\frac{1}{3}$, $\frac{2}{3}$ |

Now condition (1) is met. We find the probabilities

$$p(2) = \tfrac{1}{9}, \qquad p(1) = \tfrac{4}{9}, \qquad p(0) = \tfrac{4}{9},$$

and these are binomial probabilities.

EXAMPLE 4. The three conditions given in this section are sufficient conditions to define binomial probabilities. If they are fulfilled then the probability of $x$ successes in $n$ repetitions is the binomial probability $p(x) = \binom{n}{x} p^x q^{n-x}$. However, these conditions are not *necessary*. The probability of $x$ successes in $n$ repetitions can still be $\binom{n}{x} p^x q^{n-x}$ even though the three conditions are not met. For example, consider the tree diagram below (S, success; F, failure).

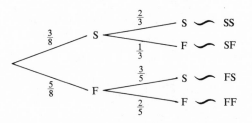

These experiments are clearly not independent. Thus condition (3) is violated. The probabilities on the sample space are

$$\{\text{SS, SF, FS, FF}\} \atop \tfrac{1}{4}, \ \tfrac{1}{8}, \ \tfrac{3}{8}, \ \tfrac{1}{4} \ .$$

The probability of a success on the first experiment is $\tfrac{1}{4} + \tfrac{1}{8} = \tfrac{3}{8}$. The probability of a success on the second experiment is $\tfrac{1}{4} + \tfrac{3}{8} = \tfrac{5}{8}$. Thus $P(\text{S})$ is not constant and condition (2) is violated. However if $x$ is the number of successes we have $p(x)$ for $x = 2, 1, 0$:

$$p(2) = \tfrac{1}{4} \qquad p(1) = \tfrac{1}{2} \qquad p(0) = \tfrac{1}{4},$$

and these are binomial probabilities with $n = 2$ and $p = \tfrac{1}{2}$. Thus binomial probabilities can arise from experiments which are not independent and which do not have the same probability of success.

### EXERCISES

1.  Six coins are flipped, each falling heads or tails. Suppose that the six flips are independent and that each coin falls heads with probability $\tfrac{1}{2}$. What is the probability that exactly 4 coins fall heads? What is the probability that 3 coins fall heads?

2.  Four coins are flipped. Each falls heads with probability $p$ and tails with probability $1 - p$. If the four flips are independent, what is the probability that exactly 2 heads occur? What is the probability that no heads occur?

3.  At each of ten gene loci a lethal gene may occur with probability $\dfrac{1}{100}$. Suppose that the occurrences at the ten loci are independent. What is the probability that no lethal genes occur? (If one or more lethal genes occur the individual never develops and dies.) What is the probability that the individual never develops? (Hint: this is the complementary event to the event no lethals occur.)

4.  Ten rats are given a dose of a drug. The number of rats dying within 24 hours is noted. Suppose that each rat has probability $\tfrac{1}{5}$ of dying and that the survival of each rat is independent of the survival of the other rats. What is the probability that eight rats die? What is the probability that all rats die?

5.  At each of $n$ gene loci, a lethal gene may occur with probability $p$. If the occurrences of the genes at the $n$ loci are independent what is the probability that the individual dies; that is, that at least one lethal gene occurs. (See the hint for Exercise 3.)

6. Consider the tree diagram below for combining two experiments. Note that $p + q = 1$, $0 < p < 1$, $0 < q < 1$, $0 < a < 1$.

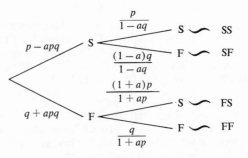

(a) Prove that the experiments are not independent.

(b) What is the probability of a success (S) in the first experiment?

(c) What is the probability of a success (S) in the second experiment?

(d) Show that the probabilities of 2, 1, and 0 successes are, respectively, $p^2$, $2pq$, $q^2$. Thus show that binomial probabilities can occur even when conditions (2) and (3) of the general statement of this section are not met.

7. Give the combined sample space and its associated probabilities for the tree diagram of Exercise 6. Set $a = 0$ and show that probabilities are those resulting from the tree below.

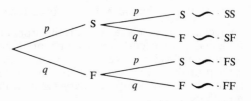

8. The sample space below is the combined space for three individual experiments. (For example, the event SFS means a success occurred on the first experiment, a failure on the second, and a success on the third.)

$$\{SSS, SSF, SFS, FSS, FFS, FSF, SFF, FFF\}$$
$$p^3, \quad 2p^2q, \quad 0, \quad p^2q, \quad 2pq^2, \quad 0, \quad pq^2, \quad q^3$$

(a) Show that the probabilities of 3, 2, 1, and 0 successes are binomial probabilities.

(b) Prove that the three experiments are not independent.

(c) What is the probability of a success in the third experiment given that exactly one success occurs?

9. The sample space below, like that of Exercise 7, is the combined space for three individual experiments.

{SSS, SSF, SFS, FSS, FFS, FSF, SFF, FFF}

$$p^3, \quad p^2q, \quad p^2q, \quad p^2q, \quad pq^2, \quad pq^2, \quad pq^2, \quad q^3$$

(a) Show that the probabilities of 3, 2, 1, and 0 successes are binomial probabilities.

(b) Prove that the probability of a success (S) on any experiment is $p$.

(Hint): Use the fact that $p + q = 1$.

(c) Construct the tree diagram for the three experiments.

(Hint: Determine conditional probabilities. Thus if S is the event "success in the first experiment" and similarly for $S_2$, show that $P(S_2 \mid S_1) = p$, etc.)

(d) From the tree diagram determine whether the three experiments are independent.

10. A bee is given a choice of landing on two colored squares — 1 blue, 1 yellow. The blue square is coated with insecticide. If the bee lands on the blue square it dies. If it lands on the yellow square it lives. If it survives the first day's test, then on the second day it is again given a choice of landing on the two colored squares.

(a) Let the probability that the bee chooses blue on the first day be $p$. Suppose also that the probability that the bee chooses blue on the second day, given that he chose yellow on the first day, is also $p$. Draw a tree diagram for the two experiments (first day and second day).

(b) Are the experiments independent? What is the probability that the bee chooses blue on the first day? What is the (unconditional) probability that the bee chooses blue on the second day? What is the probability that the bee chooses blue on both days?

11. A monkey is trained to touch one of two levers upon command. Suppose the command is given 10 times. Suppose also that each time he hears the command, he has probability $\frac{3}{5}$ of touching the correct lever. If his responses to the ten commands are independent, what is the probability that he touches the correct lever either 5 or 6 times?

12. Using the conditions of Exercise 4, determine the probability of more than two deaths occurring. (Hint: This event is the complement of the event "0, 1, or 2 deaths occur".)

PATH 5 ☞ §7.2

## 7.2  BINOMIAL AND HYPERGEOMETRIC PROBABILITIES, SAMPLING WITH AND WITHOUT REPLACEMENT

A box contains $r$ red balls and $b$ black balls. There are $N$ balls in the box, and $r + b = N$. In this section and the next we consider the two sampling schemes below:

*Sampling with replacement.* A ball is drawn from the box, and its color observed. It is then replaced in the box. Another ball is drawn, its color observed, and replaced in the box. This is continued for some fixed number of drawings. This process is called sampling with replacement. A result of this procedure is that before any drawing there are always $r$ red balls and $b$ black balls in the box. A characteristic of this procedure is that the same ball can be picked more than once.

*Sampling without replacement.* A ball is drawn from the box and its color observed. It is not replaced in the box, and is discarded. Another ball is drawn, its color observed, and likewise discarded. As a result of this procedure $N - n$ balls remain in the box after $n$ drawings. This process, which continues for some fixed number of drawings, is called sampling without replacement. It is characterized by the fact that the same ball cannot be picked more than once.

In this section, we consider the probability of selecting $x$ red balls when drawing $n$ balls from a box containing $r$ red balls and $b$ black balls ($r + b = N$). If we assume simple random sampling, (Section 4.3) we can show that sampling *with replacement* we obtain *binomial probabilities*. We have already shown in Section 4.4 that when *sampling without replacement* the probabilities obtained are *hypergeometric probabilities*.

Sampling with replacement can be modeled as follows. Before any drawing there are always $r$ red balls and $b$ black balls in the box. Each time we choose a ball simply at random from the box the sample space is

$$\{\text{red}_1, \text{red}_2, \dots, \text{red}_r, \text{black}_1, \text{black}_2, \dots, \text{black}_b\}.$$
$$\frac{1}{N}, \frac{1}{N}, \dots, \frac{1}{N}, \frac{1}{N}, \frac{1}{N}, \dots, \frac{1}{N}$$

The event R "a red ball is chosen" contains $r$ simple events and its probability is thus $r/N$. The event B "a black ball is chosen" contains $b$ simple events and its probability is $b/N$. Note that

$$\frac{r}{N} + \frac{b}{N} = \frac{N}{N} = 1.$$

A tree diagram for three drawings with replacement is given. R indicates "a red ball is chosen"; B "a black ball is chosen."

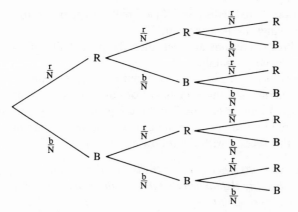

From the tree diagram it can be seen that there is a fixed number 3 of dichoto-mous experiments. This satisfies condition (1) for binomial probabilities (*cf.* Section 7.1). Secondly in any column of the tree diagram there are identical clusters (*cf.* Section 6.4); that is, R and B have the same conditional probabilities no matter what balls have been drawn previously. Hence the experiments are independent and condition (3) of Section 7.1 is satisfied. Finally, the conditional probability of a red ball R on any experiment is $r/N$. Since the experiments are independent, the unconditional probability of R on that trial is also $r/N$. The individual sample spaces for the three drawings must be

| Drawing: | 1 | 2 | 3 |
|---|---|---|---|
| | $\{R, B\}$ | $\{R, B\}$ | $\{R, B\}$ |
| | $\dfrac{r}{N}, \dfrac{b}{N}$ | $\dfrac{r}{N}, \dfrac{b}{N}$ | $\dfrac{r}{N}, \dfrac{b}{N}$ |

Thus condition (2) of Section 7.1 is also satisfied.

Since the three conditions are met we know from Section 7.1 that the pro-bability of the event "$x$ of the three balls are red" is the binomial probability:

$$p(x) = \binom{3}{x}\left(\frac{r}{N}\right)^x \left(\frac{b}{N}\right)^{3-x}, \qquad x = 0, 1, 2, 3.$$

There is nothing special about the case of three drawings. If we pick $n$ balls, the three conditions are still fulfilled. We summarize the three conditions met as follows:

(1) There is a fixed number $n$ of dichotomous experiments — $\{R, B\}$.

(2) The probability of R is the same for all individual experiments:

| Experiment: | 1 | 2 | $n$ |
|---|---|---|---|
| | $\{R, B\}$ | $\{R, B\}$ | $\{R, B\}$ |
| | $\dfrac{r}{N}, \dfrac{b}{N}$ | $\dfrac{r}{N}, \dfrac{b}{N}$ ; .... ; | $\dfrac{r}{N}, \dfrac{b}{N}$ |

(There are always $r$ red balls and $b$ black balls in the box prior to a drawing.)

(3) The drawings are independent.

Since the three conditions are met, then the probability of "$x$ successes in $n$ trials" is a binomial probability.

The notions of sampling with and without replacement can be stated in terms much more general than those of boxes of colored balls. Suppose we have a population of $N$ things, $r$ of type 1 and the remaining $N - r$ not of type 1. We take a simple random sample of $n$ things from the population of $N$ things. We can conclude this section with the following statements.

GENERAL STATEMENT (1).    *If the sampling is without replacement then the probability that exactly $x$ things in the sample are of type* 1 *is a hypergeometric probability*

$$p(x) = \frac{\binom{r}{x}\binom{N-r}{n-x}}{\binom{N}{n}}, n \leq N, x = 0, 1,...,n .$$

GENERAL STATEMENT (2).    *If the sampling is with replacement then the probability that exactly $x$ things in the sample are of type* 1 *is a binomial probability*

$$p(x) = \binom{n}{x} p^x q^{n-x}, x = 0, 1,...,n.$$

EXAMPLE 1.    A tree diagram leading to hypergeometric probabilities is given in Example 1 of Section 6.2. The preceding Section 7.1 contains ample illustrations of trees leading to binomial probabilities.

## EXERCISES

1.    A box contains two red and four green balls. A simple random sample of two balls is taken. What is the probability of no green balls in the sample
(a) if the sample is with replacement?  (b) if the sample is without replacement?

2.    A committee of four persons is to be chosen from six botanists and two zoologists. If the persons are chosen simply at random, what is the probability that no zoologists serve on the committee?

3.    A shipment of two dozen rats arrives at a laboratory. Males and females are mixed together. There are six males in the shipment. An investigator needs three rats for an experiment in which males or females can be used. If he picks three rats simply at random with-

out replacement what is the probability that three males are chosen?

4. There are six female rats. An investigator needs a blood sample from a rat. He chooses one simply at random, takes the blood sample, and then returns the rat to its cage. The next day, needing another sample, he again chooses a rat simply at random, takes the blood sample, and returns the rat. Suppose he follows this procedure on four consecutive days, and that his choice is independently made from day to day. If one of the rats is a host for a blood parasite, what is the probability that none of the four blood samples is from this rat?

5. A species of bird is near extinction. There remain only ten females and six males. While the birds are migrating to the site where they spend the winter, a storm crosses their path and seven birds are killed. If the storm kills the birds simply at random, what is the probability that all six males are killed?
Is the storm sampling with or without replacement?

6. A box contains four red and three green balls. One ball is drawn simply at random and replaced. Then, independently, two balls are drawn simply at random without replacement. What is the probability that exactly two of the three balls drawn are red? (Hint: Use a tree diagram.)

| PATH 5 ☞ §4.7, 4.8, 7.3 |

## 7.3★ APPLICATIONS OF BINOMIAL PROBABILITIES: POLLEN ANALYSIS AND VEGETATION CHANGES, BINOMIAL PROBABILITIES CAN APPROXIMATE HYPERGEOMETRIC PROBABILITIES

Paleoecology is the science of environments of the past. Changes in climate have had major effects on the evolution of entire animal and plant groups. Dramatic changes have occurred in the Pleistocene Epoch, which covers approximately the last 2,000,000 years of the earth's history. During this time there have been four major periods of glaciation. In North America, masses of ice covered large areas in Canada and the United States. Just south of the major ice masses cold climates prevailed. The last major glaciation, the Wisconsin Glaciation, reached its period of maximum glacial advance perhaps 24,000 years ago.

Concomitant with the changes in climate, striking changes occurred in the vegetation covering much of North America. An important method for studying these past vegetation changes is the study of fossil pollen grains. In many kinds of plants, the male germ cells, or pollen, are borne by the wind to their resting place on the female portion of the flower and fertilization occurs. In such wind-pollinated species, the vast majority of pollen grains fall like dust, wasted, to the surface of the earth. Many of the grains land on soil where their hard outer covering is oxidized and disintegration occurs. Others, however, fall into lakes or bogs and become part of accumulating lake mud or sediment. The outer coat of pollen grains is largely indestructible, except when oxidized. Thus the grains which accumulate in lake sediments in an environment where there is little or no oxygen become well-preserved fossils. Through time, as sediments are deposited at the bottom of a lake, a record of the pollen which fell is also accumulated.

The pollen of many kinds of plants can be recognized, although it is often not possible to identify the exact species of plant from the pollen grain alone. It is easy, for example, to distinguish a pine pollen grain (genus *Pinus*) from an oak pollen grain (genus *Quercus*) although it is extremely difficult to distinguish among the various species of pines on the basis of their pollen. Nevertheless sufficient pollen types can often be determined to enable one to infer the type of vegetation which grew in the vicinity of the lake. As the vegetation surrounding the lake changed, so also did the "pollen rain" which was deposited. For example, if pine forest surrounded the lake at a given time, the sediment deposited at that time would contain mostly pine pollen.

Suppose that pollen contained in some layer of sediment was contributed by vegetation growing 10,000 years ago. Then, barring disturbance of the layers, pollen found in the underlying layers was deposited earlier than 10,000 years ago. By analyzing the changes in proportions of the various kinds of pollen through various layers of sediments, one can, hopefully, reconstruct the sequence of past vegetation changes in the vicinity of the lake. These changes are strong indicators of the kinds of climatic change which occurred in the area.

On occasion, it may be practical to use the proportion of pine pollen as a rough indicator of the changes which occurred. In other cases the proportion of tree pollen (where pollen of arboreal species is grouped as a single category) may be useful. In most situations, however, the pollen analyst uses as detailed identifications as possible and considers all proportions simultaneously.

Pollen analysts use *sampling without replacement*. For example, a small bit of lake mud may be collected at a given depth. Pollen is extracted from the mud and a microscope slide prepared. The pollen analyst may then count some fixed number of pollen grains (say 200). For illustration, let us say that each grain is identified as "pine" or "not pine." A grain, once counted, is not counted again. Thus, the sampling is without replacement. The proportion of pine grains in the sample is used as an estimate of the proportion of pine grains in the sediment from which the mud was taken.

Suppose a pollen analyst counts a sample of $n$ grains from a layer of sediment containing $N$ pollen grains, $r$ pine grains and $N - r$ nonpine grains. The sample space for the number of pine grains observed is

$$\{0, 1, 2, ..., x, ..., n\}.$$

The pollen analyst samples *without replacement*, and if we use a *simple random sampling* model then the probabilities that exactly 0, 1, 2, etc., of the $n$ grains are pine are hypergeometric probabilities or

$$p(x) = \frac{\binom{r}{x}\binom{N-r}{n-x}}{\binom{N}{n}}, x = 0, 1, ..., n.$$

However pollen analysts rarely use the hypergeometric model in analyzing their counts. Instead they commonly use the binomial probability model, even though the sampling is without replacement. The justification for using the binomial model is the subject of this section.

Before giving a detailed argument, we can rapidly indicate the general nature of the justification. Suppose the number of pollen grains $N$ in a layer of sediment is large, say $N = 10^{12} = 1,000,000,000,000$. Suppose that 0.25 of these (or $r = 250,000,000,000$) are pine and the remaining 750,000,000,000 are nonpine. Suppose we take a simple random sample of 200 grains without replacement. Even if all 200 grains are pine, there remain 249,999,999,800 pine grains in the remaining population of 999,999,999,800 grains. Thus even with the 200 grains removed the proportion of pine grains is

$$\frac{249,999,999,800}{999,999,999,800} = 0.2499999998.$$

This is extremely close to the starting proportion of 0.25. In other words, for practical purposes, the proportion remains the same, even though 200 grains have been taken from the population. But since the proportion is effectively constant during the determination of each of the 200 grains we come *close* to meeting the conditions for binomial probabilities.

(1) There is a fixed number (200) of repetitions of a dichotomous experiment ("a grain is pine or not pine").
(2) The probability of pine is *almost* constant over the repetitions.
(3) In any column of the tree diagram for this experiment, "pine" and "not pine" have *almost* the same probabilities no matter what the previous outcomes were, hence the experiments are *almost* independent.

Suppose one samples without replacement. If the sample is small enough and the population is large enough so that the probability of pine remains almost constant, then the *with replacement model* gives approximately the same probabilities as the *without replacement* model. In other words, binomial probabilities approximate hypergeometric probabilities.

We now show this. The proof uses the definition of odds ratios (Section 5.1) and is in two parts. In the first part we define "successive odds ratios" and show that successive odds ratios uniquely determine probabilities. In the second part we show that successive odds ratios for binomial probabilities can approximate those for hypergeometric probabilities.

**Part 1**

The presentation is in general terms; however, we can readily think of the simple event $\{x\}$, in the sample space which follows, as the number of pine grains noted in counting a total of $n$ pollen grains. Consider the sample space

$$S = \{0, 1, 2, ..., x - 1, x, ..., n\}$$

in which we assume that no simple event has a probability of zero. (Recall from Section 5.1 that we defined the odds ratio of event A to event B only if both $P(A) \neq 0$ and $P(B) \neq 0$.) Consider the odds ratio of the event $\{1\}$ to $\{0\}$. This is,

$$\frac{p(1)}{p(0)}.$$

In a similar manner consider the odds ratio of the event $\{x\}$ to the event $\{x - 1\}$; this is,

$$\frac{p(x)}{p(x - 1)}.$$

Such odds ratios are called *successive odds ratios*. Suppose that we have the following successive odds ratios for the sample space S:

$$a = \frac{p(1)}{p(0)}; b = \frac{p(2)}{p(1)}; c = \frac{p(3)}{p(2)}; ... , m = \frac{p(x)}{p(x - 1)}; ... , w = \frac{p(n)}{p(n - 1)}.$$

We now show that these successive odds ratios uniquely determine the probabilities of the simple events of S. In other words they uniquely determine

$$p(0), p(1), p(2), ..., p(x), ..., p(n).$$

First, we use the successive odds ratios to determine all odds relative to $p(0)$. In other words we find

$$\frac{p(0)}{p(0)}, \frac{p(1)}{p(0)}, \frac{p(2)}{p(0)}, ... , \frac{p(x)}{p(0)}, ... , \frac{p(n)}{p(0)}.$$

These are, respectively, the odds of each simple event in S to the simple event $\{0\}$. We know that

$$p(0)/p(0) = 1, \qquad p(1)/p(0) = a.$$

To determine $P(2)/p(0)$ we can use the relation

$$\frac{p(2)}{p(0)} = \frac{p(1)}{p(0)} \times \frac{p(2)}{p(1)} \qquad \text{or} \qquad \frac{p(2)}{p(0)} = a \times b = ab.$$

Using this result and $p(3)/p(2)$ we have

$$\frac{p(3)}{p(0)} = \frac{p(2)}{p(0)} \times \frac{p(3)}{p(2)} = ab \times c = abc.$$

Continuing in this manner we can determine all the odds ratios relative to the simple event $\{0\}$. We find that

$$\frac{p(0)}{p(0)} = 1; \quad \frac{p(1)}{p(0)} = a; \quad \frac{p(2)}{p(0)} = ab; \quad \frac{p(3)}{p(0)} = abc;...;$$

$$\frac{p(x)}{p(0)} = abc...m;...; \quad \frac{p(n)}{p(0)} = abc...w.$$

These are the relative odds

$$1 : a : ab : abc : ... : abc...m : abc...m...w.$$

As in Section 5.1 we can use these relative odds to determine the probabilities of the simple events. We use the fact that

$$\frac{[p(x)/p(0)]}{1 + [p(1)/p(0)] + [p(2)/p(0)] + ... + [p(n)/p(0)]}$$

$$= \frac{[p(x)/p(0)]}{[1/p(0)][p(0) + p(1) + ... + p(n)]}$$

$$= \frac{[p(x)/p(0)]}{[1/p(0)]} = p(x).$$

Thus the probability of any simple event of S can be expressed exactly in terms of the successive odds ratios $a, b, c,...w$ or

$$p(x) = \frac{abc \, ... \, m}{1 + a + ab + ... + abc \, ... \, w} \, .$$

What we have shown is summarized in the following statement.

GENERAL STATEMENT.    *Given the sample space*

$$S = \{0, \, 1, \, 2, \, ... \, , \, x - 1, \, x, \, ... \, , \, n\},$$

*and the successive odds ratios*

$$a = \frac{p(1)}{p(0)}, \, b = \frac{p(2)}{p(1)}, \, c = \frac{p(3)}{p(2)}, \, ... \, , \, m = \frac{p(x)}{p(x-1)}, \, ... \, , \, w = \frac{p(n)}{p(n-1)},$$

*then the probabilities of the simple events of S, $p(0), p(1) ... , p(n)$, are uniquely determined, and in fact*

$$p(x) = \frac{abc...m}{1 + a + ab + abc + ... + abc...w} \, ,$$

*where it is understood that if $x = 0$ then*

$$p(0) = \frac{1}{1 + a + ab + abc + ... + abc...w} \, .$$

It follows immediately that if the two sample spaces $S_1 = \{0, 1,...,x,...,n\}$ and $S_2 = \{0, 1,...,x,...,n\}$ have the same successive odds ratios $a, b,...,w$, then they must have the same assigned probabilities $p(0), p(1),...,p(n)$.

EXAMPLE 1.   Given the sample space $\{0, 1, 2, 3\}$ and the odds ratios

$$a = \frac{p(1)}{p(0)} = 3, \qquad b = \frac{p(2)}{p(1)} = 1, \qquad c = \frac{p(3)}{p(2)} = \frac{1}{3}.$$

Determine the probabilities $p(0)$, $p(1)$, and $p(3)$. We have

$$p(0) = \frac{1}{1 + a + ab + abc} = \frac{1}{1 + 3 + 3 + 1} = \frac{1}{8};$$

$$p(1) = \frac{a}{1 + a + ab + abc} = \frac{3}{1 + 3 + 3 + 1} = \frac{3}{8};$$

$$p(2) = \frac{3 \times 1}{1 + 3 + 3 + 1} = \frac{3}{8};$$

$$p(3) = \frac{3 \times 1 \times \frac{1}{3}}{1 + 3 + 3 + 1} = \frac{1}{8}.$$

**Part 2**

We now find the successive odds ratios for binomial and hypergeometric probabilities. We first consider binomial probabilities

$$p(x) = \binom{n}{x} p^x q^{n-x}, \, x = 0, 1, ..., n.$$

Then,

$$\frac{p(1)}{p(0)} = \frac{\binom{n}{1} p^1 q^{n-1}}{\binom{n}{0} p^0 q^n} = \frac{npq^{n-1}}{q^n} = \frac{n\,p}{q},$$

and also

$$\frac{p(2)}{p(1)} = \frac{\binom{n}{2} p^2 q^{n-2}}{\binom{n}{1} p^1 q^{n-1}} = \frac{\dfrac{n(n-1)}{2}}{n} \frac{p}{q} = \frac{n-1}{2} \frac{p}{q}.$$

Generally,

$$\frac{p(x)}{p(x-1)} = \frac{\binom{n}{x} p^x q^{n-x}}{\binom{n}{x-1} p^{x-1} q^{n-x+1}} = \frac{\dfrac{n!}{x!(n-x)!}}{\dfrac{n!}{(x-1)!(n-x+1)!}} \frac{p}{q},$$

or

$$\frac{p(x)}{p(x-1)} = \frac{n-x+1}{x} \frac{p}{q}, \, x = 1, ..., n.$$

This gives the successive odds ratios for binomial probabilities.

Next we determine the successive odds ratios for hypergeometric probabilities. We suppose that $n$, the sample size, is less than $r$ and also is less than $N - r$. This assures us, for example, that all $n$ pollen grains in the sample may be pine; that is, that $p(n) > 0$. It also assures us that $p(0) > 0$, that is that none of the $n$ grains may be pine grains. In terms of the sample space $\{0, 1, ..., n\}$ it assures us that no simple event has a probability of zero. In the crucial part of the argument to follow $N$ and $r$ are both chosen large relative to $n$ so that there is no loss of generality from this condition which assures that the successive odds ratios are defined.

The successive odds ratios for hypergeometric probabilities are

$$\frac{p(x)}{p(x-1)} = \frac{\dfrac{\dbinom{r}{x}\dbinom{N-r}{n-x}}{\dbinom{N}{n}}}{\dfrac{\dbinom{r}{x-1}\dbinom{N-r}{n-x+1}}{\dbinom{N}{n}}}, x = 1, ..., n.$$

This becomes

$$\frac{p(x)}{p(x-1)} = \frac{\dbinom{r}{x}}{\dbinom{r}{x-1}} \times \frac{\dbinom{N-r}{n-x}}{\dbinom{N-r}{n-x+1}}$$

$$= \frac{(x-1)!(r-x+1)!}{x! \quad (r-x)!} \times \frac{(n-x+1)!(N-r-n+x-1)!}{(n-x)! \quad (N-r-n+x)!}$$

$$= \frac{r-x+1}{x} \times \frac{n-x+1}{N-r-n+x}$$

$$= \frac{n-x+1}{x} \left\{ \frac{r-x+1}{N-r-n+x} \right\}, x = 1, ..., n.$$

We can write these successive odds ratios in another way. Let $r/N = p$ (the proportion of pine grains). Then $q = 1 - p = (N - r)/N$. We can write

$$\frac{p(x)}{p(x-1)} = \frac{n-x+1}{x} \left\{ \frac{(r-x+1)/N}{(N-r-n+x)/N} \right\}$$

$$= \frac{n-x+1}{x} \left\{ \frac{p - [(x-1)/N]}{q - [(n-x)/N]} \right\}, x = 1, ..., n.$$

These are the successive odds of hypergeometric probabilities.

Now consider the following. Suppose we have a fixed sample size (say $n = 200$). Suppose also that we consider a fixed proportion of pine grains in the population (say $p = \frac{1}{4}$, so that $q = \frac{3}{4}$). Then how does the odds ratio $p(10)/p(9)$ change as $N$, the population size, increases. (Note that $r$ must increase with $N$ to maintain $p = \frac{1}{4}$.)

$$\frac{p(10)}{p(9)} = \frac{(200 - 9)}{10} \left\{ \frac{\frac{1}{4} - (9/N)}{\frac{3}{4} - (190/N)} \right\}$$

$$= 19.1 \left\{ \frac{\frac{1}{4} - (9/N)}{\frac{3}{4} - (190/N)} \right\}.$$

Suppose $N = 1{,}000{,}000{,}000{,}000$. Then

$$\frac{p(10)}{p(9)} = 19.1 \left\{ \frac{\frac{1}{4} - 0.000\,000\,000\,009}{\frac{3}{4} - 0.000\,000\,000\,190} \right\}.$$

Thus

$$\frac{p(10)}{p(9)} \cong 19.1 \,[\tfrac{1}{4}/\tfrac{3}{4}] = (19.1)(\tfrac{1}{3})$$

(where the symbol $\cong$ means approximately equal). But for the binomial probability, the odds ratio $p(10)/p(9)$ is exactly equal to

$$19.1 \,[\tfrac{1}{4}/\tfrac{3}{4}] = (19.1)(\tfrac{1}{3}).$$

Hence the binomial odds ratio is very nearly the same as the hypergeometric odds ratio.

This result is quite general. For *fixed* $x$, $n$, and $p$ if we choose $N$ larger and larger, then the hypergeometric successive odds

$$\frac{p(x)}{p(x-1)} = \frac{n - x + 1}{x} \left\{ \frac{p - [(x-1)/N]}{q - [(n-x)/N]} \right\}$$

can be made arbitrarily close (by choosing $N$ sufficiently large) to the binomial successive odds

$$\frac{p(x)}{p(x-1)} = \frac{n - x + 1}{x} \frac{p}{q}.$$

Thus suppose we have two models, each with the sample space $S = \{0, 1, 2,...,n\}$. Suppose that in the first model the probabilities $p(0),...,p(n)$ are hypergeometric probabilities; in the second, they are binomial probabilities $b(0),..., b(n)$. Suppose $N$ is sufficiently large (and $n$ sufficiently small) so that the successive odds for both models are very nearly equal

$$\frac{b(x)}{b(x-1)} \cong \frac{p(x)}{p(x-1)}, \, x = 1,...,n.$$

From Part 1 of this section we know that successive odds ratios determine probabilities. In both models then

$$b(x) \cong p(x), \, x = 0, 1, \dots n.$$

Hence with the population very large and the sample size small so that $(x - 1)/N$ and $(n - x)/N$ are each small relative to $p$ and $q$, binomial probabilities are for practical purposes the same as hypergeometric probabilities.

To return to pollen, $N$ the population size is usually huge (the number $N = 10^{12}$ used earlier in this section is certainly much too small as compared to the real pollen population in many cases). For all practical purposes the binomial model suffices in many pollen applications, even though the sampling is without replacement.

This section has illustrated two important results:

(1) A mathematical result, binomial probabilities can approximate hyper-geometric probabilities.

(2) A scientific result, a model whose assumptions are patently invalid (e.g., one which assumes sampling *with* replacement when it is known that the sampling is *without* replacement) under certain conditions can nevertheless be completely satisfactory for practical purposes.

EXAMPLE 2.   In the table below are binomial probabilities ($n = 4$, $p = \frac{1}{3}$) and also hypergeometric probabilities
for various values of $N$ ($n = 4$, $r/N = \frac{1}{3}$).

| | | $p(0)$ | $p(1)$ | $p(2)$ | $p(3)$ | $p(4)$ |
|---|---|---|---|---|---|---|
| Hypergeometric probabilities for | | | | | | |
| $N$ | $r$ | | | | | |
| 12 | 4 | 0.141414 | 0.452525 | 0.339394 | 0.064646 | 0.002020 |
| 30 | 10 | 0.176793 | 0.415982 | 0.311987 | 0.087575 | 0.007663 |
| 60 | 20 | 0.187415 | 0.405221 | 0.303916 | 0.093513 | 0.009936 |
| 99 | 33 | 0.191458 | 0.401150 | 0.300863 | 0.095659 | 0.010870 |
| 999 | 333 | 0.196937 | 0.395656 | 0.296742 | 0.098468 | 0.012198 |
| 9,999 | 3,333 | 0.197472 | 0.395121 | 0.296341 | 0.098736 | 0.012331 |
| 30,000 | 10,000 | 0.197511 | 0.395081 | 0.296311 | 0.098756 | 0.012341 |
| 99,999 | 33,333 | 0.197525 | 0.395068 | 0.296301 | 0.098762 | 0.012344 |
| Binomial probabilities | | | | | | |
| | | 0.197531 | 0.395062 | 0.296296 | 0.098765 | 0.012346 |

For large values of $N$, the population size $r$, the number of pine grains, must also be large. Each population considered has $r/N = \frac{1}{3}$; that is, in each case $\frac{1}{3}$ of the grains are pine. For large values of $N$, as can be seen there is close agreement between hypergeometric and binomial probabilities.

## EXERCISES

1.  Consider the sample space $S = \{0, 1, 2, 3, 4\}$. Suppose that $p(1)/p(0) = 2$; $p(2)/p(1) = 3$; $p(3)/p(2) = 4$, $p(4)/p(3) = 5/2$. Find the probability of each simple event of S.

2.  Suppose that $S = \{0, 1, \ldots, x, \ldots, n\}$ and that $p(x)/p(x - 1) = 1$ for $x = 1, 2, \ldots, n$. Determine the probability of each simple event of S.

3.  A pollen analyst takes a sample without replacement, of 20 pollen grains from sediment containing $N$ pollen grains. Half of the $N$ grains are pine pollen. Let $p(x)$ be the probability that $x$ pine grains are in the sample. Assuming simple random sampling without replacement, calculate the odds ratio $p(20)/p(19)$ for each of the values of $N$ given below. Also calculate this odds ratio for a simple random sampling model with replacement and compare the results. (a) $N = 40$; (b) $N = 100$; (c) $N = 1000$; (d) $N = 1{,}000{,}000$.

4.  A given layer of mud contains $N$ fossil pollen grains; $\frac{1}{10}$ of the grains are pine pollen. A sample of 100 grains is taken, without replacement. If $p(x)$ is the probability of exactly $x$ pine grains in the sample, then:
    (a) determine $p(50)/p(49)$ using the binomial model;
    (b) determine $p(50)/p(49)$ using the hypergeometric model with $N = 1000$; $10{,}000$; and $100{,}000$;
    (c) let A be the event "exactly 49 pine grains occur in the sample." Let B be the event "exactly 50 pine grains occur in the sample." If there are only $N = 1000$ grains in the sediment, which of the following is a more accurate statement?

    "A is about 9 times as likely as B,"

    "A is about 17 times as likely as B."

    (d) If $N = 10{,}000$, which of the statements in part (c) is more accurate?

5.  Consider the sample space $S = \{0, 1, 2\}$ where $n = 2$. Suppose that $p(0)$, $p(1)$, and $p(2)$ are hypergeometric probabilities. If $r > 2$ and $(N - r) > 2$ show that

$$p(0) = q\left[1 - \left(\frac{N}{N - 1}\right)p\right],$$

$$p(1) = 2pq\left(\frac{N}{N - 1}\right),$$

$$p(2) = p\left[p\left(\frac{N}{N - 1}\right) - \left(\frac{1}{N - 1}\right)\right],$$

where $p = r/N$ and $q = 1 - (r/N)$.

6.  Refer to the results of Exercise 5. With a binomial probability model, the probabilities of the simple events of S can be designated:

$$b(0) = q^2, \qquad b(1) = 2pq, \qquad b(2) = p^2,$$

where $p = r/N$ and $q = 1 - (r/N)$. Let $p = \frac{1}{5}$. Calculate $b(0)$, $b(1)$, and $b(2)$. Compare these with

$p(0)$, $p(1)$, and $p(2)$ of Exercise 5, where $p = \frac{1}{5}$ and $N = 1000$. (Note $1000/999 = 1.001001$.)

7. In Exercise 5, let $p = 999/1000$, and $N = 1000$. Calculate $p(0), p(1), p(2)$, and compare these with the binomial probabilities

$$b(0) = q^2 = 0.000001,$$
$$b(1) = 2pq = 0.001998,$$
$$b(2) = p^2 = 0.998001.$$

where $p = 999/1000$.

Caution: Note that $(N - r) < 2$. What does this tell us concerning $p(0)$? Is the odds ratio $p(1)/p(0)$ defined? Suppose that $p$ remains the same $999/1000$ but that $N = 2000$. Is the odds ratio $p(1)/p(0)$ then defined? (In the limit argument used in this section, there is no loss of generality in assuming that $p(x) > 0$, for $x = 0, \ldots, n$. One can always assure this by choosing $N$ sufficiently large.)

8. Consider the sample space $S = \{0, 1, 2, \ldots, x, \ldots, n\}$. Suppose that

$$p(x) = qp^x/(1 - p^{n+1})$$

Determine the successive odds ratios $p(x)/p(x - 1)$.

9. Show that hypergeometric probabilities can be written in the form

$$p(x) = \binom{n}{x} \frac{p\left(p - \dfrac{1}{N}\right) \cdots \left(p - \dfrac{x-1}{N}\right) q\left(q - \dfrac{1}{N}\right) \cdots \left(q - \dfrac{n-x-1}{N}\right)}{1\left(1 - \dfrac{1}{N}\right) \cdots \left(1 - \dfrac{n-1}{N}\right)},$$

where $p = r/N$ and $q = (N - r)/N$. Observe that there are $x$ terms involving $p$ and $n - x$ terms involving $q$. Note that if $N$ is chosen very large relative to $n$ one has approximately $\binom{n}{x} p^x q^{n-x}$.

| PATH 5 ☞ §4.7, 4.8, 6.5 |

## REFERENCES

### General

GOLDBERG, S., *Probability An Introduction* (Englewood Cliffs, N.J.: Prentice-Hall, Inc., 1960), Ch. 5.

MOSTELLER, F., ROURKE, R. E. K., and THOMAS, G. B., *Probability with Statistical Applications* (Reading, Mass.: Addison-Wesley Publishing Company, Inc., 1961), Ch. 7.

**Optional Section 7.3**

FAEGRI, K., and IVERSON, J., *Textbook of Modern Pollen Analysis* (Copenhagen: E. Munksgaard, 1950).

MARTIN, P. S., *The Last 10,000 Years* (Tucson: The University of Arizona Press, 1963).

MOSIMANN, J. E., "Statistical Methods for the Pollen Analyst: Multinomial and Negative Multinomial Techniques," in *Handbook of Paleontological Techniques*, B. Kummel, Ed. (San Francisco: W. H. Freeman and Company, 1965).

For a full understanding of the ideas presented in Section 7.3 a mathematical definition of "limit" is essential. The reader interested in pursuing or reviewing the matter may find the following book useful. The book contains biological examples.

MCBRIEN, V. O., *Introductory Analysis* (New York: Appleton-Century-Crofts, 1961).

# ANSWERS

## CHAPTER 1

Note. A dash indicates that the answer is obvious from the exercise.

### Section 1.2

1. (a) 16; (b)

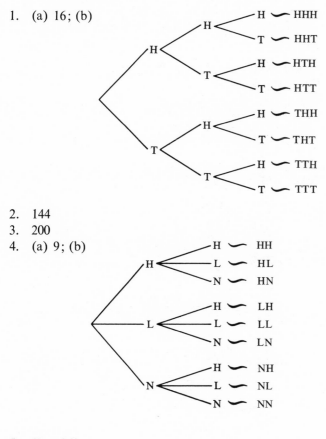

2. 144
3. 200
4. (a) 9; (b)

5. $3^5 = 243$
6. (a) $2^{10} = 1024$; (b) $2^{100}$; (c) $2^n$
7. (a) $4^8 = 65,536$; (b) $4^6 = 4096$
8. 8000

9.  (a) $20^{10} = 10,240,000,000,000$; (b) $20^5 = 3,200,000$
    (c) $20^{70}$;                              (d) $20^n$

### Section 1.3★

1.  (a) 8; (b) 8; (c) 27; (d) 64
2.  (a) $4^3 = 64$; (b) $4^5 = 1024$; (c) $4^6 = 4096$; (d) $4^{10} = 1,048,576$
3.  (a) $2^4 = 16$; (b) $2^8 = 256$
4.  (a) $2^1 = 2$; (b) $2^2 = 4$
5.  (a) $2^{10} = 1024$; (b) $2^{20} = 1,048,576$
6.  The four sperm-egg combinations are: $1-1, 1-2, 2-1, 2-2$. The fertilized eggs $1-2$ and $2-1$ are the same.
7.  (a) 16; (b) $3^2 = 9$
8.  —
9.  (a) $3^3 = 27$; (b) $3^5$; (c) $3^{10}$

### Section 1.4★

1.  (a) $4^2 = 16$; (b) —; (c) Perhaps not? $4^4 = 256$
2.  (a) $4^{12} = 16,777,216$; (b) $4^9 = 262,144$
3.  $2^6 = 64$
4.  (a) $4 \times 2^2 \times 4^9 = 4^{11} = 4,194,304$; (b) $4^{11}/4^{12} = \frac{1}{4}$
5.  (a) $4 \times 2^3 \times 2^2 \times 4^6 = 2^{19}$; (b) $2^{19}/2^{24} = \frac{1}{32}$
6.  $4^5 = 1024$
7.  (a) $2^9 = 512$; (b) $2^9/4^9 = 1/512$
8.  (a) $2^{15} = 32,768$; (b) $2^6 \times 4^3 = 2^{12} = 4096$
9.  (a) $4^{(m-1)n} \times 2^{n-1} \times 4 = 2^{2nm-n+1}$; (b) $\dfrac{1}{2^{(n-1)}}$

### CHAPTER 2

### Section 2.1

1.  (a) 6; (b)

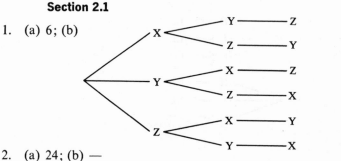

2.  (a) 24; (b) —
3.  (a) $8 \times 7 \times 6 \times 5 \times 4 \times 3 \times 2 \times 1 = 40,320$; (b) 362,880
4.  (a) 24; (b) 6; (c) 24
5.  3,628,800

6.  24
7.  (a) 6; (b) 120
8.  (a) 6; (b) 2: FDE, EFD;
    (c) 2: FED, DFE; (d) 2: EDF, DEF
9.  (a) 24; (b) 6; (c) 6

### Section 2.2

1.  (a) 40,320; (b) 24; (c) 456; (d) 0; (e) 1; (f) 3,628,800; (g) 720; (h) 4320;
    (i) 1
2.  (a) 120; (b) 2; (c) 6; (d) 360; (e) 720; (f) 25
3.  (a) 48; (b) 40,320; (c) 15; (d) 45
4.  (a) 10; (b) 1; (c) 45; (d) 252
5.  $4! = 24$                              $9! = 362,880$
    $5! = 120$                             $10! = 3,628,800$
    $6! = 720$                             $11! = 39,916,800$
    $7! = 5040$                            $12! = 479,001,600$
    $8! = 40,320$                          $13! = 6,227,020,800$
6.  (a) 24; (b) 24; (c) 720; (d) 720; (e) 5040

### Section 2.3

1.  (a) 336; (b) 56; (c) 3; (d) 6; (e) 100; (f) 970,200
2.  $10!/7! = 720$
3.  12
4.  60
5.  $7!/4! = 210$
6.  2450
7.  $10!/6! = 5040$

### Section 2.4

1.  $4!/2! = 12$
2.  (a) $4!/3! = 4$; (b)

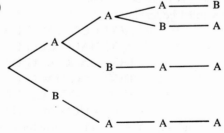

3.  (a) $7!/2! = 2520$; (b) 120
4.  $9!/6! = 504$
5.  12
6.  504

7.  $20!/19! = 20$
8.  (a) 20; (b) —;
    (c) 6, 4, 2; (d) F must be last, 4
9.  (a) $101!/100! = 101$; (b) 91; (c) 1; (d) 1

### Section 2.5

1.  (a) $6!/(2!2!) = 180$; (b) $9!/(2!2!2!) = 45,360$
2.  (a) 25,200; (b) 35; (c) 210
3.  (a) 840; (b) 7560
4.  70
5.  $27!/(10!6!2!5!4!)$
6.  252
7.  $100!/(70!5!10!12!3!)$; $100!/99! = 100$
8.  (a) 210; (b) $8!/(2!6!) = 28$; (c) $7!/(3!4!) = 35$
9.  (a) $5!/(3!2!) = 10$; (b) 5; (c) 1; (d) 10

### Section 2.6★

1.  $4^3 = 64$
2.  (a) $3! = 6$; (b) $3!/2! = 3$
3.  No, there are only $4^2 = 16$ doublets.
4.  (a) $10!/(3!3!2!2!) = 25,200$; (b) $7!/(2!2!2!) = 630$
5.  (a) $15!/(4!4!4!3!)$; (b) $11!/(3!4!3!)$
6.  (a) 8, for the succeeding triplet must start in one of two ways: UU or UC. The third letter can be any of four in either case.
    (b) No, evidence that most amino acid pairs are readily found gives strong support for a nonoverlapping code.

### Section 2.7★

1.  3, the UUA fragment must be terminal.
2.  (a) $3! = 6$, the UA must be terminal;
    (b) 60, the A must be terminal;
    (c)                    ACG UCG UACG UA
                           ACG UACG UCG UA
                           UCG UACG ACG UA
                           UCG ACG UACG UA
                           UACG ACG UCG UA
                           UACG UCG ACG UA
    The first and second sequences listed both give the observed {c, u} fragments.
3.  (a) $12!$; (b) A little over a year. The rates are 54,000/hour; 1,296,000/day and 365 days would give 473,040,000/year. The number of possible sequences is $12! = 479,001,600$. But who would read them anyway? Enumeration is not practical.

4. 5, these are not complete digest fragments, and two of the fragment permutations happen to give the same letter sequence.
5. (a) $5!/3! = 20$; (b) 4; (c) 12; (d) 24
6. (a) No, they both produce the same fragments: A, CGUA, CGUCGUA.
   (b) No, they both produce the same {C} fragments AC, GUC, GUAC, GUA and also the same {U} fragments ACGU, CGU, ACGU, A. The two sequences are examples of sequences which cannot be solved using only complete digests with enzymes cutting after specific individual letters.

## CHAPTER 3

### Section 3.1

1. (a) 3; (b) 3; (c) 3; (d) 6
2. (a) $\{1, 2, 3, 4, 5, 6, 7, 8, 9, 10, 11\}$; (b) $\{1, 3, 5, 7, 9, 11\}$; (c) $\{2, 4, 6, 8, 10\}$
3. (a) $2^3 = 8$; (b) {PPP, PPF, PFP, FPP, FFP, FPF, PFF, FFF}
4. (a) infinite; (b) finite; (c) finite; (d) finite
5. (a) $4!/3! = 4$; (b) {AAAB, AABA, ABAA, BAAA}
6. $9!/6! = 504$

### Section 3.2

1. The pair of part (a).
2. yes
3. Parts (b) and (c)
4. All of them.
5. $\{4, 5\}, \{4\}, \{5\}, \varnothing$
6. All of them.
7. There are $n$ elements, each present or absent. There are thus $2^n$ different subsets.

### Section 3.3

1. (a) $3!/(2!1!) = 3$; (b) 10; (c) 35; (d) 35; (e) $8!/(0!8!) = 1$; (f) 0; (g) 10; (h) 0; (i) 45
2. (a) $4 \times 1 = 4$; (b) 70; (c) 0; (d) 225
3. (a) $\binom{6}{2} = 15$; (b) $\binom{6}{3} = 20$; (c) $\binom{6}{7} = 0$
4. (a) $\binom{100}{4} = \dfrac{100 \times 99 \times 98 \times 97}{4 \times 3 \times 2} = 3{,}921{,}225$;
   (b) $\binom{100}{2} = 4{,}950$; (c) $\binom{100}{1} = 100$
5. $\binom{10}{3} = 120$

6. $\binom{10}{2}\binom{10}{4} = 45 \times 210 = 9450; \binom{10}{3}\binom{10}{3} = 14,400$

7. $\binom{20}{6}; \frac{\binom{10}{2}\binom{10}{4}}{\binom{20}{6}}; \frac{\binom{10}{3}\binom{10}{3}}{\binom{20}{6}}.$

8. $\binom{4}{2}\binom{3}{1}\binom{5}{1} = 6 \times 3 \times 5 = 90$

### Section 3.4

1. (a), (d)
2. Some possible sample spaces are:
   (a) {HH, HT, TH, TT}, {2, 1, 0} in which a number is the number of heads which occur.
   (b) {BCCCCC, CBCCCC, CCBCCC, CCCBCC, CCCCBC, CCCCCB}, or {e, n} in which "e" denotes that the bank swallow is on either end and "n" denotes that the bank swallow is not on the end.
   (c) {PPP, PPO, POP, OPP, OOP, OPO, POO, OOO} in which "O" is for oak and "P" for pine.
   (d) {3, 2, 1, 0} in which a number gives the number of pine grains observed.
   (e) The set of permutations of 100 M's and 1 F.
   (f) {HHH, HHT, HTH, THH, TTH, THT, HTT, TTT} or {3, 2, 1, 0} in which a number denotes the number of heads which occurs, or {3, 2, 1, 0} in which a number denotes the number of tails which occurs.
3. (a), (c)
4. (a), (c)

### Section 3.5

1. (a) {VLP, VPL}; (b) {VLP, PVL}; (c) {VPL, LPV}; (d) {VPL, LPV}; (e) {VPL}; (f) {PVL}. The events described in (c) and (d) are equal.
2. (a) {FF}; (b) {PA, PB, FA, FB}; (c) {PF, FA, FB, FC, FD}; (d) {PC, FC}; (e) {PA, PB, PC, PD, PF}
3. (a) $2^3 = 8, \binom{3}{2} = 3$; (b) $\binom{n}{r}$

### Section 3.6

1. (a) The intersection is given first, then the union:
   (i) $\varnothing$ , {a, c}
   (ii) $\varnothing$ , {a, b, c, d}
   (iii) $\varnothing$ , {a, b, c, d}
   (iv) {c} , {a, b, c, d};
   (b) the first three.
2. (a) {oo +, ooo}; (b) {ooo}; (c) {+++, +o+, o++, oo+},
   (d) {+++, +o+, ++o, +oo}; (e) {+o+, +oo}; (f) {+++}.

3. None, $A \cap B = \varnothing$; (b) None, $\varnothing$; (c) {AAF, AFA, FAA}; (d) {FAA};
   (e) {AFA, FAA}; (f) All elements of S.
4. (i) {BBTB, BTBB, TBBB}, (ii) {BBBT}, (iii) {BBTB, BTBB}, (iv) {TBBB, BBTB}
5. (ii) and (iii); yes.

6.

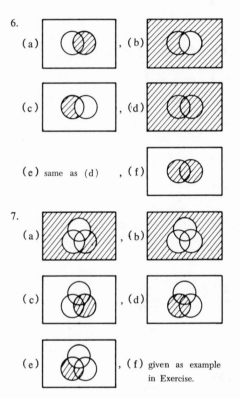

(a)      , (b)

(c)      , (d)

(e) same as (d)   , (f)

7.

(a)      , (b)

(c)      , (d)

(e)      , (f) given as example
                in Exercise.

# CHAPTER 4

## Section 4.1

1. (a) $\frac{3}{11}$;      (b) $\frac{9}{11}$;      (c) $\frac{4}{11}$;      (d) $\frac{10}{11}$;
   (e) $\frac{10}{11}$;      (f) 1;      (g) $\frac{8}{11}$;      (h) $\frac{3}{11}$
2. (a) $\frac{1}{10}$;      (b) $\frac{3}{10}$;      (c) 0
3. (a) 1;      (b) 0;      (c) $\frac{3}{5}$;      (d) $\frac{2}{5}$
4. (a) $\frac{1}{4}$;      (b) $\frac{3}{8}$;      (c) $\frac{1}{2}$;      (d) $\frac{3}{10}$
5. (a) $\frac{3}{10}$ and $\frac{1}{2}$;   (b) $\frac{7}{10}$ and $\frac{3}{10}$;   (c) $\frac{1}{5}$ and 0
6. (a) $\frac{2}{3}$;      (b) $\frac{1}{3}$;      (c) $\frac{1}{2}$;      (d) 1;
   (e) 0;      (f) $\frac{1}{3}$;      (g) 0;      (h) $\frac{2}{3}$;
   (i) 0

7.  (a) $\frac{1}{2}$;  (b) $\frac{1}{2}$;  (c) $\frac{1}{2}$;  (d) 1;
    (e) 0;  (f) $\frac{1}{4}$;  (g) 0;  (h) $\frac{3}{4}$;
    (i) 0

## Section 4.2

1.  (a) $P(A) = 0$ and $P(A') = 1$; (b) $\frac{3}{10}$ and $\frac{7}{10}$; (c) $\frac{9}{10}$ and $\frac{1}{10}$; (d) 0 and 1
2.  (a) $\frac{3}{10}$;  (b) 1;  (c) 1;  (d) $\frac{3}{10}$
3.  (a) $P(A') = \frac{2}{3}$, $P(B') = \frac{1}{3}$, $P(A \cup B) = \frac{1}{3} + \frac{2}{3} - \frac{1}{6} = \frac{5}{6}$; (b) $\frac{15}{16}$, $\frac{7}{8}$, $\frac{5}{32}$;
    (c) $0, \frac{1}{2}, 1$; (d) $0, 0, 1$; (e) $0, \frac{2}{3}, 1$
4.  (a) $\frac{2}{3}$; (b) $\frac{1}{3}$; (c) $P(A \cap B) = 0$, $P(A \cup B) = \frac{2}{3}$
5.  (a) $\frac{4}{5}$; (b) $\frac{19}{20}$
6.  —
7.  (a) 0; (b) 0; (c) $\frac{3}{10}$; (d) $\frac{7}{10}$

## Section 4.3

1.  (a) $\frac{1}{7}$; (b) $\frac{2}{7}$; (c) 1; (d) 0
2.  (a) $\frac{1}{8}$; (b) $\frac{5}{8}$; (c) 0
3.  (a) The event is {FA, FB, FC, FD, FF}. Its probability is $\frac{5}{10} = \frac{1}{2}$;
    (b) $\frac{2}{5}$; (c) $\frac{2}{5}$; (d) $\frac{3}{5}$
4.  (a) $\dfrac{91}{101}$; (b) $\dfrac{6}{101}$; (c) $\dfrac{1}{101}$
5.  (a) $\left(\dfrac{7!}{5!2!}\right) \Big/ \left(\dfrac{10!}{6!4!}\right) = \dfrac{1}{10}$; (b) $\dfrac{6}{210} = \dfrac{1}{35}$; (c) $\dfrac{1}{210}$
6.  (a) $\frac{3}{6} = \frac{1}{2}$; (b) $\frac{1}{6}$; (c) $\frac{5}{6}$
7.  (a) $\dfrac{\binom{1}{1}\binom{9}{2}}{\binom{10}{3}} = \dfrac{36}{120} = \dfrac{3}{10}$;  (b) $\dfrac{1}{15}$
8.  (a) 100; (b) $\frac{1}{100}$; (c) $\frac{12}{100}$, $\frac{88}{100}$; (d) 88
9.  (a) $\frac{1}{25}$; (b) $\frac{8}{25}$; (c) $\frac{17}{25}$; (d) 80; (e) 160
10. $\dfrac{\binom{3}{3}\binom{4}{0}}{\binom{7}{3}} = \dfrac{1}{35}$
11. $\dfrac{1}{\binom{5}{2}\binom{5}{3}} = \dfrac{1}{100}$

## Section 4.4

1.  (a) $\dfrac{\binom{4}{0}\binom{3}{2}}{\binom{7}{2}} = \dfrac{3}{21}$;  (b) $\dfrac{\binom{4}{2}\binom{3}{0}}{\binom{7}{2}} = \dfrac{6}{21}$;  (c) $\dfrac{\binom{4}{1}\binom{3}{1}}{\binom{7}{2}} = \dfrac{12}{21}$
2.  (a) $\dfrac{990}{1225}$; (b) $\dfrac{10}{1225}$; (c) $\dfrac{225}{1225}$
3.  (a) $\dfrac{\binom{5}{0}\binom{45}{3}}{\binom{50}{3}}$; (b) $\dfrac{\binom{5}{3}\binom{45}{0}}{\binom{50}{3}}$; (c) $\dfrac{\binom{5}{1}\binom{45}{2}}{\binom{50}{3}}$; (d) $\dfrac{\binom{5}{2}\binom{45}{1}}{\binom{50}{3}}$

4.  (a) $\binom{4}{2} = 6$; (b) $\{S_1S_2, S_1H_1, S_1H_2, S_2H_1, S_2H_2, H_1H_2\}$; (c) $\{H_1H_2\}$;

(d) $\{S_1H_1, S_1H_2, S_2H_1, S_2H_2\}$; (e) $\{S_1S_2\}$

5.  (a) $\frac{1}{6}, \frac{4}{6}, \frac{1}{6}$; (b) $\frac{\binom{2}{0}\binom{2}{2}}{\binom{4}{2}} = \frac{1}{6}, \frac{\binom{2}{1}\binom{2}{1}}{\binom{4}{2}} = \frac{4}{6}, \frac{\binom{2}{2}\binom{2}{0}}{\binom{4}{2}} = \frac{1}{6}$

6.  $\frac{\binom{3}{1}\binom{1}{0}}{\binom{4}{1}} = \frac{3}{4}, \frac{\binom{3}{0}\binom{1}{1}}{\binom{4}{1}} = \frac{1}{4}$

7.  (a) $\frac{\binom{10}{2}\binom{990}{18}}{\binom{1000}{20}}$; (b) $\frac{\binom{10}{0}\binom{990}{20}}{\binom{1000}{20}}$; (c) $\binom{1000}{20}$

8.  (a) $\frac{35}{120}$, (b) $\frac{63}{120}$; (c) 120, (d) 35

9.  (a) $\frac{\binom{50}{6}\binom{150}{0}}{\binom{200}{6}}$; (b) $\frac{\binom{50}{2}\binom{150}{4}}{\binom{200}{6}}$; (c) $\binom{200}{6}$

### Section 4.5

1.  $p(0) = \frac{\binom{4}{0}\binom{3}{6}}{\binom{7}{6}} = 0, p(1) = 0, p(4) = \frac{3}{7}, p(5) = 0$

2.  $\frac{1}{10}, 0, 0$

3.  $0, 0, 0$

4.  $p(150) = \binom{100}{150}\binom{1900}{50}/\binom{2000}{200} = 0, p(170) = 0, p(200) = 0$

5.  $0, \frac{3}{5}, \frac{2}{5}, 0, 0$

6.  $p(2) = 0$

7.  (a) 0; (b) 0

### Section 4.6

1.  (a) $15 + 6 = 21$; (b) $56 + 28 = 84$; (c) $2 + 1 = 3$; (d) $3 + 3 = 6$

2.  (a) $0 + 4 + 12 + 4 = 20$; (b) $0 + 2 + 2 + 0 = 4$; (c) $\frac{1}{10} + \frac{6}{10} + \frac{3}{10} + 0 = 1$

3.  (a) $6 + 45 + 60 + 15 + 0 + 0 = 126$; (b) $499,500 + 1000 = 500,500$

### Section 4.7★

1.  (a) $\binom{20}{4} = 4845$; (b) $\binom{20}{17} = 1140$

2.  (a) $\binom{9}{5} = 126$; (b) $\binom{9}{7} = 36$; (c) $\frac{35}{126} = \frac{5}{18}$; (d) $\frac{10}{36} = \frac{5}{18}$

3.  (a) Model I: $\frac{408}{4845} = \frac{24}{285}$. Model II: $\frac{96}{1140} = \frac{24}{285}$

(b) I: $\frac{\binom{17}{6}\binom{3}{-2}}{\binom{20}{4}} = 0$; II: $\frac{\binom{4}{6}\binom{16}{11}}{\binom{20}{17}} = 0$.

4.  (a) Model I: $\{S_1S_2N_1, S_1S_2N_2, N_1N_2S_1, N_1N_2S_2\}$ in which "S" stands for smoker, "N" for nonsmoker. Model II: $\{L_1L_2, L_1L_3, L_2L_3, L_1N, L_2N, L_3N\}$ in which "L" stands for lung-cancer-death and "N" for non-lung-cancer-death.

(b) $p(0) = 0, p(1) = \frac{1}{2}, p(2) = \frac{1}{2}, p(3) = 0$

5. (a) $\binom{1}{1}\binom{199}{124}$; (b) $\frac{\binom{199}{124}}{\binom{200}{125}} = \frac{125!199!}{124!200!} = \frac{125}{200}$; (c) $\frac{125}{200}$

### Section 4.8★

1. (a) $S = \frac{3}{5}, PT = \frac{2}{5}, FRF = \frac{1}{4}$; (b) $\frac{3}{5}, \frac{6}{65}, \frac{3}{62}$; (c) $\frac{3}{5}, \frac{6}{65}, \frac{3}{62}$;
   (d) $\frac{6}{7}, \frac{6}{7}, \frac{3}{4}$; (e) $\frac{1}{2}, \frac{1}{2}, \frac{1}{3}$; (f) $0, 0, 0$
2. (a) $\frac{2}{5}$; (b) No, 0; (c) $\frac{3}{5}$, yes
3. $p(0) = 0, p(1) = \frac{1}{5}, p(2) = \frac{3}{5}, p(3) = \frac{1}{5}, p(4) = 0$
4. (a) A-B: $S = 1, PT = \frac{8}{9}, FRF = \frac{4}{5}$. A-C: $\frac{1}{3}, \frac{2}{7}, \frac{1}{6}$. B-C: $\frac{2}{3}, \frac{1}{2}, \frac{1}{3}$. A and B most closely, then B and C. A and C least closely.
   (b) : (i) $\frac{1}{3}$, (ii) $\frac{1}{5}$, (iii) $\frac{1}{2}$
5. —

# CHAPTER 5

### Section 5.1

1. (a) 4: 2: 3: 1: 10; (b) 10
2. (a) 9: 11; (b) 11: 4; (c) 9:4; (d) 9:1
3. $\frac{7}{25}, \frac{6}{25}, \frac{1}{5}, \frac{4}{25}, \frac{3}{25}$
4. (a) 6:1; (b) 7:1; (c) 7:8; (d) undefined; (e) undefined; (f) undefined
5. (a) 3:1; (b) $\frac{9}{16}, \frac{3}{16}, \frac{3}{16}, \frac{1}{16}$. The odds are 3:1.
6. (a) $\frac{27}{64}, \frac{9}{64}, \frac{9}{64}, \frac{3}{64}, \frac{9}{64}, \frac{3}{64}, \frac{3}{64}, \frac{1}{64}$; (b) $\frac{13}{16}$

### Section 5.2

1. $\frac{10}{11}, 0, \frac{1}{2}, 1, \frac{5}{7}$
2. (a) $P(B|A) = \frac{2}{5}, P(A|B) = \frac{3}{16}$; (b) 1, $\frac{3}{4}$; (c) 0, 0
3. (a) $\frac{1}{30}, \frac{9}{30}$; (b) $r(1 - s)$
4. —
5. (a) The probabilities are, respectively, $\frac{9}{1000}, \frac{1}{40}, \frac{891}{1000}, \frac{3}{40}$; (b) $\frac{966}{1000}$

### Section 5.3

1. A, C, and C, D
2. (a) not independent, neither; (b) mutually and also pairwise; (c) pairwise but not mutually independent
3. The probabilities on S are, respectively, $\frac{4}{27}, \frac{4}{27}, \frac{4}{27}, \frac{2}{27}, \frac{2}{27}, \frac{2}{27}, \frac{1}{27}, \frac{8}{27}$
4. (a) yes; (b) $\frac{1}{3}, \frac{1}{3}$; (c) no
5. (a) $\frac{1}{3}, \frac{3}{5}$, greater; (b) no
6. —
7. $P(A) = 1$ or 0

## CHAPTER 6

### Section 6.1

1. (a) 3; (b) 2; (c) —
2. (a) {ADG, ADH}; (b) {ADG}; (c) none, $\varnothing$; (d) {BEK}; (e) {BEK};
   (f) {BEK, BEL, ADG, ADH}; (g) {ADG, ADH}; (h) {ACF, BEK, BEL}
3. —
4. —

### Section 6.2

1. (a) $\frac{3}{8}$; (b) $\frac{1}{8}$; (c) $\frac{1}{2}$; (d) $\frac{1}{3}$; (e) $\frac{1}{4}$; (f) $\frac{3}{8}$; (g) $\frac{1}{4}$; (h) $\frac{3}{4}$; (i) 0

2. (a)

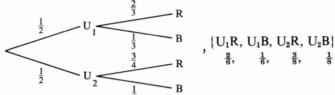

$\{U_1R, U_1B, U_2R, U_2B\}$
$\frac{2}{6}, \quad \frac{1}{6}, \quad \frac{3}{8}, \quad \frac{1}{8}$

   (b) $\frac{7}{24}$; (c) $\frac{1}{3}$
3. (a) $\frac{6}{11}$; (b) $\frac{5}{11}$
4. (a) The combined space is $\{1D, 1L, 2D, 2L\}$; (b) $\frac{2}{3}$
   $\frac{1}{4}, \quad \frac{1}{4}, \quad \frac{5}{12}, \quad \frac{1}{12}$
5. (a) $\frac{5}{8}$; (b) $\frac{1}{2}$; (c) $\frac{3}{8}$

### Section 6.3

1. (a) $\dfrac{wx}{20}$; (b) 0; (c) $\dfrac{1}{120}$
2. (a) $\frac{1}{2}$; (b) $\frac{1}{6}, \frac{2}{3}, 1$;
   (c) {ACF, ADG, ADH, ADI, BER, BES}
   $\frac{1}{3}, \quad \frac{1}{12}, \quad \frac{1}{36}, \quad \frac{1}{18}, \quad \frac{1}{4}, \quad \frac{1}{4}$
3. (a) {AHE, AHD, ATF, BTE, BTD, BTF, CHD, CTF}
   $\frac{1}{120}, \quad \frac{9}{120}, \quad \frac{3}{12}, \quad \frac{1}{9}, \quad \frac{1}{9}, \quad \frac{1}{9}, \quad \frac{3}{12}, \quad \frac{1}{12}$
   (b) —
4. (a) $\frac{1}{4}$; (b) $\frac{1}{12}$; (c) $\frac{1}{9}$; (d) $\frac{41}{120}$; (e) $\frac{1}{3}$; (f) $\frac{1}{3}$

5. (a) {SS, SG, SO, GS, GG, GC, 00}

$s^2$, $sr$, $sv$, $ru$, $rw$, $ry$, $v$

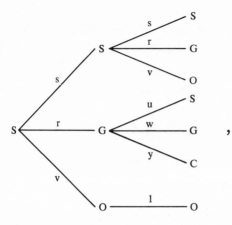

(b) $1 - vs - v = s^2 + sr + ru + rw + ry$; (c) $s^2 + sr + ru + rw$;

(d) $s$; (e) $sv$

6. $uv + ym$

7. 1

8. $s^3 + s^2r + sr + rus + r^2u + rw + ryz + ryt$

### Section 6.4

1. Yes. Clusters of a given experiment are identical.

2. (a) no; (b) yes; (c) no

3. {WWW, WWB, WBW, WBB, BWW, BWB, BBW, BBB}

     $\frac{4}{15}$,     $\frac{4}{15}$,     $\frac{2}{15}$,     $\frac{2}{15}$,     $\frac{1}{15}$,     $\frac{1}{15}$,     $\frac{1}{30}$,     $\frac{1}{30}$

4. (a) $\frac{4}{15}$; (b) $\frac{4}{15}$; (c) $\frac{7}{15}$

5. (a) $\frac{1}{8}$; (b) $\frac{3}{8}$; (c) $\frac{3}{8}$

6. "R" stands for real eggs, "W" for wooden eggs.

{RA, RB, RC, WA, WB, WC}

     $\frac{3}{14}$,     $\frac{1}{14}$,     $\frac{2}{7}$,     $\frac{1}{7}$,     $\frac{1}{7}$,     $\frac{1}{7}$

7. {RA, RB, RC, WA, WB, WC}

     $\frac{9}{40}$,     $\frac{1}{20}$,     $\frac{9}{40}$,     $\frac{9}{40}$,     $\frac{1}{20}$,     $\frac{9}{40}$

### Section 6.5★

1. When males and females have the same gene frequency: $p = p'$.

2. $p^2 + pq = p(p + q) = p$

3. —

4. —

5. {AAMS, AAMD, AAFS, AAFD} = AA

{AaMS, AaMD, AaFS, AaFD, aAMS, aAMD, aAFS, aAFD} = Aa

{aaMS, aaMD, aaFS, aaFD} = aa
{AAMS, AaMS, aAMS, aaMS} = X
{AAFS, AaFS, aAFS, aaFS} = Y
$P(X) = mu$, $P(Y) = nu$. (AA) $\cap$ X = AAMS and $P(AA|X) = pp'mu/mu$
$= pp'$. Similarly $P(Aa|X) = pq' + qp'$, and $P(aa|X) = qq'$. $P(AA|Y)$
$= pp'$, $P(Aa|Y) = pq' + qp'$, and $P(aa|Y) = qq'$.

6. A tree diagram for the four independent experiments is

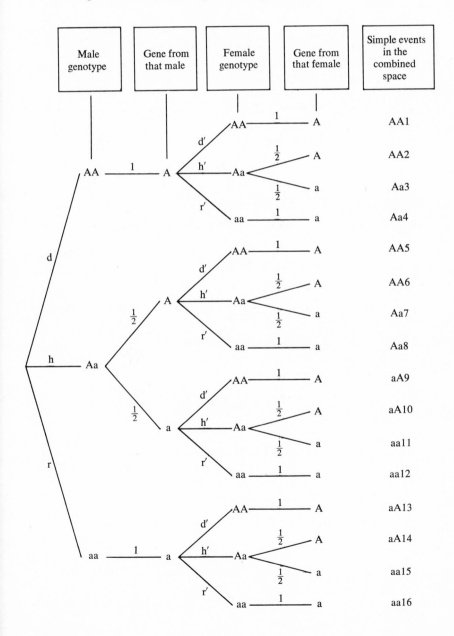

For example,
$$AA = \{AA1, AA2, AA5, AA6\}$$
and the sum of the probabilities of its simple events is
$$
\begin{aligned}
P(AA) &= dd' + \tfrac{1}{2} dh' + \tfrac{1}{2} hd' + \tfrac{1}{4} hh' \\
&= (d' + \tfrac{1}{2} h') d + (d' + \tfrac{1}{2} h') \tfrac{1}{2} h \\
&= (d + \tfrac{1}{2} h) (d' + \tfrac{1}{2} h') \\
&= pp'
\end{aligned}
$$

### Section 6.6★

1.  A model is as follows. Long wings (L) is dominant to short wings (l). The mating could be Ll × Ll. Then the sample space for the phenotype of an offspring is {D, R}. "D" for dominant, "R" for recessive
    $$\tfrac{3}{4}, \ \tfrac{1}{4}$$

2.  The mating could be ll × ll. The offspring sample space is {R}. That l is recessive is consistent with Exercise 1.

3.  The mating could be Ll × ll with sample space for the offspring:
    $$\{D, R\}$$
    $$\tfrac{1}{2}, \ \tfrac{1}{2}$$

4.  A possible model is as follows. If rough (H) is dominant to smooth (h), and if the mating is Hh × hh then the sample space would be
    $$\{D, R\}$$
    $$\tfrac{1}{2}, \ \tfrac{1}{2}$$

    The number of offspring is small. The mating might also be Hh × Hh with sample space
    $$\{D, R\}$$
    $$\tfrac{3}{4}, \ \tfrac{1}{4}$$

5.  (a) A possible model is that of the dihybrid cross with "long" dominant to "vestigial" and "gray" dominant to "ebony":
    $$\{DD, DR, RD, RR\}$$
    $$\tfrac{9}{16}, \ \tfrac{3}{16}, \ \tfrac{3}{16}, \ \tfrac{1}{16}$$

    (b) It seems very unlikely.

6.  A mating of LlGg × llgg in which the L gene is determined independently of the G gene.

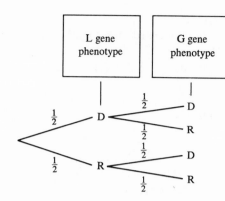

, {DD, DR, RD, RR}
  $\frac{1}{4}$, $\frac{1}{4}$, $\frac{1}{4}$, $\frac{1}{4}$

7. A mating LLGG × llgg: {DD}.
   1

8. {DDD, DDR, DRD, RDD, DRR, RDR, RRD, RRR}
   $\frac{27}{64}$, $\frac{9}{64}$, $\frac{9}{64}$, $\frac{9}{64}$, $\frac{3}{64}$, $\frac{3}{64}$, $\frac{3}{64}$, $\frac{1}{64}$,
   The relative odds are 27 : 9 : 9 : 9 : 3 : 3 : 3 : 1

9. (a) {AABBCC, AABBCc, AABBcc, AABbCC, AABbCc, AABbcc,
   $\frac{1}{64}$, $\frac{2}{64}$, $\frac{1}{64}$, $\frac{2}{64}$, $\frac{4}{64}$, $\frac{2}{64}$,
   AAbbCC, AAbbCc, AAbbcc, AaBBCC, AaBBCc, AaBBcc, AaBbCC,
   $\frac{1}{64}$, $\frac{2}{64}$, $\frac{1}{64}$, $\frac{2}{64}$, $\frac{4}{64}$, $\frac{2}{64}$, $\frac{4}{64}$,
   AaBbCc, AaBbcc, AabbCC, AabbCc, Aabbcc, aaBBCC, aaBbCc,
   $\frac{8}{64}$, $\frac{4}{64}$, $\frac{2}{64}$, $\frac{4}{64}$, $\frac{2}{64}$, $\frac{1}{64}$, $\frac{2}{64}$,
   aaBBcc, aaBbCC, aaBbCc, aaBbcc, aabbCC, aabbCc, aabbcc}
   $\frac{1}{64}$, $\frac{2}{64}$, $\frac{4}{64}$, $\frac{2}{64}$, $\frac{1}{64}$, $\frac{2}{64}$, $\frac{1}{64}$
   (b) 8 : 1; (c) 1 : 1

### Section 6.7★

1. (a) A model is as follows. Let the two genes be on the same chromosome.
   The first mating is CCgg × ccGG: The sample space for the offspring
   is {CgcG}. The second mating is CgcG × CgcG. The sample space for the
   1
   offspring is {CgcG, CgCg, cGcG}.
   $\frac{1}{2}$ , $\frac{1}{4}$ , $\frac{1}{4}$
   (b) It seems reasonable, otherwise we would expect 9 : 3 : 3 : 1 odds.

2. (a) A model is as follows. Let the two genes be on different chromosomes.
   The first mating is as in 1. The second mating is a dihybrid cross (Section
   6.6★) the odds are 9 : 3 : 3 : 1.
   (b) No. The observed odds are close to 9 : 3 : 3 : 1.

3. (a) A model of a mating of an hhll with an individual having HL on one
   chromosome and hl on the other. p is the crossover probability:
   {hairy-light, hairy-dark, smooth-light, smooth-dark}
   $\frac{1}{2} - \frac{1}{4}p$      $\frac{1}{4}p$      $\frac{1}{4}p$      $\frac{1}{2} - \frac{1}{4}p$

    (b) $9 : 1 : 1 : 9$.
4.  (a) Same as 3(a), substituting "marked" for "light" etc.;
    (b) $47 : 3 : 3 : 47$; (c) H
5.  (a) $\frac{9}{17}p$; (b) $\frac{13}{17}p$; (c) $\frac{3}{17}p$; (d) $9 : 13 : 3$; (e) yes, to M

# CHAPTER 7

## Section 7.1

1.  $\binom{6}{4}(\frac{1}{2})^4(\frac{1}{2})^2 = \frac{15}{64}$, $\binom{6}{3}(\frac{1}{2})^3(\frac{1}{2})^3 = \frac{20}{64}$
2.  $\binom{4}{2}p^2(1-p)^2 = 6p^2(1-p)^2$, $(1-p)^4$
3.  $(\frac{99}{100})^{10}$, $1 - (\frac{99}{100})^{10}$
4.  $\binom{10}{8}(\frac{1}{5})^8(\frac{4}{5})^2$, $(\frac{1}{5})^{10}$
5.  $1 - (1-p)^n$
6.  (a) —; (b) $p - apq$; (c) $p^2 + pq(1 + a)$; (d) The sample space is
    $\{$SS,      SF,         FS,       FF$\}$. The rest follows.
    $p^2$,  $(1 - a)pq$, $(1 + a)pq$,  $q^2$
7.  —
8.  (a) —; (b) —; (c) $\frac{2}{3}$
9.  (a) —; (b) —; (c) —; (d) They are independent.

10. (a)

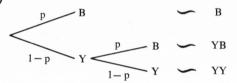

    (b) no, $p$, $(1 - p)p$, $0$
11. $\binom{10}{5}(\frac{3}{5})^5(\frac{2}{5})^5 + \binom{10}{6}(\frac{3}{5})^6(\frac{2}{5})^4$
12. $1 - [(\frac{4}{5})^{10} + 10(\frac{1}{5})(\frac{4}{5})^9 + 45(\frac{1}{5})^2(\frac{4}{5})^8]$

## Section 7.2

1.  (a) $\frac{1}{9}$; (b) $\frac{1}{15}$
2.  $\frac{15}{70}$
3.  $\binom{6}{3}/\binom{24}{3}$
4.  $(\frac{5}{6})^4$
5.  $\binom{6}{6}\binom{10}{1}/\binom{16}{7}$, without replacement
6.  $\dfrac{66}{147} = \dfrac{22}{49}$

### Section 7.3★

1. Respectively: $\frac{1}{93}, \frac{2}{93}, \frac{6}{93}, \frac{24}{93}, \frac{60}{93}$

2. Each has probability $1/(n+1)$

3. (a) $(0.05) \times (0.05) = 0.0025$;   (b) $(0.05) \times (0.62) = 0.031$;
   (c) $(0.05) \times (0.962) = 0.0481$; (d) $(0.05) \times (0.999962) = 0.0499981$.
   The corresponding ratio with replacement is 0.05.

4. (a) $\left(\frac{51}{50}\right) \times \left(\frac{1}{9}\right) = \frac{51}{450}$; (b) $N = 1000$: $\left(\frac{51}{50}\right) \times \left(\frac{51}{850}\right)$; $N = 10,000$:
   $\left(\frac{51}{50}\right) \times \left(\frac{951}{8950}\right)$; $N = 100,000$: $\left(\frac{51}{50}\right) \times \left(\frac{9951}{8995}\right)$; (c) 17 times;
   (d) about 9 times

5. —

6. $b(0) = \frac{16}{25} = 0.64, b(1) = \frac{8}{25} = 0.32, b(2) = \frac{1}{25} = 0.04. p(0) =$
   $0.63983984; p(1) = 0.32032032, p(2) = 0.03983984$

7. $p(0) = 0, p(1) = \dfrac{\binom{999}{1}\binom{1}{1}}{\binom{1000}{2}} = 0.002, p(2) = 0.998$
   The odds ratio $p(1)/p(0)$ is undefined when $N = 1000$. When $N = 2000$,
   $p(0) > 0$ and $p(1)/p(0)$ is defined.

8. $p(x)/p(x-1) = p$

9. —